HEAT ENGINES

BY

S. H. MOORFIELD
M.Sc. (Manch.), A.M.I.Mech.E.

HEAD OF THE MECHANICAL AND ELECTRICAL ENGINEERING
DEPARTMENTS, WIGAN AND DISTRICT MINING AND
TECHNICAL COLLEGE

AND

H. H. WINSTANLEY
B.Sc. (Lond. 1st Cl. Hons.), A.M.I.Mech.E.

LECTURER IN MECHANICAL ENGINEERING,
WIGAN AND DISTRICT MINING AND TECHNICAL COLLEGE

SECOND EDITION

LONDON
EDWARD ARNOLD & CO.

First published 1931
Second edition 1935
Reprinted 1938, 1940 *and* 1942

PRINTED IN GREAT BRITAIN
BY BRADFORD AND DICKENS, LONDON, W.C.1

PREFACE TO THE SECOND EDITION

The chief departure from the first edition is the addition of a chapter on the steam turbine. This has been rendered necessary by the inclusion of the subject in the syllabuses of a number of examining bodies ; some teachers have also suggested that such an addition would be an improvement.

In treating of the turbine the authors have deemed it necessary to devote a proportion of the text to descriptive matter, since but few students have the opportunity of seeing more than the external parts of such plant in which almost every working part is of necessity enclosed.

As regards the remainder of the book such errors as have come to the notice of the authors have been corrected.

Thanks are due to the following firms : Messrs. Metropolitan-Vickers Electrical Co., Ltd., who supplied drawings for the preparation of figures 114, 115, 116, 117 and 118 ; Messrs. C. A. Parsons & Co., Ltd., for figures 119, 120 and 121.

S. H. MOORFIELD.
H. H. WINSTANLEY.

TECHNICAL COLLEGE,
    WIGAN,
        September, 1935.

PREFACE TO THE FIRST EDITION

The object of this work is to provide a self-contained course in Heat Engines for students who aim at obtaining the Ordinary National Certificate in Mechanical Engineering. As there are several examining bodies for the purpose of awarding these certificates, it has been necessary to deal with the subject more extensively than is required by the syllabus of any one such body. The authors hope, however, that it will be possible to meet these conditions by the omission of certain sections, in accordance with the instructions of a teacher.

It is expected that the reader will have obtained some previous knowledge of the subject such as is gained in the First and Second Year Senior Courses for Part Time Technical Students, hence, terms are frequently used in the earlier part of the book without explanation. Whilst the needs of the part time student have been primarily considered, it is thought that the book will cover a suitable First Year Course in Heat Engines for Full Time Day Students.

No attempt has been made to give detailed instructions for experimental work since at this stage so much depends upon the equipment available.

Mere description of plant and machinery has been avoided to allow for a clear and concise presentation of the essential underlying principles of Heat Engines. Only such descriptions, therefore, as are necessary to the development of the theory are included.

It will be noted that no special chapter deals with the steam turbine. This is in keeping with the aim of the authors as stated above, for at this stage we feel that nothing more than a description of details could be attempted without going beyond the desired scope. At the same time, the student should recognize that, where the subject is not obviously treating only of the reciprocating engine, the turbine may be included in the term steam engine.

In many cases the examples at the end of the chapters amplify the text, and the student is recommended to work through most of these to obtain full benefit from the use of the book. A number of examples may, on a first reading, prove too difficult owing to the phraseology not being fully understood until the latter part of the work has been read. These should be especially useful for revision purposes.

The thanks of the authors are due to Messrs. Babcock & Wilcox, Ltd., Messrs. Hick, Hargreaves & Co., Ltd., and Messrs. The National Gas Engine Co., Ltd., for the use of blocks and diagrams ; to the Union of Lancashire and Cheshire Institutes, the Union of Educational Institutions and the Northern Council of Technical Education Committees for permission to print recent examination questions ; to His Majesty's Stationery Office for permission to print the entropy chart and to the holders of the copyright of Callendar's Steam Tables for the reproduction of values contained therein. We are also indebted to the students of the Mining and Technical College, Wigan, who have gathered experimental data and worked examples, and especially to Mr. Fred Caunce and Mr. Arthur Parkes, two of our degree students.

S. H. MOORFIELD.
H. H. WINSTANLEY.

TECHNICAL COLLEGE,
  WIGAN.
    August, 1931.

CONTENTS

HEAT ENGINES

CHAPTER I

WORK

1. The work of this chapter should be thoroughly understood before passing on to the study of the subject of Heat Engines.

All heat engines are built for the definite purpose of utilizing heat in the doing of work, such as hauling a load by a locomotive, lifting weights by colliery winding engines, operating ship winches, excavators, etc., lifting and forcing water by pumps, driving shafts in mills and factories. A thorough understanding of the methods of calculating the sizes of engine cylinders cannot be obtained until the student has quite clear ideas of Work and Power.

2. Definition. Work is a result of the application of effort or force. A further definition often given is as follows : Work is the result of expenditure of energy.

This is the best definition for our purpose because we must later consider heat as a form of energy. The necessary condition that work may be done is that movement shall take place. An effort or force may be applied to a body, but no work is done unless the body moves at the point where the force is applied. The amount of movement may be large or small.

3. Measurement of Work. The engineer measures the work done by or on any of his productions by observing and measuring the force acting, and also measuring the distance moved in the direction of action of the force.

For example, let F — a uniform force, applied whilst a

distance S is traversed. Then a measure of the work done is obtained by multiplying F and S.

Thus, work done $= F \times S$.

The units of the work are important and depend upon the units chosen for F and S.

When F is in tons and S inches, the work is in inch-tons.

When F is in pounds and S inches, the work is in inch-pounds.

When F is in pounds and S feet, the work is in foot-pounds.

The last-named unit is most commonly used. Other units, not needed for our present purpose, are often used.

EXAMPLE. The area of a steam engine piston is 30 square inches, and the uniform effective pressure upon the piston is 40 lbs. per square inch. The piston moves 4 inches. Find the work done during the movement.

Force on piston = Intensity of pressure $\times$ area of piston.
$$= 40 \text{ lbs. per sq. in.} \times 30 \text{ sq. ins.}$$
$$= 1,200 \text{ lbs. force.}$$

Work done = Force acting $\times$ distance moved.
$$= 1,200 \text{ lbs.} \times 4 \text{ inches}$$
$$= 4,800 \text{ inch-lbs.}$$

If we divide this result by 12, thus converting the inches to feet we shall get

$$\text{Work done} = \frac{4,800 \text{ inch-lbs.}}{12 \text{ inches per ft.}} = 400 \text{ ft.-lbs.}$$

Alternatively, we may proceed as follows, changing the unit of distance.

$$4 \text{ inches} = \tfrac{4}{12} \text{ ft.} = \tfrac{1}{3} \text{ ft.}$$
Then work done $= 1,200 \text{ lbs.} \times \tfrac{1}{3} \text{ ft.} = 400 \text{ ft.-lbs.}$

4. Work done during Change of Volume. In heat-engine work, the student is constantly being called upon to recognize PdV and $P(V_1 - V_2)$ as quantities of work done, and for this purpose the units must be very carefully considered.

When we speak of pressure in this book, intensity of pressure is meant. The word pressure itself is often used to denote force, so that the student must be careful to get correct ideas as to pressure, or intensity of pressure.

Pressure intensity, or (briefly) pressure, is the load per unit of area, e.g. pressure in lbs. per square inch is the force in lbs. on one square inch ; pressure in lbs. per square foot is the force in lbs. on one square foot.

EXAMPLE. The pressure of the atmosphere is 14·7 lbs. per square inch. What is the pressure in lbs. per square foot ?

Let P = pressure in lbs. per square foot ;

p = pressure in lbs. per square inch.

Since there are 144 square inches in one square foot, and on each square inch a force of 14·7 lbs., then pressure in lbs. per sq. ft.

$$= 144 \times 14\cdot7$$
$$= 2,116\cdot8$$

or $\qquad$ P $= 144p$.

EXAMPLE. A mercury U-tube pressure gauge gives a reading of 3 inches difference in level when denoting the pressure of air in a vessel. What is the pressure difference represented in lbs. per square inch, if mercury is 13·6 times as heavy as water, and water weighs 62·4 lbs. per cubic foot ?

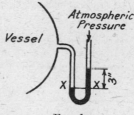

This type of example is very important.

First notice that the area of the tube is not given.

The pressure at level XX (fig. 1) is the same in both limbs.

On the left, it is the pressure in the vessel. On the right, it is the atmospheric pressure, plus the pres-

FIG. 1.

sure due to the weight of a 3-inch column of mercury.

Consider the weight of mercury covering an area of 1 sq. ft. to a depth of 3 inches.

Then weight of mercury = 1 ft. × 1 ft. × $\frac{3}{12}$ ft. × 13·6 × 62·4

$$= \tfrac{1}{4} \times 13\cdot6 \times 62\cdot4$$
$$= 212\cdot16 \text{ lbs.}$$

Hence the pressure in the vessel is 212·16 lbs. per square foot above atmospheric pressure.

Again, 212·16 lbs. per sq. ft.

$$= \frac{212\cdot16}{144} \text{ lbs. per sq. inch}$$

$= 1\cdot478$ lbs. per sq. inch above atmospheric pressure.

Note that the area of the tube is not involved because we are concerned with the *intensity* of pressure which is independent of this area.

We may now consider work done when volume changes at uniform pressure.

Imagine a cylinder, with its axis horizontal, fitted with a piston and supplied with gas at constant pressure through the opening at B (fig. 2). Let the piston move, and, hence, the volume between piston and cover change as the gas is supplied.

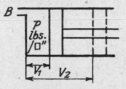

Fig. 2.

Let a = area of piston surface in contact with gas in square inches.

p = intensity of pressure of gas in lbs. per sq. in.

Let L = linear horizontal movement of piston in *feet*.

Now the force on piston = $p \times a$ lbs.

Work done = $p \times a \times$ L ft.-lbs.

Again, let A = area of piston in square feet.

P = pressure of gas in lbs. per square foot.

We then have $p = \dfrac{P}{144}$

and $a = 144$ A

$\therefore$ work done = $p \times a \times$ L ft.-lbs.

$$= \frac{P}{144} \times 144 \text{ A} \times \text{L ft.-lbs.}$$

$$= \text{PAL ft.-lbs.}$$

The units of this equation are lbs. per square foot for pressure, square feet for area, and feet for distance.

The product of P and A is force and L is distance.

$\therefore$ the above (PA) $\times$ L = force $\times$ distance.

But, again, we may regard the product of A and L as the change of volume, or the volume " swept " by the piston.

$$\therefore \text{ PAL becomes P} \times \text{AL ft.-lbs.}$$

$$= \text{P} \times \text{ volume change, ft.-lbs.}$$

$$= \text{P} \times (\text{V}_2 - \text{V}_1) \text{ ft.-lbs.}$$

EXAMPLE.   Four cubic feet of water at 700 lbs. per square inch are supplied to a hydraulic engine. Find the work done during the supply.

Work = P × change in volume
    = 144p × change in volume
    = (144 × 700) × 4

(Brackets are used to keep the pressure distinct.)

    = 403,200 ft.-lbs.

EXAMPLE. Three cubic feet of steam at a uniform pressure of 100 lbs. per square inch are supplied to the cylinder of an engine. Find the work done during the supply. Neglect clearance.

Here let $V_1 = 0$ and let $V_2 = 3$ cubic feet.

Then change in volume = $(V_2 - V_1) = 3 - 0 = 3$ cubic feet.

    Work done = $P(V_2 - V_1)$
        = $144p(V_2 - V_1)$
        = 144 × 100 × 3 ft.-lbs.
        = 43,200 ft.-lbs.

It will be seen from the above example, that when the cylinder contains no steam initially, and a volume V cubic feet is admitted at a pressure P lbs. per square foot,

Work done during admission = PV ft.-lbs.

In considering examples such as the above, relating to engine cylinders, it is very helpful to draw the Pressure-Volume diagram.

5. The Pressure Volume Diagram as a Work Diagram. When a gas, a mixture of gases, or a vapour is operating in an engine cylinder, it is known as the working substance. The pressure-volume diagram is a diagram in which the pressure of the working substance is plotted vertically and its volume plotted horizontally. Lines drawn upon the field enclosed by the rectangular

FIG. 3.

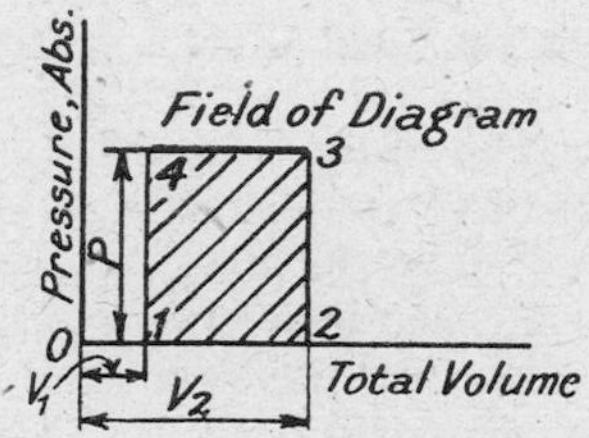

co-ordinates then have definite meaning, and represent the behaviour of the working substance in the cylinder of an engine. By means of such lines it is possible at a glance to convey to the mind a large amount of precise information. The practice of drawing or sketching the lines fixes the problem, and enables the initial and final states of the substance to be kept quite distinct. In fig. 3, O is the origin, and the volume scale is set out towards the right. The pressure scale is set up on the perpendicular line from O. Thus the diagram will be on the right of the pressure scale and above the volume scale. If a point be chosen anywhere in the field of the diagram, two dimensions are fixed at once, one denoting the pressure, and the other denoting the volume of the substance for which the diagram is drawn. These dimensions are P (pressure) and V (total volume) in fig. 3. The position of this point establishes the " state " of some given quantity of substance as regards pressure and volume. The amount of the substance will be dealt with after discussing the characteristic equation for gases, see article 28.

The " state " point is regarded as movable, and its path from the initial state to some final state can be traced out by a line known as a pressure-volume line. The pressure-volume line is used to denote a " process " in the changing state of a gas in an engine cylinder.

The state point in fig. 3 may now be considered to have arrived at (3) by moving horizontally from (4) to (3), and the area of the enclosed rectangle (1, 2, 3, 4) is proportional to the product $P \times (V_2 - V_1)$. This shows that an area in the field of the diagram can be made to represent a quantity of work done, as the state point moves from (4) to (3).

This is a very important process line, and could represent the supply of steam or gas to a cylinder at constant pressure, from volume V_1 until the quantity supplied occupied volume V_2.

The quantity $(V_2 - V_1)$ is called the *volume swept* by the piston, and is the product of the area of the piston and the distance it moves during the increase of volume. The work done during the process is shown by the shaded area, and the magnitude of that work is obtained by multiplying the shaded area by the " work scale " in the appropriate units.

6. Work Scale of a Pressure-Volume Diagram.

Definition. The work scale of a pressure-volume diagram is the number of foot-lbs. represented by one square inch of the diagram, when inches are used as the units in plotting and foot-lbs. as the unit of work. Other units may be employed, but the student is advised to use one set of units throughout, until he becomes proficient in the subject itself.

The work scale is obtained as follows :

Let p_s = pressure scale in lbs. per sq. in. per inch of vertical measurement.

V_s = volume scale in cu. ft. per inch of horizontal measurement.

Then 1 square inch = 1 vertical inch × 1 horizontal inch. Now writing the equivalents of these we have

$$\text{Foot-lbs. per sq. in.} = (p_s \times 144) \times V_s$$
$$= 144 \; p_s \; V_s \text{ ft.-lbs.}$$

Since $P_s = 144 \, p_s$, we have

$$1 \text{ square inch} = P_s V_s \text{ ft.-lbs.,}$$

where P_s is the scale of absolute pressure in lbs. per sq. ft. and V_s is the scale of volume in cubic feet.

EXAMPLE. A pressure volume diagram is plotted to a scale of 1 inch = 25 lbs. per sq. in. abs. and 1 inch = 2 cu. ft. Find the work scale.

1 square inch represents $P_s V_s$ ft.-lbs.

∴ ,,   ,,   ,,   ,, $25 \times 144 \times 2 = 7{,}200$ ft.-lbs.

EXAMPLE. The area under a certain line on a pressure-volume diagram is 3·13 square inches. The scales of pressure and volume are 20 lbs. per square inch per inch, and 2·5 cubic feet per inch, respectively. Find the work represented by the given area.

Work scale = $144 p_s V_s$ ft.-lbs. per sq. in.

$$= 144 \times 20 \times 2 \cdot 5 = 7{,}200 \text{ ft.-lbs. per sq. in.}$$

Work represented by area = $3 \cdot 13 \times 7{,}200 = 22{,}536$ ft.-lbs.

7. Work done when both Pressure and Volume Change.

We may now return to the state point of the substance. Consider the point to move along the curved path (1) to (2), fig. 4. At some point where the pressure is P lbs. per sq. ft., let an increase in volume of δV cu. ft. be taken.

If, during the increase in volume, the pressure remained constant, the work done would be $P \times \delta V$ ft.-lbs., and $P \times \delta V$ would also be proportional very nearly to the area of the strip shown. By making δV smaller the error would be less. If the whole shaded area be divided into strips, each could be made to represent the work done during a slight increase in volume as nearly as we choose by making δV sufficiently small. Adding all these strips together, the total amount of work repre-

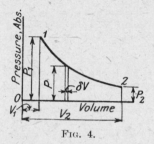

FIG. 4.

sented by them may be made as near the actual amount of work done as we choose, when the volume increases from (1) to (2).

Also, by choosing smaller values of δV, the sum of the areas of all strips approaches more nearly to the actual area under the curve. Hence, when δV is infinitely small, and we have an infinite number of strips, the sum of all $P\delta V$ products equals the work done, and the sum of all strips equals the area under the curve. Thus the area under the curve, to the proper work scale, equals the work done during the process.

It will be shown later that when we know the law connecting pressure and volume, this work can be calculated.

The indicator diagram from an engine cylinder is a pressure-volume diagram, and the student is advised to treat it as such, and not as a pressure-stroke diagram. As pressure volume lines will be largely used to illustrate what is happening in engine cylinders, an appreciation of their value, and knowledge of their use, will be of great service in future consideration of the important engine cycles.

EXAMPLES I

1. A draught gauge in the form of a U-tube containing water shows a difference of level in the two limbs of 0·75 inch. Calculate

the difference in pressure in lbs. per sq. ft. indicated by this reading. Express the answer also in lbs. per sq. in. One cu. ft. of water weighs 62·4 lbs.

2. A mercury U-tube gauge is used to test the pressure of air in a pipe. The reading of the gauge is 3·5 inches difference of level. Find the absolute pressure of the air in lbs. per sq. in. Assume the outside atmospheric pressure to be 14·7 lbs. per sq. in.

3. The ram of a boiler feed pump is 4 inches diameter and the stroke is 8 inches. Find the work done per stroke by this pump when forcing water into a boiler whose pressure gauge reads 150 lbs. per sq. in.

4. How much work is required to pump 1 cubic foot of water into a boiler the gauge pressure being 200 lbs. per sq. in. ?

5. A quantity of gas is heated at constant pressure and under these conditions the volume changes from 3·2 cu. ft. to 3·8 cu. ft. The pressure is 180 lbs. per sq. in. absolute. Find the total work done during the heat supply period.

6. A pressure volume diagram for a gas is set down to a scale of $1'' = 200$ lbs. per sq. in. and $1'' = 0.4$ cu. ft. The total area under the expansion line on this diagram is 2·31 sq. ins. Find the work done during the expansion.

7. The area of a gas engine indicator card is 0·68 sq. in. The volume swept by the piston is 0·23 cu. ft. and the diagram is set down to a pressure scale of 300 lbs. per sq. in. per inch. Find the work per cycle, the length of the diagram being 2·25 inches.

8. What do you understand by the " work scale " of a diagram ? An ideal indicator diagram for a gas engine is plotted to a scale of $1'' = 0.3$ cu. ft. and $1'' = 75$ lbs. per sq. in. The area of the enclosed figure is 2·5 sq. ins., and the length of the diagram is 5½ inches. What is the work scale of the diagram ? Find from this the hypothetical mean effective pressure.   W. & D.M.T.C.

CHAPTER II

POWER AND ENERGY

8. Power is the Rate of Doing Work. This statement introduces the idea of time. The amount of work done in unit time is a measure of the power. If one engine does twice as much work as another in one minute, then it has twice the power. Hence

$$\text{Power} = \frac{\text{Work done}}{\text{Time}}.$$

If an engine, working at a uniform rate, does 270,000 ft.-lbs. of work in 3 minutes,

$$\text{then work done per minute} = \frac{270,000}{3}$$

$$= 90,000 \text{ ft.-lbs. per min.}$$

The power of this engine may be said to be 90,000 ft.-lbs. per minute.

9. Unit of Power. The unit of power which has been chosen as convenient for practical engineering purposes is 33,000 ft.-lbs. *per minute.*

Note well that it is not merely 33,000 ft.-lbs.

This unit is called one *horse power.*

The horse power of the above engine is

$$\frac{90,000}{33,000} = 2 \cdot 72 \text{ horse power.}$$

One horse power, being 33,000 ft.-lbs. per minute, is also 550 ft.-lbs. per second, or 33,000 × 60 ft.-lbs. per hour = 1,980,000 ft.-lbs. per hour.

Although these numbers are different, the *rate* is the same, and all are one horse power.

10. Useful Horse Power. The power delivered at

the coupling, or driving pulley, of an engine, or at the brake when the engine is under test, is called the Brake Horse Power. This is less than the horse power developed in the engine cylinder. This is because work has been absorbed at various points in the working parts of the engine, that is, a proportion of the power has been lost. It should be clearly understood, therefore, that the number of brake horse power units is less than that produced in the cylinder, but this is not because a brake horse power is less than any other. The value of the horse power is exactly the same, namely, 33,000 ft.-lbs. per minute.

EXAMPLE. The work produced in an engine cylinder in 7 minutes is 287,000 ft.-lbs., and the work done against the engine brake in 10 minutes is 280,000 ft.-lbs. Find the horse power produced in the cylinder, and that delivered to the brake.

Cylinder horse power, or Indicated horse power

$$= \frac{\text{work done per minute}}{33,000}$$

$$= \frac{287,000}{7} \div 33,000 = \frac{41,000 \text{ ft.-lbs. per min.}}{33,000}$$

$$= 1 \cdot 24 \text{ H.P.}$$

Work done at brake $= \dfrac{280,000}{10}$ ft.-lbs. per min.

$$= 28,000 \quad ,, \quad ,, \quad ,,$$

Brake horse power $= \dfrac{28,000}{33,000} = 0 \cdot 848$ H.P.

Note that the value of the horse power is the same, whether in the cylinder or at the brake. It is the number of units of power which is less at the brake.

11. Energy. This may be defined as the capacity for doing work. It may be regarded as a store of something upon which we may draw, when suitable conditions are created, for the purpose of doing work. These conditions depend upon the nature of the source of energy, and they will be discussed as they affect our subject.

The many forms of energy known to science include (1) mechanical energy, (2) thermal or heat energy, (3) electrical energy, (4) chemical energy. Our concern is chiefly with the relationships existing between mechanical and thermal energy and the transformation of the latter into the former. It is generally possible to change one of the above forms of energy into another form.

The transformation of thermal into mechanical energy is the fundamental principle underlying all the work of Heat Engines, and its study is of vital importance to the engineer.

Transformation of mechanical energy into thermal energy in an engine is not of service. Heat thus produced is said to be degraded and is rendered useless.

12. Conservation of Energy. Energy appears to be indestructible, and observation leads to the general conclusion which is known as the " Principle of the Conservation of Energy." It may be stated as follows : " Energy cannot be created or destroyed." This principle is essential in establishing many very important results in the theory of heat engines. It must be remembered that energy transformation is not energy loss. Clear recognition of this fact will avoid difficulty later.

13. Conversion of Energy. Because energy is convertible, it is necessary to know something of equivalent amounts of energy in its different forms. We therefore have to use conversion factors, when we wish to change an amount of energy, expressed in one kind of unit, into the corresponding amount, expressed in some other unit. Thus if energy is given in electrical units, we must use a conversion factor to change it into mechanical units.

The factor with which we are mainly concerned is the one for converting heat units into units of mechanical energy, usually foot-lbs. This particular factor is known as Joule's Mechanical Equivalent of Heat, and has been obtained as the result of careful experimental measurement.

The value of the equivalent is—

One British Thermal Unit = 778 ft.-lbs. or

One Centigrade Heat Unit = 1,400 ft.-lbs.

The Centigrade Heat Unit may be defined as the mean value of the quantity of heat required to raise the temperature of 1 lb. of water through 1° C.

The British Thermal Unit may be defined as the mean value of the quantity of heat required to raise the temperature of 1 lb. of water through 1° F.

EXAMPLE. It is found by experiment that 1 lb. of a certain coal will give out 8,000 centigrade heat units (C.H.U.) when completely burned. How much energy is this equal to in ft.-lbs., and how far would this energy raise a weight of 1 ton vertically, supposing the whole of it could be applied to this purpose ?

Heat energy available in coal per lb. = 8,000 C.H.U.

Equivalent mechanical energy available in coal per lb.

$$= 8,000 \times 1,400 \text{ ft.-lbs.}$$
$$= 11,200,000 \text{ ft.-lbs.}$$

If the weight of 2,240 lbs. is raised " h " feet

$$2,240h = 11,200,000 \text{ ft.-lbs.}$$

$$h = \frac{11,200,000 \text{ ft.-lbs.}}{2,240 \text{ lbs.}} = 5,000 \text{ feet.}$$

We shall see later that only a fraction of this energy could be expended in doing mechanical work.

EXAMPLE. The thermal energy stored in 1 lb. of petrol is 18,000 B.T.U. A petrol engine consumes 15 lbs. of petrol per hour, and converts into mechanical energy 20 per cent. of that supplied. What is the power of the engine ?

Heat energy supplied to engine per hour = $18,000 \times 15$

$$= 270,000 \text{ B.T.U.}$$

Heat energy supplied per min. = $\frac{270,000}{60} = 4,500$ B.T.U.

Mechanical energy supplied per min. = $4,500 \times 778$
$$= 3,501,000 \text{ ft.-lbs.}$$

Since only 20 per cent. of energy is converted, we have

Work done by petrol engine per min. = $\frac{3,501,000 \times 20}{100}$

$$= 700,200 \text{ ft.-lbs.}$$

H.P. of engine = $\frac{700,200}{33,000} = 21 \cdot 2$ H.P.

EXAMPLE. An engine of 200 I.H.P. is supplied with steam, each pound of which carries 640 C.H.U. to the engine. If 12 per cent. of the heat supplied is converted into work on the pistons, how much steam is required by this engine per hour ?

Work to be done on engine piston per min. $= 200 \times 33,000$ ft.-lbs.

,,   ,,   ,,   ,,   ,,   ,, hour

$= 200 \times 33,000 \times 60$ ft.-lbs.

Heat equivalent of this work $= \dfrac{200 \times 33,000 \times 60}{1,400}$ C.H.U. per hr.

$= 200 \times 1,414$ C.H.U. per hour.

$= 282,800$,,   ,,   ,,

Heat carried to engine per lb. of steam $= 640$ C.H.U.

Heat converted into work per lb. of steam $= \frac{12}{100} \times 640$ C.H.U.

$= 76 \cdot 8$,,

Weight of steam required per hour

$$= \frac{282,800}{76 \cdot 8} = 3,683 \cdot 5 \text{ lbs. per hour.}$$

EXAMPLES II

1. The area of an indicator diagram is $2 \cdot 46$ sq. ins. The pressure scale is $1'' = 64$ lbs. per sq. in., and the volume scale is $1'' = 0 \cdot 5$ cu. ft. The engine completes 220 of these cycles per minute. Calculate its indicated horse power.

2. The draw-bar pull of a locomotive when travelling at 30 miles per hour is 12,000 lbs. Find the horse power expended by the engine upon the train.

3. A pump lifts 10,000 gallons of water per minute through a vertical height of 200 feet. Calculate the horse power thus expended. For the purpose of pumping, coal whose calorific value is 7,800 C.H.U. per lb. is used. Only 10 per cent. of this heat is effectively used by the plant. Find the weight of coal burned per hour. 1 gallon of water weighs 10 lbs.

4. An alternator generates 15,000 kilowatts. The overall efficiency of boilers, engines and dynamo may be taken as 16 per cent. What weight of coal, whose calorific value is 12,000 B.Th.U., will be burned per hour ? 1 kilowatt $= 1\frac{1}{3}$ horse power.

5. Express 1,414 C.H.U. per hour in horse power.

6. A fan delivers air at a water-gauge pressure of 3 inches. The volume of air passing through the fan is 200,000 cu. ft. per minute. Find the horse power required to drive the fan.

7. One pound weight of steam contains 670 C.H.U. Of this quantity, 31 C.H.U. are changed into kinetic energy. Find the velocity of the steam in feet per second.

8. The area of an indicator diagram taken from a double-acting steam engine is $2 \cdot 1$ sq. ins., and its length is $3 \cdot 5$ inches. The strength of the spring used is 60 lbs. per inch of height. The diameter of the cylinder is 18 inches, and the piston stroke is 26 inches. Speed, 150 revs. per min. Find the indicated horse power of the engine and, if the mechanical efficiency is 78 per cent., the brake horse power.   U.L.C.I.

9. A double acting steam engine has a cylinder diameter of 6 inches and the stroke of the piston is 10 inches. The mean effective pressure of the steam in the cylinder is 40 lbs. per sq. in. At what speed in revolutions per minute should the engine run in order to develop 20 horse power. U.L.C.I.

10. At what level is the " feed check " valve generally fitted to a boiler and why ?

Find the horse power required to drive a boiler feed pump which delivers 800 gallons of water per hour against a boiler pressure of 185 lbs. per sq. in. by gauge. Efficiency of pump, 75 per cent. U.L.C.I.

CHAPTER III

HEAT AND ITS MEASUREMENT

14. Heat as Energy. Heat has been described as a form of energy, and must, therefore, be capable of doing work. In order that work may be done motion is essential, and this motion must be associated with applied force.

According to the kinetic theory of heat, heat is a measure of the molecular activity within a substance ; it is said to be equal to the kinetic energy of the molecules of which the heated substance consists.

15. Specific Heat. The quantity of heat, which is taken in by, or removed from a body, depends upon three things :

(1) The mass of substance in the particular body.

(2) A property of the substance known as its Specific Heat.

(3) The change of temperature which takes place.

To assist the student in forming a conception as to how these three points affect the problem, we may consider a quantity of water being heated by a gas burner, or some other agency, which ensures the transmission of heat to the water at a uniform rate. A definite time will be needed to raise the water to boiling point, but if the mass of water be doubled, or increased in any other ratio, then the time of heating will be increased in the same ratio. This is because the heat added must be in proportion to the mass. The change of temperature or temperature range is the same in both cases. Again, if we take a mass of water, and apply the heat to raise its temperature from 20° C. to 50° C., and note the time taken, we should find on replacing the water by the same mass of some other liquid and raising the temperature of this liquid from 20° C. to

50° C., that the time would be different—usually less. This is due to the fact that different substances have different capacities for absorbing heat, or different specific heats. If the quantity of heat taken in by the water is a quantity 1, say, and the other substance has absorbed a quantity C, then the ratio $\frac{C}{I} = C$ is called the specific heat of the substance. The specific heat of water is taken as unity in general.

Finally, if with the uniform flow of heat, we heat a mass of water from 20° C. to 50° C., thus giving a temperature range of 30°, and then, taking an equal quantity of water, we heat it up from 20° C. to 80° C., thus giving a range of 60°, we find the time doubled because the temperature range is doubled. Thus we see that the quantity of heat is proportional to the increase in temperature.

All the above reasoning would apply equally well if the substances were being cooled, and thus giving out, instead of absorbing heat at a definite rate.

16. Heat Calculation. In consideration of the preceding article, we should expect to find that the following equation holds :

Heat added = mass of substance × specific heat × temperature rise,

and all experiment tends to prove it true.

We have seen that specific heat may be regarded as a ratio, but it is sometimes convenient to treat it as a quantity of heat.

Definition. The specific heat of a substance is the *ratio of the quantity of heat* required to raise a definite mass of that *substance* through a given temperature range to the *quantity of heat required* to raise the same mass of *water* through the same temperature range.

Let   C = specific heat of substance which may be a gas, liquid, or solid.

        C_w = specific heat of water.

        W = a given mass of water and also mass of substance.

$T_1 - T_2$ = rise in absolute temperature.

Then specific heat of substance $= \dfrac{C \times W \times (T_1 - T_2)}{C_w \times W \times (T_1 - T_2)}$

$$= C, \text{ when } C_w = 1$$

EXAMPLE. The specific heat of air at constant pressure is 0·238. Find the amount of heat necessary to raise the temperature of $1\frac{1}{2}$ lb. of air from 200° absolute to 250° absolute.

Heat added = mass × sp. ht. × temperature rise

$\qquad = 1\frac{1}{2} \times \cdot238 \times (250 - 200)$

$\qquad = 1\frac{1}{2} \times \cdot238 \times 50 = 17\cdot85$ C.H.U.

The absolute temperatures are in centigrade degrees, and the student may note that the temperature rise would be exactly the same, if the temperatures were on the ordinary centigrade scale.

Let us now treat specific heat as a heat quantity instead of a ratio.

Definition. The specific heat of a substance is the quantity of heat required to raise one pound of that substance through one degree.

Thus 1 pound of iron requires 0·1146 centigrade heat unit to raise its temperature through one degree centigrade, or it requires 0·1146 British Thermal Unit to raise its temperature through one degree Fahrenheit. Hence the specific heat of iron = 0·1146 heat units per lb. per degree. Since one centigrade heat unit is required to raise 1 lb. of water through one degree centigrade, and one British Thermal Unit to raise 1 lb. of water through one degree Fahrenheit, we see that both definitions of specific heat give the same numerical value.

17. Water Equivalent. It is often necessary to find the mass of water which has the same heat capacity as a given mass of some other substance. Here the idea of specific heat as a ratio has a direct application.

This mass of water is the *water equivalent* of the given mass of substance. We may define the water equivalent of a body as the mass of water which requires the same quantity of heat to raise its temperature one degree as would be required to raise the temperature of the body one degree.

EXAMPLE. Find the water equivalent of an iron container which weighs 20 lbs. Specific heat of iron = 0·1146.

Water equivalent of container = 20 × 0·1146
= 2·292 lbs.

That means that 2·292 lbs. of water would absorb the same amount of heat as 20 lbs. of iron, when the temperature rise is the same, or that 20 lbs. of iron is the *equivalent in heat capacity* of 2·292 lbs. of water.

EXAMPLE. An empty copper vessel weighs 2·19 lbs. and 8·5 lbs. of water are poured into it. The temperature of the water and vessel is then raised 20° C. Find the heat supplied to the system. Specific heat of copper = 0·0965.

Water equivalent of copper vessel = 0·0965 × 2·19 = 0·211 lbs.
Total water equivalent of system = 8·5 + 0·211 = 8·711 lbs.
Heat required to raise temperature 20° C. = 8·711 × 20 = 174·22 C.H.U.

EXAMPLE. The parts of a simple calorimeter for testing fuels consist of 4·6 lbs. of glass and 1·2 lb. of steel. Water weighing 2,560 grams is poured in. Find the heat required to raise the temperature of the whole system 3½° C., if the specific heat of steel = 0·1158 and of glass = 0·198.

Water equivalent of glass = 4·6 × 0·198 = 0·912 lbs.
,, ,, ,, steel = 1·2 × 0·1158 = 0·139 lbs.
2,560 grams of water = $\frac{2,560}{454}$ lbs. of water = 5·64 lbs.

Total water equivalent of system = 6·691 lbs.
Heat required to raise calorimeter and water through 3½° C.
= 6·691 × 3·5 = 23·4 C.H.U.

18. Calorimetry.

The above examples indicate the method of using specific heats in the calculation of quantities of heat, and in heat measurement.

The measurement of heat quantities is a portion of science known as calorimetry, and whenever the term is met with, it should at once convey the idea of measuring heat quantity.

19. Thermometry.

The measurement of heat will be seen to involve the measuring of a temperature change, and this requires the use of either a thermometer or a pyrometer. The student is supposed to be familiar with the ordinary type of glass thermometer containing mercury,

or some other liquid.   Such thermometers can only measure
moderate temperatures.   Some form of pyrometer is
generally used for measuring high temperatures, such as
the temperatures of molten metals or of furnaces, and such
temperature measurement is generally known as *pyrometry*.

The most convenient pyrometers for use by engineers
are based upon some electrical phenomenon.   A full discussion of these is outside the scope of this book, and for
fuller information the student may refer to books on
electricity.   We may, however, point out that electrical
pyrometers depend, either upon the measuring of the
increase in the resistance of a platinum wire when it is
heated, or upon the measurement of a small electric current
generated when the junction of two dissimilar metals is
heated.   As the latter can be measured by a form of

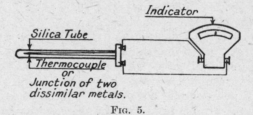

Fig. 5.

voltmeter, which is calibrated directly in temperatures,
it requires no electrical knowledge to read it, and thus
is very convenient for use in either engineering practice,
or the engineering laboratory.

A table of specific heats of substances commonly met
with in engineering is appended.

TABLE I

Water	.	.	.	.	.	1·0	Copper	.	.	.	.	.	0·0965
Ice	.	.	.	.	.	0·504	Brass	.	.	.	.	.	0·0940
Aluminium	.	.	.	.	0·2143	Zinc	.	.	.	.	.	0·0956
Cast iron	.	.	.	.	0·125	Gunmetal	.	.	.	.	0·0952
Cast steel	.	.	.	.	0·117	Nickel	.	.	.	.	0·1086
Mild steel	.	.	.	.	0·1158	Mercury (liquid)	.	.	0·0333
Wrought iron	.	.	.	0·1146	Coal	.	.	.	.	.	0·2412
Tin	.	.	.	.	.	0·0562	Petroleum	.	.	.	.	0·434

20. Specific Heat of a Gas. Hitherto we have dealt with specific heats in a general way, and have made no special reference to any peculiar property of the substance concerned. In treating solids and liquids, for all practical purposes nothing need be added, but our study of specific heats in relation to gases and vapours needs extending.

A vapour may be regarded as a gas near its temperature of liquefaction, and for the present, we need make no difference between them.

Typical vapours are steam and ammonia, and typical gases are air, oxygen, nitrogen.

In converting heat into mechanical energy, we find it necessary to use some working substance, and so far, gases and vapours have been found to be our most convenient working substances. This is because their expansion or increase in volume is so marked in contrast to that of solids and liquids. An exact discussion of the expansion of gases will be found in the next chapter.

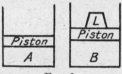

Fig. 6.

Let us now consider a quantity of gas enclosed in the space A, fig. 6. Let the piston shown be considered fixed so that the volume of space A cannot change nor can any gas escape. Suppose the gas in A to be heated from an initial temperature T_1 to a final temperature T_2; the pressure will vary but the volume cannot; hence we say that the gas in A is heated at *constant volume*. Our former equation for the heat added will hold here, namely:

Heat added = weight of gas × specific heat at constant volume × rise in temperature.

Let W = weight of gas, let C_v = sp. ht. at constant volume.

Then, heat added = $W \times C_v \times (T_2 - T_1)$ heat units.

Now suppose the piston in B to be movable, and let there be a load L upon it. This will ensure that the pressure in B remains constant.

On heating the gas in B, expansion will now occur, and

again we will suppose that the initial temperature is T_1, and the final temperature T_2.

We now see that the volume changes and the piston will rise, thus doing work on the weight L. Let us note that the rise in temperature is the same as before $(T_2 - T_1)$, but in addition work has been done, hence, we may expect that more heat has been passed into the gas if the weight of gas is W as before. Our equation for the heat added, therefore, can only be satisfied if the specific heat is greater than in the case of the cylinder A. We have, then,

Heat added = W × sp. ht. at constant pressure ×
$$(T_2 - T_1)$$

or putting C_p = sp. ht. at constant pressure

Heat added = W × C_p × $(T_2 - T_1)$

Experiment proves our expectation that C_p is greater than C_v.

If the student will now thoroughly grasp the following three points it will greatly facilitate his work later.

(1) A gas has two specific heats.
(2) The conditions under which a gas is heated have an important bearing on the quantity of heat required to produce a certain rise in temperature.
(3) That, otherwise, the method of calculating heat added to a gas is the same as that for a solid or liquid.

For the purposes of this work, we shall assume that the specific heats of any gas are constant throughout the whole temperature range. This is not strictly true of the gases we meet with in heat engines, but in dealing with the questions we shall consider, the results will not be materially affected. We have seen that C_p is greater than C_v, because in heating a gas at constant pressure, work is done on an external body in addition to raising the temperature. As the doing of work necessitates expenditure of energy, some of the heat *supplied* to the gas has not remained in it, or has not *entered* permanently into it. We may thus distinguish between heat *supplied* to a gas and heat *entering* a gas.

EXAMPLE. Heat is supplied to 5 lbs. of air first at constant pressure and then at constant volume, so as to raise the temperature from 300° abs. to 375° abs.   Find the difference in heat supplied in the two cases. $C_p = 0\cdot237$; $C_v = 0\cdot169$.

Express the difference in ft.-lbs.

Heat supplied at constant pressure =

$5 \times 0\cdot237 \times (375 - 300) = 5 \times 0\cdot237 \times 75 = 88\cdot87$ C.H.U.

Heat supplied at constant volume =

$5 \times 0\cdot169 \times (375 - 300) = 5 \times 0\cdot169 \times 75 = 63\cdot37$ C.H.U.

Difference $= 88\cdot87 - 63\cdot37 = 25\cdot5$ C.H.U.

Expressed in ft.-lbs., 25·5 C.H.U. $= 25\cdot5 \times 1,400$ ft.-lbs.

$$= 35,700 \text{ ft.-lbs.}$$

We shall see later that this is the work which would be done on an external body.

The student may note here that when a portion of the atmosphere is heated, such as the air in an ordinary room, it is heated at constant pressure, and therefore the value C_p must be used.

Examples III

1. A block of copper weighing 5 lbs. is taken from a furnace and dropped into a copper calorimeter weighing 0·75 lb. and containing 6·5 lbs. of water. Initial temperature of calorimeter and water was 14° C. and after the copper had been added it rose to 58° C. Find the temperature of the furnace.

2. Mercury at a temperature of 60° C. and weighing 1·5 lb. is poured into 2·4 lbs. of water at 15° C. Find the final temperature of the mixture.

3. A copper vessel weighs 2·8 lbs. and contains 4 lbs. of petroleum and 8·56 lbs. of aluminium. Find the water equivalent of the whole. How much heat is needed to raise the temperature 18·24° C.?

4. Cooling water is supplied to a condenser at 11° C. and leaves it at 31·5° C. The supply is 1,250 lbs. per minute. Find the heat carried away in ft.-lbs. per minute and express it in horse power.

5. The air supplied to boiler furnaces is sometimes pre-heated. In a similar case, the boiler-house temperature was 18° C. and the heated air was at a temperature of 195° C. The weight of air supplied per lb. of coal is 18·4 lbs. Find the quantity of heat supplied by the air to the furnace per lb. of coal burnt, if the specific heat of air at constant pressure is 0·238.

6. An oil-fired boiler takes 21·6 lbs. of air per lb. of oil. The products of combustion may be taken as equal in weight to oil and air. The oil-supply and air-supply are both fed at boiler room temperature, which is 16° C. If the temperature of the flue gases is 260° C. and their specific heat is 0·24, calculate the quantity of heat carried away per lb. of oil consumed.

CHAPTER IV

THERMAL PROPERTIES OF PERFECT GASES

21. First Law of Thermodynamics. This law states a principle with which the student has already gained some familiarity, and may be expressed as follows : Heat and mechanical energy are mutually convertible.

The conversion factor is called Joule's Mechanical Equivalent, and is such that one centigrade heat unit = 1,400 ft.-lbs.

22. Principle of the Heat Engine. Mention has already been made (see art. 5) of a working substance. At the present time engineers always use a gas or vapour as the working substance in a heat engine, nothing else having been found as yet to be practicable. Moreover, we have not yet discovered any practical method of changing large quantities of heat into work without the agency of a working substance.

This working substance receives and gives up heat, changing its pressure, volume and temperature to suit the circumstances, but it should be clearly understood that none of the working substance is destroyed or reduced in quantity.

The study of heat engines is largely directed to calculations relating to the changing pressure, volume, and temperature of the working substance. These quantities are determined when we know the *state* of the gas, and it is vital to know what relationships exist between the state of a gas, and its heat content.

We are, on this account, deeply concerned with the *properties* of the *working substance*.

23. State of a Substance. By the state, we mean the condition of *pressure*, *volume*, *temperature* and *heat* *content* at any instant. Unless otherwise stated, the amount of substance considered in calculations relating to the working substance is generally 1 lb., and most tables of properties, and standard diagrams, are prepared for 1 lb. of substance. Omission of a weight generally means assuming the weight to be unity, and failure to recognize this sometimes causes the student some difficulty.

Knowledge of the state of a substance will fix the properties of unit weight necessary to determine the amount of work done by 1 lb., or by 1 cu. ft., as the case may be.

Again, the state leads to a knowledge of the energy contained in unit weight of the substance. For example, the state of steam is known when its pressure and temperature, or pressure and dryness fraction are known, and from this the volume and energy content can be deduced.

The state of a perfect gas is defined when we know the pressure, volume of 1 lb., and the temperature. From this information we can determine the energy content, when we know certain figures which are properly called gas constants.

We may summarize by stating the following facts:

(1) The heat engine uses heat and converts it into mechanical work.

(2) The working substance is not destroyed, though its state, and, therefore, its heat content changes.

(3) The heat content gives valuable information, which can only be extracted when we know the thermal properties of the working substance.

24. Laws of Perfect Gases. A perfect gas is one which obeys Boyle's Law and to which Joule's law of energy is applicable. Both these laws are dealt with below.

25. Boyle's Law. The volume of a given mass of a perfect gas varies inversely as the absolute pressure *when the temperature is constant*.

Let P = the absolute pressure of the gas.

V = volume occupied when pressure = P.

Then the above law states that $V \propto \dfrac{1}{P}$.

This may be written as an equation by introducing a constant C.

$$\text{Then } V = \frac{C}{P} \text{ or } PV = C.$$

This shows that the product of the absolute pressure

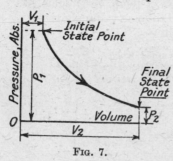

FIG. 7.

and volume of a *given quantity* of gas is constant, when the temperature does not change.

Let a quantity of gas at pressure P_1 and volume V_1 (see fig. 7) change its pressure and volume in a cylinder without change of temperature.

Let P_2 and V_2 be the final pressure and volume respectively.

Then anywhere on the curve $PV = C$.

$$\therefore P_1V_1 = C \text{ and } P_2V_2 = C.$$
$$\therefore P_1V_1 = P_2V_2$$

This is a useful working form of Boyle's Law as it avoids the necessity for calculating C.

EXAMPLE. Four cubic feet of gas at a pressure of 120 lbs. per square inch absolute expand at constant temperature until the volume is 20 cubic feet. Find the final pressure.

Since temperature is constant the expansion is according to Boyle's Law, and fig. 7 may represent the change.

Initial state is P_1V_1. Final state is P_2V_2.

$$P_1V_1 = P_2V_2.$$
$$\therefore P_2 = P_1 \frac{V_1}{V_2}$$

$$\left(\text{It may be noted that } P_2 = P_1 \div \text{ a volume ratio, } \frac{V_2}{V_1} \right).$$

$$\therefore P_2 = 120 \text{ lbs. per sq. inch} \times \frac{4 \text{ cu. ft.}}{20 \text{ cu. ft.}}$$

$$= 24 \text{ lbs. per sq. in. absolute.}$$

26. **Charles's Law of Gases.** Equal volumes of different gases expand equally for equal increases of

temperature, provided that the *pressure remains constant* during the expansion.

It is found by experiment that the change in volume per degree centigrade of temperature change is $\frac{1}{273}$ of the volume of the gas at $0°$ C. Thus 5 cu. ft. of any gas at $0°$ C. would expand to $5 + (\frac{5}{273} \times$ temp. rise) cubic feet when the temperature increased to some value above $0°$ C., the pressure remaining constant.

EXAMPLE. Find the volume occupied when a given quantity of gas exists at a temperature of $400°$ C., if the volume of this quantity of gas at $0°$ C. is 20 cu. ft., the pressure being the same at both temperatures.

Since the pressure is the same throughout Charles's Law is applicable.

Increase in volume $= \frac{1}{273} \times 20$ cu. ft. per degree C.

Total increase in volume $= \frac{1}{273} \times 20 \times 400$ cu. ft.

$$= \frac{8,000}{273} = 29·3 \text{ cu. ft.}$$

$\therefore$ Final volume $= 20 + 29·3 = 49·3$ cu. ft.

Alternative View of Charles's Law.

The above method of using Charles's Law is not the most convenient.

Imagine 273 cu. ft. of gas at $0°$ C., and at a pressure which remains constant whilst the temperature is reduced. Let the temperature be $- t°$ C. and the volume at this temperature V. Then, if we assume that Charles's Law holds until the temperature reaches its lowest limit, we should get the following values of V and $- t°$ C.

V					$- t$	T
273 cu. ft.	.	.	.	.	$0°$ C.	$273°$
272 ,,	.	.	.	.	$- 1°$ C.	$272°$
270 ,,	.	.	.	.	$- 3°$ C.	$270°$
200 ,,	.	.	.	.	$- 73°$ C.	$200°$
100 ,,	.	.	.	.	$- 173°$ C.	$100°$
10 ,,	.	.	.	.	$- 263°$ C.	$10°$
0 ,,	.	.	.	.	$- 273°$ C.	$0°$

(It will be noticed that the volume has disappeared. In practice this cannot occur for the gas would become liquid before $- 273°$ C. was reached.)

If we constructed a new scale of temperature with its

zero at $-273°$ C., we should get the values under T in the third column. All that has been done is that 273 has been added to each value of $-t°$ C.

We now see that volumes and temperatures rise together in the same proportion and that

$$\frac{V}{T} = 1$$

If the volume is made some multiple of 273, say 273 C, where C is a constant having any positive value whatsoever,

then $\frac{V}{T} = C$ or $V = CT$

Thus the law of Charles may be stated as follows : The total volume of a given quantity of gas varies directly as the absolute temperature when the pressure is kept constant.

Stated algebraically the law is $V \propto T$ or $V = CT$ when pressure does not vary.

The useful form in the working of examples is

$$\frac{V}{T} = C \text{ or } \frac{V_1}{T_1} = \frac{V_2}{T_2}.$$

EXAMPLE. Five cubic feet of gas at 40° C. receives heat at constant pressure so that the final temperature is 200° C. Find the final volume, and write down the increase during the supply of heat.

This is Charles's Law, because the pressure is constant.

The pressure-volume diagram for this change is shown in fig. 8.

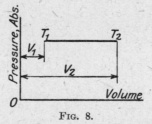

FIG. 8.

Since temperatures are not absolute, 273 must be added.

$$\therefore T_1 = 40 + 273 = 313° \text{ abs.}$$
$$\text{and } T_2 = 200 + 273 = 473° \text{ ,,}$$

Now
$$\frac{V_2}{T_2} = \frac{V_1}{T_1}$$

$$\therefore V_2 = \frac{V_1}{T_1}T_2 = \frac{5 \times 473}{313} \text{ cu. ft.}$$

$$= \frac{2,365}{313} = 7 \cdot 556 \text{ cu. ft.}$$

$\therefore$ Increase in volume $= 7 \cdot 556 - 5 = 2 \cdot 556$ cu. ft.

EXAMPLE. The temperature of the charge of gas at the beginning of fuel admission in a Diesel engine cylinder is 350° C., and the volume of the gas charge at the end of the heat supply is 1·9 times the volume at the beginning. If the heat is supplied at constant pressure, find the temperature at the end of the heat supply period.

This again is Charles's Law. This application to an engine problem shows that these fundamental laws have their practical applications later. The P — V diagram is shown in fig. 8.

$$\frac{V_2}{V_1} = 1 \cdot 9 \text{ and } T_1 = 350 + 273 = 623° \text{ abs.}$$

$$\frac{T_2}{V_2} = \frac{T_1}{V_1}$$

$$\therefore T_2 = \frac{V_2}{V_1}T_1 = 1 \cdot 9 \times 623$$

$$= 1183 \cdot 7° \text{ absolute}$$

$$= (1183 \cdot 7 - 273)° \text{ C.}$$

$$= 910 \cdot 7° \text{ C.}$$

The working forms of Boyle's Law and Charles's Law are worthy of note for comparison.

Boyle's Law	*Charles's Law*

$$\left.\begin{array}{c} \dfrac{P_1}{V_2} = \dfrac{P_2}{V_1} \\ \text{or} \\ \dfrac{P_1}{P_2} = \dfrac{V_2}{V_1} \end{array}\right\} \begin{array}{c}\text{Temperature}\\\text{Constant}\end{array} \qquad \left.\begin{array}{c} \dfrac{T_1}{T_2} = \dfrac{V_1}{V_2} \\ \text{or} \\ \dfrac{V_2}{T_2} = \dfrac{V_1}{T_1} \end{array}\right\} \begin{array}{c}\text{Pressure}\\\text{Constant}\end{array}$$

27. Combination of the Laws of Boyle and Charles.

The pressure, volume and temperature of a gas may all change at once. In this case, because pressure changes, Charles's Law will not apply and because the temperature changes Boyle's Law will not apply. We require some principle by which to treat this important case.

This change of state may be regarded as taking place in two stages.

(a) by a change according to Boyle's Law, followed by

(b) a change according to Charles's Law.

Let us consider a given quantity of a perfect gas at pressure P_1, volume V_1, and temperature T_1, in a cylinder A (fig. 9); the same gas is found later to be in the state P_2, V_2, T_2, as in cylinder C.

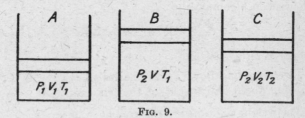

Fig. 9.

We may imagine an intermediate state as having existed —shown at B. Then because the temperature is the same in A and B, the change from A to B follows Boyle's Law.

Hence
$$P_1 V_1 = P_2 V$$

$$\therefore V = \frac{P_1}{P_2} V_1 \quad \cdots \quad (1)$$

In the change from B to C the pressure remains the same whilst the temperature changes; hence Charles's Law applies.

$$\therefore \frac{V}{V_2} = \frac{T_1}{T_2}$$

$$\therefore V = \frac{T_1}{T_2} V_2 \quad \cdots \quad (2)$$

In equations (1) and (2), the volume V is that in B, and hence is the same quantity for both equations.

$$\therefore \frac{P_1}{P_2} V_1 = \frac{T_1}{T_2} V_2 \quad \cdots \quad (3)$$

$$\therefore \frac{P_1 V_1}{T_1} = \frac{P_2 V_2}{T_2} \quad \cdots \quad (4)$$

It is obvious, by similar reasoning, that if this quantity of gas underwent a further change to the state P_3, V_3, T_3, the equation (4) could be added to as below.

$$\frac{P_1V_1}{T_1} = \frac{P_2V_2}{T_2} = \frac{P_3V_3}{T_3}$$

This result may be expressed thus : **The product of the pressure and volume of a quantity of gas divided by its absolute temperature is a constant**, and this again may be written algebraically

$$\frac{PV}{T} = K \text{ or } PV = KT \quad . \quad . \quad . \quad . \quad (5)$$

where K is a constant.

In considering Boyle's and Charles's Laws we have said nothing about the weight of the gas concerned.

The weight contained in the volume V depends upon the density, that is upon the specific volume of the gas.

Definition. The density of a gas or vapour is the weight of unit volume at a given temperature and pressure.

Usually we shall state it as the weight of one cubic foot.

Definition. The specific volume of a gas or vapour is the volume of unit weight at some stated temperature and pressure.

We shall generally state it in cubic feet per lb.

28. Characteristic Equation of a Gas. We shall now show that the constant K in equation (5) includes the weight of the gas.

Let V_s = the specific volume of a particular gas, whilst P and T are its pressure and temperature.

Then $V = wV_s$ where w is the weight of gas used.

Then we have $\quad PV = KT$

$$\therefore \ PwV_s = KT$$

$$\therefore \quad PV_s = \frac{K}{w}T \quad . \quad . \quad . \quad . \quad (6)$$

$\dfrac{K}{w}$ is a new constant. If, then, we deal with 1 lb. of gas which is represented by V_s, the value $\dfrac{K}{w}$ will always be the same for any given kind of gas.

$$\text{Let } \frac{K}{w} = R, \text{ then } K = wR$$

and equation (5) becomes

$$PV = wRT \quad . \quad . \quad . \quad . \quad (7)$$

and we may also write equation (7) in the form

$$PV_s = RT \quad . \quad . \quad . \quad . \quad (8)$$

Both equations (7) and (8) are very important ones, whilst equation (8) is known as the *Characteristic Equation* of a gas, and the value of R is called the *Characteristic Constant* for the gas.

29. Units of the Characteristic Equation. In using this equation, careful attention needs to be given to the units, and the student is recommended to make himself familiar with one system, confining himself to that system throughout.

The following are the most convenient units for our purpose.

P = absolute pressure in lbs. per sq. ft.

T = absolute temperature in centigrade degrees.

V_s = volume of 1 lb. wt. of gas in cu. ft.

We may interpret the meaning of R in the following way.

Let 1 lb. of gas be enclosed in a cylinder fitted with a piston, and let it be heated at constant pressure so that its temperature is increased by one degree from some value T, to $(T + 1)$. The volume will increase from, say, V_1 to V_2, moving the piston against whatever resistance exists.

Now $PV_1 = RT$

and $PV_2 = R(T + 1)$

∴ subtracting $P(V_2 - V_1) = R(T + 1) - RT = R$.

We have seen (art. 4) that $P(V_2 - V_1)$ is work done. Hence, we see that R is the work done against external resistance when 1 lb. of gas is heated through one degree at constant pressure. The constant, R, thus stands for a quantity of energy, and, with the units adopted in this article, will be in ft.-lbs.

If one pound of a gas is heated at constant pressure through a temperature range $(T_2 - T_1)$, the external energy given to the gas is $R(T_2 - T_1)$.

The numerical value of R will vary according to the temperature scale used. If the Fahrenheit degree is used, then, since it represents a smaller temperature rise, the work done per degree will be less and hence R will have a smaller value.

When air is the gas, the value of R is 96 ft.-lbs. per centigrade degree, and 53·2 ft.-lbs. per Fahrenheit degree.

EXAMPLE. The pressure, volume and temperature of a quantity of gas are respectively 100 lbs. per sq. in. abs., 3 cu. ft., and 150° C. ordinary temperature. A change of state results in the following, volume 9 cu. ft., temperature 10° C. What is the pressure?

Note that no weight is given, hence we use equation (4).

$$\frac{P_1 V_1}{T_1} = \frac{P_2 V_2}{T_2}$$

$$\therefore P_2 = P_1 \times \frac{V_1}{V_2} \times \frac{T_2}{T_1}$$

$$= (100 \times 144) \times \frac{3}{9} \times \frac{283}{423}$$

$$= 3,210 \text{ lbs. per sq. ft.}$$
$$= 22\cdot3 \text{ lbs. per sq. in.}$$

EXAMPLE. The state of a quantity of gas enclosed in a gas engine cylinder at the beginning of compression is volume 1·8 cu. ft., temperature 80° C., and pressure 14 lbs. per sq. in. What will be the temperature after the volume is reduced to 0·5 cu. ft., and the pressure raised to 105 lbs. per sq. in.?

Fig. 10 indicates the change on the P–V diagram.

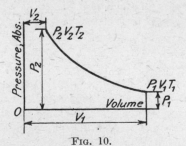

FIG. 10.

D

Equation (4) is again used.

$$\frac{P_1 V_1}{T_1} = \frac{P_2 V_2}{T_2}$$

$$T_2 = T_1 \times \frac{P_2}{P_1} \times \frac{V_2}{V_1}$$

$$= 353 \times \frac{105 \times 144}{14 \times 144} \times \frac{0.5}{1.8}$$

$$= \frac{353 \times 7.5}{3.6} = 736° \text{ C. absolute}$$

$$= 736 - 273 = 463° \text{ C. ordinary.}$$

The student may note that the pressure ratio and the volume ratio are the important factors in this example, and the units chosen are immaterial.

EXAMPLE. The characteristic equation of a certain gas is $PV = 98T$, T being in centigrade degrees. Find the weight of this gas which occupies 200 cu. ft. at 100 lbs. per sq. in. abs. and 200° C. (ordinary temperature).

Equation (7) gives the desired result.

$$PV = wRT$$

$$\therefore w = \frac{PV}{RT} = \frac{100 \times 144 \times 200}{98 \times 473}$$

$$= 62.2 \text{ lbs.}$$

We may proceed thus :

Vol. of 1 lb. of gas at 100 lbs. per sq. in. and 473° abs.

$$= V_s = \frac{RT}{P}$$

$$\therefore V_s = \frac{98 \times 473}{100 \times 144} = 3.22 \text{ cu. ft.}$$

$$\therefore \text{ Density of gas} = \text{wt. per cu. ft.} = \frac{1}{3.22} \text{ lbs. per cu. ft.}$$

$$\therefore \text{ Weight} = \text{volume} \times \text{density} = \frac{200}{3.22} = 62.2 \text{ lbs.}$$

EXAMPLE. Three pounds of gas at 120 lbs. per sq. in. and 80° C. are placed in a cylinder. What is the volume of the cylinder if the characteristic constant is 97 ?

$$PV_s = RT$$

$$\therefore \text{ vol. of 1 lb.} = \frac{RT}{P} = \frac{97 \times 353}{120 \times 144}$$

$$= 1.98 \text{ cu. ft.}$$

$$\therefore \text{ Volume occupied by 3 lbs.} = 1.98 \times 3$$

$$= 5.94 \text{ cu. ft.}$$

$$= \text{volume of cylinder.}$$

EXAMPLES IV

1. Air, occupying 12·4 cu. ft. at 14·7 lbs. per sq. in. pressure, is compressed into a space of 2·6 cu. ft. without change of temperature. What is the pressure ?

2. A room measures 30 ft. × 25 × 12 ft. The temperature of the air in the room is raised from 6° C. to 16° C. What volume of air at the higher temperature passes out of the room ?

3. A pound of hydrogen occupies 178·2 cu. ft. at 0° C. and 14·7 lbs. per sq. in. pressure. What is the volume at 15° C. and 14·5 lbs. per sq. in. pressure ?

4. A gas at 0° C. and 14·7 lbs. per sq. in. is said to be at normal temperature and pressure (N.T.P.). Reduce 56 cu. ft. of carbon dioxide at 30° C. and 18 lbs. per sq. in. to its volume at normal temperature and pressure.

5. A volume of air, 12·39 cu. ft. at 0° C. and 14·7 lbs. per sq. in. is raised to a temperature of 20° C. without change of pressure. Find the new volume, and the work done by the air during the expansion in foot-lbs. What is the work done per degree rise of temperature in this case ?

6. The characteristic constant of hydrogen is 1,382 ft.-lbs. per degree centigrade. A quantity of hydrogen occupies 89·1 cu. ft. at 29·8 lbs. per sq. in. and 0° C. What weight of gas is present ?

7. The cylinder of an air compressor is 24 ins. dia. and 4 ft. long. At the end of the suction stroke it is filled with air at 13·5 lbs. per sq. in. pressure, and at a temperature of 22° C. When 3 ft. of the compression stroke have been completed the pressure is 60 lbs. per sq. in. Find the temperature of the air.

8. The specific volume of oxygen at N.T.P. is 11·21 cu. ft. What weight of oxygen is contained in a cylinder 5 ft. long by 5 ins. diameter when the pressure is 1,400 lbs. per sq. in. and the temperature 15° C. ?

9. Calculate the volume of 15 lbs. weight of air at 100 lbs. per sq. in. absolute pressure and at a temperature of 25° C.

If this air is now heated to 50° C. at constant volume, what will be its new pressure ? R = 96.   N.C.T.E.C.

10. What is the law connecting the pressure, volume and temperature of 1 lb. of air, given that at atmospheric pressure (14·7 lbs. per sq. in.) and at 0° C. the volume of 1 lb. of air is 12·39 cu. ft. Four cubic feet of air at a pressure of 30 lbs. per sq. in. absolute and at a temperature of 35° C. are heated at constant volume. Calculate the number of units of heat added if the final temperature is 120° C.

Specific heat of air at constant volume is 0·169.   U.E.I.

11. State separately and distinctly Boyle's and Charles's Laws. Give the rule relating the pressure, volume and temperature of a

gas, which is derived from these laws, stating exactly the meaning of each letter, and the unit in which it is expressed.

If at 0° C., and standard atmospheric pressure of 14·7 lbs./sq. in. the weight of dry air is 0·0807 lb. per cu. ft., obtain the value of the constant in the equation connecting the pressure, volume and temperature of a gas.

If one ounce of air at a certain pressure, volume 88 cu. ins., and temperature 13° C. be compressed to volume 48 cu. ins. and the temperature raised to 39° C., find the ratio of the final to the initial pressure.

U.E.I.

12. During a test of a gas engine working on the "Otto Cycle," 8,449 cu. ft. of mixture (air and gas) at atmospheric pressure and at a temperature of 13·8° C. entered the cylinder per hour. The engine was running at 165·8 revs. per min. and there was an impulse stroke every cycle ; diameter of cylinder 14 ins. and piston stroke 22 ins.

Determine the increase of temperature of the charge which took place during the suction stroke, assuming that "wire drawing" is negligible.

U.L.C.I.

13. The clearance volume of a gas engine is 750 cu. ins., and immediately after explosion the temperature and pressure of the gases are found to be 1,120° C. and 220 lbs. per sq. in. abs. respectively. When the piston has swept a volume of 2,250 cu. ins., the pressure is shown by the indicator diagram to be 48 lbs. per sq. in. abs. What is the temperature of the gases in the cylinder at this point ?

CHAPTER V

HEAT CHANGES IN GASES

30. Introductory. Having considered separately the quantity of heat absorbed by a gas, and the changes in pressure volume and temperature as related to each other, in this chapter we combine the two aspects. The student is reminded that gases and vapours are used as working substances because they can readily absorb or yield up heat, and because the change in heat content produces changes in pressure and volume which are appreciable in amount. It should be understood, however, that the heat in the gas is the dominating factor, and that the pressure and volume changes are the results, which we find it convenient to use when the work is done in a cylinder. Consideration of the steam turbine will enable us to see that we are not compelled to obtain energy from a gas or vapour merely through its pressure, for in this case, change of momentum in the steam supplies the necessary propelling force.

The student is here warned against the common error of supposing that the pressure determines the energy contained in a working substance ; that quantity depends upon the heat in the substance.

31. Effects of Heat Supply to a Gas. When heat is supplied to a given weight of a gas, several effects are possible. The following three cases cover these possibilities and the third is capable of further subdivision.

CASE I. The temperature may rise without change in volume. The pressure will rise but no work is done since there is no movement.

Case II. The temperature may rise and the volume increase whilst the pressure remains constant. Work is done as heat is being added.

Case III. The temperature, volume and pressure may all change during the supply of heat. This is the most general case and requires extended treatment.

We shall now consider in detail cases I and II.

32. Heating a Gas at Constant Volume. This case has been mentioned in article 20. Let us consider 1 lb. of gas. Let the initial state be denoted by the suffix (2) and final state by suffix (1). Let T be absolute temperature.

Then heat supplied $= 1 \times C_v \times (T_1 - T_2)$
$$= C_v (T_1 - T_2) \text{ heat units per lb.}$$

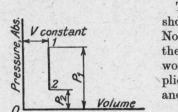

The PV diagram, fig. 11, shows this change of state. Note that there is no area under the " curve " and no external work is done. The heat supplied all enters into the gas and we may write

Fig. 11.

Heat supplied
$$= \text{heat entering gas.}$$
$$= C_v(T_1 - T_2).$$

33. Heating a Gas at Constant Pressure. In the cylinders a and b, fig. 12, we have 1 lb. of gas. The initial state is as in (a) and the final state as in (b). Note that P is the pressure in both cases so that the piston must be free to move. As the temperature increases the volume increases. In these circumstances

Heat supplied to 1 lb. of gas $= 1 \times$ sp. ht. at constant pressure $\times$ temperature rise $= C_p \times (T_1 - T_2)$.

The change in the state of the gas is shown in the P – V diagram, fig. 13.

Owing to the increase in volume work has been done against external resistance, and the increase in volume is the direct result of supplying heat. Work would not have been done if heat had not been added.

Here we have the vital principle of all heat engines, viz. that work is done because heat is supplied.

If we know the initial and final volumes V_2 and V_1 then we know that

External work done $= P(V_1 - V_2)$ ft.-lbs.

$$= \frac{P}{J}(V_1 - V_2) \text{ heat units.}$$

where $J =$ Joule's mechanical equivalent.

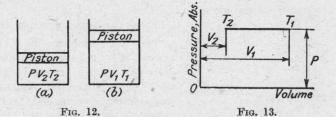

FIG. 12.   FIG. 13.

Here we may distinguish between the heat supplied to a gas and the heat entering a gas.

The heat has all been received by the gas, but a portion has been transformed into mechanical work, and has not entered permanently into the gas. The heat which is thus retained in the gas is spoken of as Internal Energy; that which is done against external resistance or pressure is called External Energy.

In this case we may say that

Increase in Internal Energy

= Heat supplied — Heat transformed into work.

$$= C_p(T_1 - T_2) - \frac{P}{J}(V_1 - V_2)$$

EXAMPLE. How much heat will be necessary to raise the temperature of 3 lbs. of gas from 200° C. to 500° C., the volume remaining

constant during the heat supply. Sp. ht. at constant volume
= 0·17.

Heat required = 3 lbs. × 0·17 × (500° − 200°)
= 3 × 0·17 × 300 = 153 C.H.U.

34. Energy of Gases. The internal energy of a
quantity of gas is the heat in it at a stated temperature,
reckoned from some temperature chosen as a base.

Experiments made by Dr. Joule led him to the conclusion
that the internal energy of a gas was dependent on temperature alone. It does not depend on pressure and volume.
The external energy, however, does depend on pressure and
volume.

Joule's Energy Law for Gases. "The internal energy
of a given quantity of a gas depends entirely on temperature."

Generally we are not concerned with total internal energy
but rather with change of internal energy. In calculations
we may choose any suitable temperature as a base. In
some cases we choose 100° C. as base, whilst in others,
particularly with permanent gases, we calculate internal
energies with reference to the absolute zero of temperature.

Thus if 1 lb. of gas has an absolute temperature of T_2
and it is raised to T_1, the increase in internal energy

$$= C_v(T_1 - T_2).$$

This is true no matter what happens to the volume, for
Joule's Law tells us that the internal energy depends on
temperature alone.

The external work done by a gas is the energy expended
by the gas on outside matter in expanding against the
constant pressure under which the gas exists. For doing
this work heat is required, which must be supplied from
some outside source.

If we start from some temperature as a base, and raise
the temperature to some definite value at constant pressure,
we shall

(1) put internal energy into the gas,

(2) expend energy in doing external work.

The first will be the internal energy gained by the gas and the second will be the increase of external energy of the gas, and the sum of these two quantities will be the total heat energy supplied.

If T_2 be our starting or base temperature, and T_1 the final temperature, we shall have

$$\text{Internal energy increase} = C_v(T_1 - T_2)$$
$$\text{Total heat supplied} = C_p(T_1 - T_2)$$
$$\therefore \; C_p(T_1 - T_2) = C_v(T_1 - T_2) + \text{External work done.}$$

EXAMPLE. How much heat must be supplied to 3 lbs. of gas to raise its temperature from 200° C. to 500° C. at constant pressure ? Find also the external work done during the supply of heat. Specific heat at constant pressure = $C_p = 0\cdot24$. $C_v = 0\cdot17$.

Heat required = Weight × sp. ht. × temperature rise
= $3 \times 0\cdot24 \times (500 - 200)$
= 216 C.H.U.

Heat entering gas as internal energy

= Weight × sp. ht. at const. vol. × temp. rise
= $3 \times 0\cdot17 \times (500 - 200)$
= 153 C.H.U.

External work done = (216 − 153) C.H.U.

= 63 C.H.U.

This should be compared with the last example.

EXAMPLE. The characteristic constant for a gas is 98 ft.-lbs. per lb. per degree centigrade, and 2·2 lbs. of this gas receive heat at constant pressure of 120 lbs. per sq. in. abs., the temperature rising from 30° C. to 200° C. (ordinary temperatures) as a result of the heat supply. If $C_v = 0\cdot17$ for this gas, find (a) the increase in internal energy, (b) increase in external energy, (c) increase in total energy.

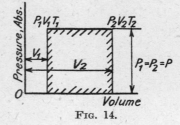

FIG. 14.

Fig. 14 shows the P–V diagram.

Increase in internal energy = wt. × C_v $(T_2 - T_1)$
= $2\cdot2 \times 0\cdot17 \times (473 - 303)$
= $2\cdot2 \times 0\cdot17 \times 170$ = 63·6 C.H.U.

To find V_1.

$$P_1 V_{s1} = RT_1$$

$$\therefore V_{s1} = \frac{RT_1}{P_1} = \frac{98 \times 303}{144 \times 120}$$

$$= 1 \cdot 718 \text{ cu. ft.} = \text{specific volume.}$$

$$\therefore V_1 = 1 \cdot 718 \times 2 \cdot 2 = 3 \cdot 78 \text{ cu. ft.}$$

V_2 may be found by using Charles's Law.

$$\frac{V_2}{T_2} = \frac{V_1}{T_1}$$

$$\therefore V_2 = \frac{V_1 T_2}{T_1}$$

$$= \frac{3 \cdot 78 \times 473}{303} \text{ cu. ft.} = 5 \cdot 9 \text{ cu. ft.}$$

Increase in external energy $= P(V_2 - V_1)$
$$= 144 \times 120(5 \cdot 9 - 3 \cdot 78)$$
$$= 17,280 \times 2 \cdot 12$$
$$= 36,634 \text{ ft.-lbs.} = 26 \cdot 17 \text{ C.H.U.}$$

Total energy increase $= 26 \cdot 17 + 63 \cdot 6 = 89 \cdot 77$ C.H.U.
Note that the total energy increase is the heat supplied.
We may thus proceed to calculate the specific heat at constant pressure.

Total heat supplied $= 89 \cdot 77$ C.H.U.
$$= w \times C_p \times (T_2 - T_1)$$
$$= 2 \cdot 2 \times (473 - 303) \times C_p$$
$$= 2 \cdot 2 \times 170 \times C_p$$

$$\therefore C_p = \frac{89 \cdot 77}{2 \cdot 2 \times 170} = 0 \cdot 24.$$

From the example we gather that we may write
Heat supplied = External work done + Gain in Internal Energy.

Let us now write the internal energy equation below the total energy equation.

Total energy $=$ $89 \cdot 77 = w \times C_p(T_2 - T_1)$
Internal energy $=$ $63 \cdot 6 = w \times C_v(T_2 - T_1)$
subtracting $26 \cdot 17 = w(C_p - C_v)(T_2 - T_1)$

from which $\quad C_p - C_v = \dfrac{26 \cdot 17}{w(T_2 - T_1)} = \dfrac{26 \cdot 17}{2 \cdot 2 \times 170}$

$$= 0 \cdot 07 \text{ C.H.U.}$$
$$= 98 \text{ ft.-lbs. per degree.}$$

From this result it may be observed that the difference
in specific heats is the same as the characteristic constant,
when all units are in ft.-lbs. or heat units.

35. Gas Energy Equation. Summarizing the foregoing results we may say that on heating a gas we may
  (1) raise the temperature and therefore increase the
     internal energy,
  (2) raise the temperature and cause external work to be
     done,
  (3) cause external work to be done whilst the tempera-
     ture remains constant.

All these results are covered by the gas energy equation
given below.

Heat supplied to gas = External work done by gas + in-
                                          crease in internal energy of gas.

This equation may be written in a negative form for
heat abstracted as follows :

Heat abstracted from gas = Work done on gas + Re-
                                          duction in internal energy
                                          of gas.

In general applications of this equation any of the
quantities may be negative relative to the others.

Let H = heat added to a gas and − H = heat ab-
                    stracted,
      W = work done by gas and − W = work done on
                    gas,
      E = gain of internal energy and − E = loss of
                    internal energy.

Then the equation can be written to cover all cases

$$\pm \mathrm{H} = \pm \mathrm{W} \pm \mathrm{E}.$$

It is, of course, necessary in numerical work to give
each term its appropriate sign. Thus, when volume is
increasing, work is being done by the gas and W is positive ;
when volume is decreasing, work is being done on the gas
and W is negative ; when temperature is rising, internal
energy is increasing and E is positive ; when temperature
is falling, internal energy is decreasing and E is negative.

The proper sign can only be inserted when we know the circumstances in each case.

The student should note that this equation is based upon, and is consistent with, the Principle of the Conservation of Energy.

36. Relationship between Gas Constants. The last numerical example showed us some relationship between specific heats and the characteristic constant. We now proceed to treat this generally.

In the reasoning which follows we are dealing with 1 lb. of gas.

Let T_2 = initial absolute temperature.
T_1 = final   ,,   ,,
J = Joule's mechanical equivalent of heat.
R = characteristic constant in ft.-lbs. per degree.
C_p = specific heat at constant pressure in heat units.
C_v = specific heat at constant volume in heat units.
V_2 = initial volume in cu. ft.
V_1 = final   ,,   ,, ,, ,,
P = pressure in lbs. per sq. ft.

Now consider that heat is supplied to one pound of gas at constant pressure, so that work is done by the gas and internal energy is gained. Then

Heat supplied = work done + gain in internal energy.

$$C_p(T_1 - T_2) = \frac{P}{J}(V_1 - V_2) + \text{gain in internal energy.}$$

We have seen, article 34, that gain in internal energy

$$= C_v(T_1 - T_2)$$

$$\therefore \; C_p(T_1 - T_2) = \frac{P}{J}(V_1 - V_2) + C_v(T_1 - T_2)$$

(Note that J is introduced because all units must be either in ft.-lbs. or in heat units.)

$$\therefore \; C_v(T_1 - T_2) = C_p(T_1 - T_2) - \frac{P}{J}(V_1 - V_2).$$

Now from the characteristic equation $P_1V_1 = RT_1$ and $P_2V_2 = RT_2$
and since the pressure is constant $P_1 = P_2 = P$

$$\therefore \ PV_1 = RT_1 \text{ and } PV_2 = RT_2$$
$$\therefore \ PV_1 - PV_2 = RT_1 - RT_2$$
$$\therefore \ P(V_1 - V_2) = R(T_1 - T_2)$$
$$\therefore \ \frac{P}{J}(V_1 - V_2) = \frac{R}{J}(T_1 - T_2)$$

Hence substituting

$$C_v(T_1 - T_2) = C_p(T_1 - T_2) - \frac{R}{J}(T_1 - T_2)$$

$$\therefore \ C_v = C_p - \frac{R}{J}$$

$$\therefore \ C_p - C_v = \frac{R}{J} \text{ or } (C_p - C_v)J = R$$

EXAMPLE. The values of C_p and C_v for a gas are 0·2375 and 0·1691 respectively. Find the density of this gas at 15° C. and 14·7 lbs. per sq. in. absolute.

$$\text{Density} = \frac{1}{\text{specific volume}}$$
$$PV_s = RT \text{ (article 28)}$$
$$\therefore \text{ Specific volume} = \frac{RT}{P}$$

$$\therefore \text{ Density} = \frac{P}{RT} \text{ lbs. per cu. ft.}$$

$$= \frac{14·7 \times 144}{(0·2375 - 0·1691)1,400 \times 288}$$
$$= \frac{14·7 \times 144}{95·76 \times 288}$$
$$= 0·077 \text{ lbs. per cu. ft.}$$

EXAMPLE. A quantity of gas occupies 5 cu. ft. at 180 lbs. per sq. in. and 100° C. Find the change in internal energy if the temperature is increased to 300° C. $C_p = 0·24$ and $C_v = 0·17$.

$$R = (C_p - C_v)J = (0·24 - 0·17) \times 1,400$$
$$= 0·07 \times 1,400 = 98$$
$$PV = wRT \text{ (article 28)}$$

$$\therefore \ w = \text{wt. of gas in lbs.} = \frac{PV}{RT} = \frac{144 \times 180 \times 5}{98 \times 373}$$
$$= 3·55 \text{ lbs.}$$

Change in internal energy $= C_v(T_1 - T_2) \times$ wt.
$$= 0.17 \times (573 - 373) \times 3.55$$
$$= 0.17 \times 200 \times 3.55$$
$$= 120.7 \text{ C.H.U.}$$

EXAMPLE. A quantity of gas occupying 3 cu. ft. at 120 lbs. per sq. in. receives heat at constant pressure until the volume increases to 6 cu. ft. The initial temperature is 200° C. and $C_p = 0.237$ and $C_v = 0.169$. Find the change in internal energy and the external work done during the heat supply.

(There are alternative methods of solving this problem which are instructive.)

(i) $R = (C_p - C_v)J = (0.237 - 0.169)1,400 = 95.2$ ft.-lbs.

$$\text{Weight of gas} = \frac{\text{volume occupied}}{\text{specific volume}}$$

$$\text{Specific volume} = \frac{RT}{P} = \frac{95.2 \times 473}{144 \times 120} = 2.6 \text{ cu. ft.}$$

$$\text{Weight of gas} = \frac{3}{2.6} = 1.153 \text{ lb.}$$

Final temperature $(T_1) = T_2 \times \frac{6}{3} = 473 \times 2 = 946°$ C. abs.
Change in Internal Energy $= w \times C_v(T_1 - T_2)$
$$= 1.153 \times 0.169 \times (946 - 473)$$
$$= 1.153 \times 0.169 \times 473$$
$$= 92.4 \text{ C.H.U.}$$

External work = Heat supplied − Internal energy gain.
$$= wC_p(T_1 - T_2) - 92.4$$
$$= [1.153 \times 0.237 \times 473] - 92.4$$
$$= 129.5 - 92.4 = 37.1 \text{ C.H.U.}$$

(ii) The external work done may also be found as follows :—
External work $= P(V_1 - V_2)$
$$= 120 \times 144 \times (6 - 3)$$
$$= 120 \times 144 \times 3$$
$$= 51,840 \text{ ft.-lbs.}$$
$$= 37 \text{ C.H.U.}$$

(iii) Again $PV_1 = wRT_1$ and $PV_2 = wRT_2$.
$$\therefore PV_1 - PV_2 = wRT_1 - wRT_2$$
$$= w \times R \times (T_1 - T_2)$$
$$= 1.153 \times 95.2 \times 473$$
$$= 51,840 \text{ ft.-lbs.} = 37 \text{ C.H.U.}$$

EXAMPLES V

1. Six pounds of gas at temperature 200° C. and pressure 120 lbs. per sq. in. receive heat at constant pressure until the final tempera-

ture is 600° C. If $C_p = 0.24$ and $C_v = 0.17$, find the external work done during the heat supply.

2. Five pounds weight of gas with specific heats as above receive heat at constant volume and the temperature rises from 150° C. to 400° C. How much heat is supplied ? The same weight of gas is now heated at constant pressure from 150° C. to 400° C. How much heat is supplied in this case ? What becomes of the difference in the two cases ?

3. A cylinder contains 2 lbs. of air occupying a volume of 18 cu. ft. at a temperature of 11° C. Later it has a volume of 5 cu. ft. and a temperature of 85° C. Find the increase in internal energy if $C_v = 0.17$.

4. A gas has its temperature raised at constant pressure of 60 lbs. per sq. in. absolute from 10° C. to 400° C. Its initial volume is 10 cu. ft. Find the external work done.

5. The values of C_p and C_v for a gas are 0.239 and 0.169 respectively. Find the specific volume at 0° C. and 14.7 lbs. per sq. in. absolute of this gas. What is its density ?

6. A quantity of gas occupying 10 cu. ft. at 180 lbs. per sq. in. absolute receives heat at constant pressure until the volume increases to 16 cu. ft. The initial temperature is 150° C. If $C_p = 0.239$ and $C_v = 0.169$, find the change in internal energy and the external work done during the heat supply.

7. A gas is heated at constant pressure from a temperature of 100° C. to 400° C. Find the external work done per lb. of gas if $R = 98$.

8. 2 lbs. of gas at 15° C. and 30 lbs. per sq. in. absolute occupy a volume of 8.68 cu. ft. If the specific heat of the gas at constant volume is 0.153, find the specific heat at constant pressure.

N.C.T.E.C.

9. Four cubic feet of air at a pressure of 300 lbs. per sq. in. absolute and a temperature of 180° C. expand at constant pressure to a volume of 12 cu. ft. Find the temperature at the end of the expansion and the heat absorbed. (Gas constant $R = 96$ ft.-lbs. per lb. per degree C. ; specific heat of air at constant volume = 0.17).

N.C.T.E.C.

CHAPTER VI

EXPANSION AND COMPRESSION OF GASES

37. When a gas undergoes expansion or increases in volume, work is done by the gas. When a gas undergoes compression or decreases in volume, work is done on the gas. This may be illustrated by means of a cylinder fitted with a piston which allows no leakage and which is loaded with a number of weights as shown in fig. 15.

The number of weights on the piston determines the

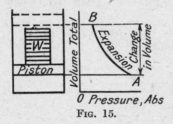

0 Pressure, Abs

Fig. 15.

pressure of the gas. Now remove the weights one by one. Reduction in pressure and, therefore, expansion occur. Movement of the remaining weights on the piston has resulted and hence work has been done in lifting the weights.

The curve AB shows the general outline of the curves of pressure and volume representing such processes. If the piston were started opposite B, and weights were added the gas would be compressed, and the descending weights would do work on the gas. In these changes

$$\text{Ratio of expansion} = \frac{\text{Volume at end of expansion}}{\text{Volume at beginning of expansion}}.$$

$$\text{Ratio of compression} = \frac{\text{Volume at beginning of compression}}{\text{Volume at end of compression}}.$$

Note that both ratios give a value greater than unity since the larger quantity is in the numerator.

38. Laws of Expansion and Compression. The relationship between the pressure and volume of a given quantity of gas can generally be written

$$PV^n = C,$$

where n and C are constants. This equation is known as the law of expansion or compression. The value of n is important and is controlled by the nature of the gas, and the circumstances under which the change takes place. Generally the value of n must be found experimentally. Some typical values of n are given below.

(1) Perfect gas expanding at constant temperature $n = 1$.

(2) Perfect gas expanding without receiving or emitting heat $n = \dfrac{C_p}{C_v}$.

(3) Dry steam expanding, remaining dry throughout $n = \frac{16}{15}$.

(4) Dry steam expanding, without receiving or emitting heat $n = 1 \cdot 135$.

When n has a value greater than unity, the curves of expansion and compression become steeper. Fig. 16 shows

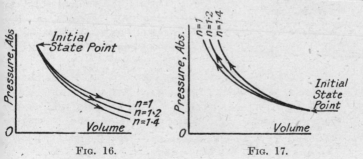

FIG. 16.   FIG. 17.

approximately what occurs during expansion, whilst fig. 17 shows the changes occurring during compression.

39. Working Form of Equation. The working form of the general law of expansion or compression is obtained by writing it for initial and final states.

E

Let suffix (1) denote initial state of gas (see fig. 18).

  ,, ,, (2) ,, final ,, ,, ,,

Then $P_1V_1^n = C$, also $P_2V_2^n = C$.

$$\therefore \ P_1V_1^n = P_2V_2^n.$$

Note that an expression such as V_1^n is not a volume but a mere number.

EXAMPLE. The pressure of a quantity of gas enclosed in a cylinder is 100 lbs. per sq. in. by gauge, and the volume occupied is 3 cu. ft. The gas expands according to the law $PV^{1.3} = C$ until the volume is 12 cu. ft. Find the final pressure.

Draw and dimension the P–V diagram as in fig. 19.

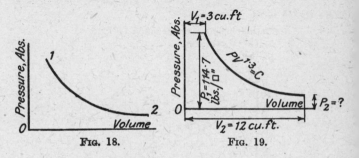

FIG. 18.   FIG. 19.

Pressure given is by gauge, but the pressure used in the equation is always absolute.

$$\therefore \ P_1 = 100 + 14.7 = 114.7 \text{ lbs. per sq. in.}$$
$$P_1V_1^{1.3} = P_2V_2^{1.3}$$
$$\therefore \ P_2 = P_1\left(\frac{V_1}{V_2}\right)^{1.3}$$
$$\therefore \ P_2 = 114.7 \times \left(\frac{3}{12}\right)^{1.3} = 114.7 \times \frac{1}{4^{1.3}}$$

Note that the figure 4 is the expansion ratio, a mere number.

$$1.3 \times \log 4 = 1.3 \times .6021 = 0.7827$$
$$\therefore \ 4^{1.3} = 6.063$$
$$\therefore \ P_2 = \frac{114.7}{6.063} = 18.9 \text{ lbs. per sq. in. abs.}$$
$$= 18.9 - 14.7 = 4.2 \text{ lbs. per sq. in. gauge.}$$

EXAMPLE. The absolute pressure of a quantity of gas is 120 lbs. per sq. in., and the initial volume is 1.5 cu. ft. The gas is expanded according to the law $PV^{1 \cdot 17} = C$ until the pressure is 15 lbs. per sq. in. absolute. Find the final volume.

Fig. 20 shows the P–V curve for the operation.

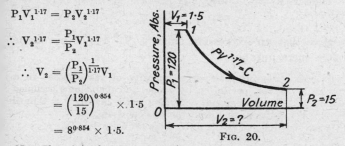

$$P_1 V_1^{1 \cdot 17} = P_2 V_2^{1 \cdot 17}$$

$$\therefore V_2^{1 \cdot 17} = \frac{P_1}{P_2} V_1^{1 \cdot 17}$$

$$\therefore V_2 = \left(\frac{P_1}{P_2}\right)^{\frac{1}{1 \cdot 17}} V_1$$

$$= \left(\frac{120}{15}\right)^{0 \cdot 854} \times 1 \cdot 5$$

$$= 8^{0 \cdot 854} \times 1 \cdot 5.$$

Fig. 20.

Note that 8 is the pressure ratio.

$$0 \cdot 854 \ \log 8 = 0 \cdot 854 \times 0 \cdot 9031 = 0 \cdot 7713$$
$$\therefore 8^{0 \cdot 854} = 5 \cdot 906$$
$$\therefore V_2 = 5 \cdot 906 \times 1 \cdot 5 = 8 \cdot 86 \text{ cu. ft.}$$

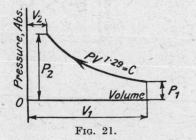

Fig. 21.

EXAMPLE. The " charge " in a gas engine cylinder is compressed through a volume ratio of $4\frac{1}{2}$. Find the final pressure if the initial pressure is 13 lbs. per sq. in. absolute and the law of compression is $PV^{1 \cdot 29} = C$.

$$P_1 V_1^{1 \cdot 29} = P_2 V_2^{1 \cdot 29} \text{ (fig. 21)}.$$

$$P_2 = P_1 \left(\frac{V_1}{V_2}\right)^{1 \cdot 29}$$

$$= 13 \times 4 \cdot 5^{1 \cdot 29}$$

$$1 \cdot 29 \ \log 4 \cdot 5 = 1 \cdot 29 \times 0 \cdot 6532 = 0 \cdot 8426$$
$$\therefore 4 \cdot 5^{1 \cdot 29} = 6 \cdot 96$$
$$\therefore P_2 = 13 \times 6 \cdot 96 = 90 \cdot 48 \text{ lbs. per sq. in. abs.}$$

The above examples show the method of using the given law. In all cases the volume ratio or pressure ratio has been used. The lesser quantity has been made unity and this simplifies the logarithmic work.

The whole equation may be put in logarithmic form thus—

$$\log P_1 + n \log V_1 = \log P_2 + n \log V_2.$$

By transposing we may find an expression for n.

$$n \log V_1 - n \log V_2 = \log P_2 - \log P_1$$
$$n(\log V_1 - \log V_2) = \log P_2 - \log P_1$$
$$\therefore n = \frac{\log P_2 - \log P_1}{\log V_1 - \log V_2}$$

EXAMPLE. The following measurements were made of two points A and B on the expansion curve of a gas engine indicator diagram.

Vertical distance of A above atmospheric line   = 1·44 in.
  ,,   ,,   ,, B ,,   ,,   = 0·33 in.
Horizontal distance of A from zero volume line = 1·775 in.
  ,,   ,,   ,, B ,,   ,,   ,,   = 4·445 ins.

The clearance volume was 140 cubic inches and the swept volume 400 cubic inches. The length of the indicator diagram was 3·7

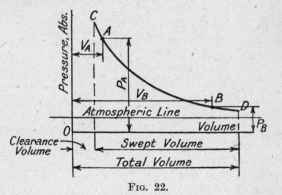

FIG. 22.

inches and the scale of the spring was 120 lbs. per sq. in. per in. Find the value of n in the law of expansion. Sketch and dimension the expansion line to illustrate the problem.

We require to find the pressures and volumes at A and B (fig. 22). CD is the whole expansion line.

Pressure $P_A = (1\cdot44 \times 120) + 14\cdot7 = 187\cdot5$ lbs. per sq. in.
Pressure $P_B = (0\cdot33 \times 120) + 14\cdot7 = 54\cdot3$ lbs. per sq. in.

Volume at $A = V_A = 1\cdot775'' \times \dfrac{400}{3\cdot7} = 192$ cu. ins.

$= 0\cdot111$ cu. ft.

,,   ,, $B = V_B = 4\cdot445'' \times \dfrac{400}{3\cdot7} = 481$ cu. ins.

$= 0\cdot278$ cu. ft.

$$\log P_A + n \log V_A = \log P_B + n \log V_B$$
$$n (\log V_A - \log V_B) = \log P_B - \log P_A$$
$$n(\log 0\cdot111 - \log 0\cdot278) = \log 54\cdot3 - \log 187\cdot5$$
$$n(\bar{1}\cdot0453 - \bar{1}\cdot4440) = 1\cdot7348 - 2\cdot2729$$
$$n = \frac{-0\cdot5381}{-0\cdot3987} = 1\cdot35.$$

40. Work done during Expansion or Compression.

The object of this article is to establish expressions for the work done when expansion or compression occurs according to the law $PV^n = C$. The student who has not yet done sufficient integral calculus to understand the proofs may note the results and examples, and return to the proofs later.

Two cases arise (1) when $n = 1$ (unity).

(2) when n is not unity.

CASE I.   When $PV = C$.

Fig. 23 shows the curve of expansion from volume V_1 to volume V_2 according to the law PV $= C$. We require to find the work done during the expansion.

Let us consider a point where the vol-
ume is V and the pressure P. Let a very small increase δV in the volume occur. The pressure

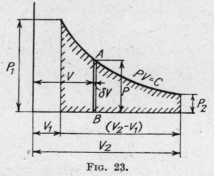

FIG. 23.

P will decrease a very small amount and we may say (very approximately)

Work done during increase δV, in volume, $= P.\delta V$. When δV becomes infinitely small we may adopt the calculus notation and write

$$dW = P.dV \text{ where } W = \text{work done.}$$

$\therefore$ Total work done during expansion

$$= W = \int_{V_1}^{V_2} P.dV.$$

but

$$P = \frac{C}{V}$$

$\therefore$

$$W = C \int_{V_1}^{V_2} \frac{dV}{V} = C \left[\log_e V \right]_{V_1}^{V_2}$$

$$= C(\log_e V_2 - \log_e V_1)$$

But $C = PV$

$\therefore$

$$W = PV(\log_e V_2 - \log_e V_1)$$

$$= PV\log_e \frac{V_2}{V_1}$$

$$\frac{V_2}{V_1} = \text{expansion ratio} = r$$

$\therefore$ Work done $= PV \log_e r$.

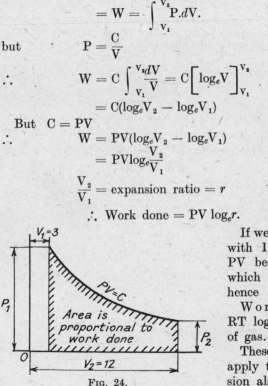

Fig. 24.

If we are dealing with 1 lb. of gas PV becomes PV_s which equals RT, hence

Work done $=$ RT $\log_e r$ per lb. of gas.

These results apply to compression also.

EXAMPLE. A quantity of gas, occupying 3 cu. ft. at a pressure of 120 lbs. per sq. in. absolute, expands until the volume is 12 cu. ft. according to the law $PV = C$. Find the work done during expansion.

$$P_1 V_1 = P_2 V_2 = PV \text{ (fig. 24).}$$

Thus we can take any product of P and V which we happen to know.

Work done $= P_1 V_1 \log_e r$

$$= 120 \times 144 \times 3 \times \log_e \frac{12}{3}$$
$$= 120 \times 144 \times 3 \times \log_e 4$$
$$= 120 \times 144 \times 3 \times 2{\cdot}3026 \times \log_{10} 4$$
$$= 120 \times 144 \times 3 \times 2{\cdot}3026 \times 0{\cdot}6021$$
$$= 72{,}000 \text{ ft.-lbs.}$$

EXAMPLE. The characteristic constant for a gas is 96 ft.-lbs. per degree centigrade. One pound of this gas expands at constant temperature of 200° C. through a volume ratio of 6. Find the work done.

Work done per lb. $= PV_e \log_e r$
$$= RT \log_e r$$
$$= 96 \times 473 \times 2{\cdot}3026 \times \log_{10} 6$$
$$= 96 \times 473 \times 2{\cdot}3026 \times 0{\cdot}7782$$
$$= 81{,}500 \text{ ft.-lbs.}$$

CASE II. When n is not unity. $PV^n = C$ (fig. 25). With the same notation and reasoning as in Case I we get

$$dW = P.dV$$

$$\therefore \text{ Work done} = W = \int_{V_1}^{V_2} P.dV$$

$$PV^n = C \therefore P = \frac{C}{V^n} = CV^{-n}$$

$$\therefore \text{ Work done} = C \int_{V_1}^{V_2} V^{-n} dV = C \left[\frac{V^{-n+1}}{-n+1} \right]_{V_1}^{V_2}$$

$$= C \left(\frac{V_2^{1-n} - V_1^{1-n}}{1-n} \right)$$

but $C = P_1 V_1^n = P_2 V_2^n$

$$\therefore W = \frac{P_2 V_2^n . V_2^{1-n} - P_1 V_1^n . V_1^{1-n}}{1-n}$$

$$= \frac{P_2 V_2 - P_1 V_1}{1-n}$$

$$= \frac{P_1 V_1 - P_2 V_2}{n-1}$$

This equation will give a positive result if P_1 and V_1 refer to initial state and expansion occurs. It will give a negative result if P_1 and V_1 refer to initial state and compression occurs. If P_1 refers to the higher pressure

and V_1 the smaller volume it will give a positive result
in all cases. The negative result in connection with compression means that work is done on the gas and not by
the gas. Pressures must be absolute and if they are in

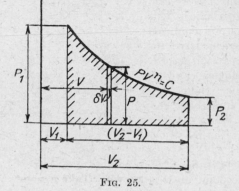

Fig. 25.

lbs. per square foot and volumes in cubic feet the work
done will be in ft.-lbs.

The student is warned against using this formula when
$n = 1$, for then the work done would be indeterminate.

EXAMPLE. Three cubic feet of gas expand according to the law
$PV^{1\cdot3} = C$ from a pressure of 100 lbs. per sq. in. absolute to a
pressure of 20 lbs. per sq. in. absolute. Find the final volume and
the work done.

$$P_1V_1{}^{1\cdot3} = P_2V_2{}^{1\cdot3}$$

$$\therefore V_2 = \left(\frac{P_1}{P_2}\right)^{\frac{1}{1\cdot3}}.V_1$$

$$= \left(\frac{100}{20}\right)^{0\cdot77} \times 3 = 5^{0\cdot77} \times 3$$

$$= 3\cdot453 \times 3 = 10\cdot359 \text{ cu. ft.}$$

$$\text{Work done} = \frac{P_1V_1 - P_2V_2}{n - 1}$$

$$= \frac{(144 \times 100 \times 3) - (144 \times 20 \times 10\cdot359)}{1\cdot3 - 1}$$

$$= \frac{43,200 - 29,834}{0\cdot3} = \frac{13,366}{0\cdot3}$$

$$= 44,553 \text{ ft.-lbs.}$$

41. Hyperbolic Expansion. When values of P and V are plotted from the equation PV = C, the curve obtained is known as a rectangular hyperbola, and expansion or compression according to this law is said to be hyperbolic. This must not be confused with Boyle's Law, for whilst expansion according to Boyle's Law is hyperbolic, there are possible hyperbolic expansions which do not accord with Boyle's Law.

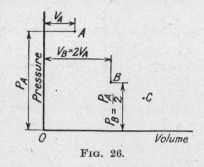

FIG. 26.

Any hyperbolic expansion curve may be readily plotted when one point on it is known. Take a point A, fig. 26, the co-ordinates of which are P_A and V_A. To find a new point, double the volume and halve the pressure. Thus $V_B = 2V_A$ and $P_B = \frac{1}{2}P_A$.

Repeat the process taking three times the volume and $\frac{1}{3}$ the pressure. In this way a large number of points may be obtained using the actual dimensions of P_A and V_A on the diagram.

A graphical construction for finding the hyperbolic curve is given in fig. 27.

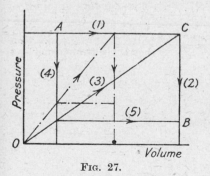

FIG. 27.

Let O be the point of zero volume and pressure, and let A be the point given on the curve.

Draw the horizontal AC where C represents a point immediately above the final volume. Drop a perpendicular from C. Join CO. Drop a perpendicular from A. From where this cuts the line CO, draw horizontally to B on CB. B is the required point on the hyperbola. Thus any number of points may be found.

42. Isothermal Expansion. An isothermal operation is one carried out at constant temperature; that is, in an isothermal expansion or compression the temperature remains the same throughout. Boyle's Law assumes constant temperature of the gas, and hence expansion according to Boyle's Law is isothermal. This is where some hyperbolic expansions differ from Boyle's Law, for hyperbolic expansion is not necessarily isothermal, though it often is so.

Since temperature is unchanged it follows that in a perfect gas the internal energy is unchanged. Because, however, there is expansion or compression, work is done by or on the gas.

The gas energy equation tells us (Art. 35)

Heat added = work done + gain in internal energy.

When the temperature does not change the last term becomes zero (Art. 34).

Hence   heat added = work done by gas.

This means that during isothermal expansion the work done, expressed in heat units, is exactly equal to the heat supplied to the gas. With isothermal compression we obtain similarly,

Heat abstracted = work done on gas.

Thus heat is given out equal to the work done on the gas. We see, then, that the heat is immediately transformed into mechanical work or, on compression, the work is transformed immediately into heat.

EXAMPLE. A quantity of gas expands isothermally and receives 15 C.H.U. during the expansion. How much work is done ?

Work done = heat supplied
         = 15 C.H.U.
         = 15 × 1,400 ft.-lbs. = 21,000 ft.-lbs.

EXAMPLE. The amount of work expended in the isothermal compression of a quantity of gas is 70,000 ft.-lbs. How much heat is given out from the gas during compression ?

$$\text{Heat removed} = \text{work done on gas}$$
$$= \frac{70,000}{1,400} = 50 \text{ C.H.U.}$$

EXAMPLE. A quantity of gas is compressed isothermally from initial conditions of 20 cu. ft. and 14·7 lbs. per sq. in. absolute, to a final pressure of 102·9 lbs. per sq. in. absolute. Find the work done on the gas.

$$\text{Ratio of compression} = \frac{102·9}{14·7} = 7 = r$$

$$\begin{aligned}
\text{Work done} &= PV \log_e r \\
&= 144 \times 14·7 \times 20 \times \log_e 7 \\
&= 144 \times 14·7 \times 20 \times 2·3026 \times 0·8451 \\
&= 82,850 \text{ ft.-lbs.}
\end{aligned}$$

This, in work units, is also the heat emitted by the gas.

43. Adiabatic Expansion.

Another important special case of expansion or compression is that known as adiabatic. In this case the gas neither receives nor gives out heat. We may imagine the gas to be contained in some cylinder made of a material which is a perfect non-conductor of heat. The gas can then expand or be compressed, but no heat can either be given to or taken from the gas. Students very frequently misunderstand the meaning of adiabatic expansion or compression. Taking first the case of expansion ; here the temperature falls and there is loss of internal energy, but no heat is lost in the form of heat. Heat, however, is transformed into work and so the gas has given up heat in the form of work.

The gas energy equation is again applied.

Heat added = work done + gain in internal energy. Since the operation is adiabatic no heat is added, hence the equation becomes

$$0 = \text{work done} + \text{gain in internal energy.}$$

∴ Work done = − (gain in internal energy). Negative gain is the same as loss.

∴ Work done by gas = loss of internal energy.

In the case of compression,

Work done on gas = gain in internal energy, hence the work done passes into the gas and increases its internal energy, thus raising its temperature. It has received no heat from any external heat supply, but it has transformed the work done upon it into heat.

EXAMPLE. The temperature of $1\frac{1}{2}$ lb. of gas at the beginning of an adiabatic expansion is 700° C. absolute, and at the end is 300° C. absolute. Find the work done during expansion. $C_v = 0\cdot169$.

$$\text{Change in internal energy} = 1\tfrac{1}{2} \times 0\cdot169 \times (700 - 300)$$
$$= 1\tfrac{1}{2} \times 0\cdot169 \times 400$$
$$= 600 \times 0\cdot169$$
$$= 101\cdot4 \text{ C.H.U.}$$
$$\therefore \text{Work done} = 101\cdot4 \times 1,400 \text{ ft.-lbs.}$$
$$= 141,960 \text{ ft.-lbs.}$$

EXAMPLE. A quantity of gas weighing $1\frac{1}{4}$ lb. expands from a pressure of 120 lbs. per sq. in. absolute to a pressure of 15 lbs. per sq. in. absolute, in such a way that the gas does not receive or reject any heat. The initial temperature is 200° C. Find the work done and the change in internal energy. $C_p = 0\cdot24$ and $C_v = 0\cdot17$.

Initial specific volume $= \dfrac{RT}{P}$ and $R = J(C_p - C_v)$

$$\therefore \text{ Specific volume} = \frac{1,400 \times (0\cdot24 - 0\cdot17) \times 473}{144 \times 120}$$
$$= \frac{1,400 \times 0\cdot07 \times 473}{144 \times 120}$$
$$= 2\cdot686 \text{ cu. ft. at 120 lbs./sq. in. and 200° C.}$$
$$\therefore \text{ Initial volume} = 1\cdot25 \times 2\cdot686$$
$$= 3\cdot36 \text{ cu. ft.}$$

The value of n for adiabatic change $= \dfrac{C_p}{C_v}$, see Article 38.

$$\therefore n = \frac{0\cdot24}{0\cdot17} = 1\cdot41.$$

Hence
$$P_1 V_1^{1\cdot41} = P_2 V_2^{1\cdot41}$$
$$V_2 = \left(\frac{P_1}{P_2}\right)^{\frac{1}{1\cdot41}} V_1 = \left(\frac{120}{15}\right)^{0\cdot71} \times 3\cdot36$$
$$= 8^{0\cdot71} \times 3\cdot36 = 4\cdot377 \times 3\cdot36$$
$$= 14\cdot7 \text{ cu. ft.}$$

Work done during expansion

$$= \frac{P_1V_1 - P_2V_2}{n-1}$$

$$= \frac{144 \times 120 \times 3\cdot36 - 144 \times 15 \times 14\cdot7}{1\cdot41 - 1}$$

$$= \frac{58{,}200 - 31{,}800}{0\cdot41} = \frac{26{,}400}{0\cdot41}$$

$$= 64{,}400 \text{ ft.-lbs.}$$

$$= 46 \text{ C.H.U.}$$

Final temperature is found from

$$\frac{P_1V_1}{T_1} = \frac{P_2V_2}{T_2}$$

$$T_2 = \left(\frac{P_2}{P_1}\right)\left(\frac{V_2}{V_1}\right)T_1 = \frac{4\cdot385}{8} \times 473$$

$$= 258\cdot7^\circ \text{ C. abs.}$$

$\therefore$ Reduction in internal energy $= 1\cdot25 \times 0\cdot17(473 - 259)$
$$= 1\cdot25 \times 0\cdot17 \times 214$$
$$= 45\cdot6 \text{ C.H.U.}$$

This quantity is equal to the work done above. The slight difference of $0\cdot4$ is due to slide rule error.

44. If a gas is expanding and receiving heat, the curve will be above the adiabatic, and if losing heat, below the adiabatic (fig. 28).

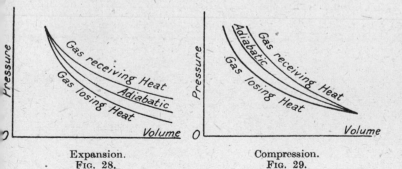

Expansion.
Fig. 28.

Compression.
Fig. 29.

If the gas is being compressed, the curve lies above the adiabatic when the gas receives heat, and below the adiabatic when heat is being rejected (fig. 29).

EXAMPLE. Five cubic feet of gas expand in a cylinder from a pressure of 200 lbs. per sq. in. absolute, and temperature of 300° C. to a pressure of 25 lbs. per sq. in. absolute, according to the law $PV^{1.2} = C$. $C_p = 0.238$ and $C_v = 0.169$. Find the heat interchanged between the gas and the cylinder wall.

To find the final volume. $P_1V_1^{1.2} = P_2V_2^{1.2}$

$$V_2 = \left(\frac{P_1}{P_2}\right)^{0.835} \times 5 = \left(\frac{200}{25}\right)^{0.835} \times 5$$

$$= 8^{0.835} \times 5 = 5.676 \times 5$$

$$= 28.38 \text{ cu. ft.}$$

$$\text{Work done} = \frac{P_1V_1 - P_2V_2}{n - 1}$$

$$= \frac{144 \times 200 \times 5 - 144 \times 25 \times 28.38}{1.2 - 1}$$

$$= \frac{144{,}000 - 102{,}000}{0.2}$$

$$= 210{,}000 \text{ ft.-lbs.} = 150 \text{ C.H.U.}$$

Now find weight of gas.

$$PV = wRT$$

$$w = \frac{PV}{RT} = \frac{200 \times 144 \times 5}{1{,}400(0.238 - 0.169) \times 573}$$

$$= 2.6 \text{ lbs.}$$

To find final temperature.

$$\frac{P_1V_1}{T_1} = \frac{P_2V_2}{T_2}$$

$$T_2 = \frac{P_2V_2}{P_1V_1} . T_1$$

$$= \frac{25}{200} \times \frac{28.38}{5} \times 573 = \frac{5.676}{8} \times 573$$

$$= 407° \text{ C. abs.}$$

The temperature is lower than at the commencement, hence, internal energy is less.

Reduction in internal energy $= w \times C_v(T_1 - T_2)$
$$= 2.6 \times 0.169 \times (573 - 407)$$
$$= 2.6 \times 0.169 \times 166$$
$$= 73.0 \text{ C.H.U.}$$

Heat added = work done by gas + gain in internal energy
$$= 150 - 73$$
$$= 77 \text{ C.H.U.}$$

Referring to fig. 16, it will be seen that the curve for $n = 1.2$ lies between the isothermal, where $n = 1$, and the adiabatic, where $n = 1.41$.

In the isothermal case, heat would be added equal to the external work done. In the adiabatic case, no heat would be added.

The case of this example is that where some amount of heat less than the external work must be added.

EXAMPLES VI

1. A quantity of gas, enclosed in a cylinder, is at 150 lbs. per sq. in. by gauge and has a volume of 4 cu. ft. The gas expands according to the law $PV^{1.25} = C$ until the volume is 10 cu. ft. Find the pressure after expansion.

2. Air at a pressure of 160 lbs. per sq. in. absolute is confined in a space of 1·5 cu. ft. It expands according to the law $PV^{1.4} = C$ until the pressure is 30 lbs. per sq. in. Find the final volume.

3. The same quantity of gas is found at different times during an expansion in the following two states :—(a) Pressure 160 lbs. per sq. in. by gauge, volume 2·4 cu. ft. ; (b) Pressure 40 lbs. per sq. in. by gauge, volume 7 cu. ft. Find the law of expansion.

4. 4 lbs. of air expand according to the law $PV = 96T$ at an absolute temperature of 305° C. The expansion ratio is 4. Find the work done during expansion.

5. Steam in a cylinder is cut off at ⅓ stroke. The clearance space is 0·25 cu. ft. and the swept volume is 3·5 cu. ft. Admission pressure, 80 lbs. per sq. in. absolute. Assuming expansion according to the law $PV = C$, find the work done during the expansion.

6. Air at a pressure of 180 lbs. per sq. in. absolute and occupying a volume of 12 cu. ft. expands according to the law $PV^{1.4} = C$ until its volume is 32 cu. ft. Find the work done during expansion.

7. A quantity of air at 13·5 lbs. per sq. in. absolute pressure and volume 14 cu. ft. is compressed according to the law $PV^{1.2} = C$ until the pressure is 80 lbs. per sq. in. absolute. Calculate the work done on the air during compression.

8. If 2 lbs. of gas expand isothermally at a temperature of 14° C. with an expansion ratio of 5, determine the amount of heat in heat units which must be supplied to the gas. $R = 96$.

9. An internal combustion engine has a clearance volume of 774 cu. ins., diameter of cylinder 15 ins., stroke 19 ins. Compression takes place according to the law $pv^{1.3} = $ constant.

The pressure at the commencement of compression is 14 lbs. per sq. in. absolute and the temperature 100° C. Find the pressure and temperature at the end of compression.   U.L.C.I.

10. A motor-car engine has a diameter of cylinder of 3¾ ins. and a stroke of 5 ins. The clearance volume is 14·4 cu. ins. Determine the compression ratio of the engine. If the temperature of the mixture at the commencement of compression is 60° C., find the

temperature at the end of the compression stroke, assuming compression follows the law $PV^{1.3}$ = constant. Atmospheric pressure = 14·7 lbs. per sq. in. U.L.C.I.

11. At the commencement of the compression stroke of a gas engine the pressure is 14·7 lbs. per sq. in. and the temperature is 90° C. If the compression follow the law $pv^{1.3}$ = constant, find the pressure and temperature of the gas when it is compressed to $\frac{1}{5}$ of its volume. U.L.C.I.

12. A gas-engine cylinder has a bore of $6\frac{1}{2}$ ins. and a stroke of 12 ins. The volume of the combustion chamber is 120 cu. ins. At the beginning of the compression stroke the mixture enclosed has a temperature of 120° C. and a pressure of 13·5 lbs. per sq. in. If the law connecting the pressure and volume during the compression stroke is $PV^{1.4}$ = constant, find the pressure and temperature at the end of the compression stroke.

State the laws of gases on which your determinations depend. U.E.I.

13. One pound of a gas at a pressure of 15 lbs. per sq. in. (absolute) and a temperature of 15° C. is compressed adiabatically to 400 lbs. per sq. in. (absolute). Assuming that $PV = 96T$, and that the index for adiabatic compression is 1·408, calculate the final volume and temperature.

What is the ratio of compression and how much work has been done during the compression ? U.L.C.I. (A.)

14. The characteristic equation of a certain gas is $PV = 100T$, and the specific heat at constant volume is 0·175. One pound of this gas at a pressure of 75 lbs. per sq. in. (absolute) is expanded from a volume of 6 cu. ft. to a volume of 36 cu. ft. and the equation of the curve of expansion is $PV^{1.31}$ = constant. Find the number of C.H.U.'s interchanged between the gas and the cylinder walls during the expansion, and the direction of the flow.

U.L.C.I. (A.)

CHAPTER VII

THE WORKING CYCLE

45. Meaning of Cycle. A cycle may be defined as a series of operations occurring in unchanging order. When the series is complete the cycle may be repeated, the processes being repeated in the same order.

The action of all engines is cyclic and may be represented by lines upon the field of a Pressure-Volume diagram, or Temperature-Entropy diagram (see Chapter XII).

The cycles may be those of imaginary perfect engines, or of actual engines. In the former case they are called ideal cycles and in the latter actual cycles. Examples of ideal cycles are the Carnot or Constant Temperature cycle, the Otto or Constant Volume cycle, and the Rankine cycle. The ideal cycles are used as bases of comparison for the performance of actual engines.

The cycles are often named in accordance with the conditions under which the heat is supplied, for example, in the Constant Temperature cycle the heat is received at constant temperature. In ideal cycles all accidental heat losses are prevented, and the working substance is assumed to behave like a perfect working substance, and to follow simple laws.

46. The Carnot Cycle. This cycle consists of four simple operations, namely, Isothermal Expansion, Adiabatic Expansion, Isothermal Compression, Adiabatic Compression, carried out in the order given. The adiabatic compression brings the substance back to the same state as that in which it existed at the beginning of the isothermal expansion.

The efficiency of the Carnot cycle is the maximum possible efficiency attainable by a perfect heat engine using a perfect working substance. It is the ultimate standard of comparison for all heat engines. No engine works upon this cycle, because the mean effective pressure is low, and it is impossible to achieve the conditions necessary to carry out the cycle.

The conditions of the Carnot cycle may be imagined to occur in the following manner.

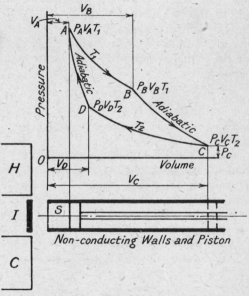

Fig. 30.

One pound weight of a perfect gas is placed in the cylinder at S (fig. 30). The cylinder material is supposed to be perfectly non-conducting, except at the end. A source of heat H is supposed to produce unlimited heat at constant temperature. A non-conducting cover I and a sump for heat are also required. The sump is of infinite capacity, its temperature thus remaining constant.

The temperature of H is T_1 and the temperature of the working substance is also T_1 when receiving heat from the source. The sump is at temperature T_2 and the working substance has that temperature when rejecting heat to it.

The four stages of the cycle are as follows :

Stage (1). Line AB in fig. 30. The source of heat is applied to the end of the cylinder and isothermal expansion occurs at T_1.

Heat supplied $= RT_1 \log_e r$.   (Arts. 40 and 42.)

Stage (2). Line BC. The non-conducting cover is applied to the end of the cylinder. Adiabatic expansion occurs, the temperature falling from T_1 to T_2.

Stage (3). Line CD. The sump C is applied to the end of the cylinder and isothermal compression occurs at temperature T_2.

$$\text{Heat rejected} = RT_2 \log_e r.$$

Stage (4). Line DA. The non-conducting cover is applied and adiabatic compression occurs, the temperature rising from T_2 to T_1.

In stage (3) the compression must stop at a point on an adiabatic curve through A, so that the substance shall be returned to its initial state of pressure, volume and temperature when the compression of stage (4) occurs. This will be the case when the ratio of isothermal compression is equal to the ratio of isothermal expansion.

By the principle of the conservation of energy

Work done $=$ heat supplied $-$ heat rejected.

$$= RT_1 \log_e r - RT_2 \log_e r$$

$$\text{Efficiency of the cycle} = \frac{\text{work done}}{\text{heat supplied}}$$

$$= \frac{RT_1 \log_e r - RT_2 \log_e r}{RT_1 \log_e r}$$

$$= \frac{T_1 - T_2}{T_1}$$

This result is very important, and shows that the efficiency of the ideal engine depends on temperatures only. The wider the range of temperature the greater will be the efficiency.

EXAMPLE. The temperature limits of an engine are 1,700° C. absolute and 500° C. absolute. What is the maximum possible efficiency?

$$\eta = \frac{T_1 - T_2}{T_1} = \frac{1,700 - 500}{1,700}$$

$$= \frac{1,200}{1,700} = 0 \cdot 706.$$

47. Carnot Cycle for Vapour.

This is the same as that for gases, but when a vapour is expanded or compressed at constant temperature, its pressure is also constant. Hence, on a P–V diagram, the isothermal expansion and compression lines become horizontal as in fig. 31.

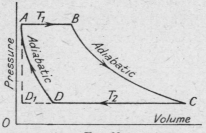

FIG. 31.

AB is isothermal expansion. At A the substance is all liquid, and at B it is dry vapour.

BC is adiabatic expansion, and at C the substance has become wet vapour.

CD is isothermal compression, which is condensation, since the volume is diminishing at constant temperature. At D the substance is nearly all liquid.

DA is adiabatic compression, and the temperature rises from T_2 to T_1, whilst the substance changes from the state of mixture to that of all liquid at A.

Under these conditions the heat supplied is the latent heat L_1 of the substance at temperature T_1. As the efficiency is still

$$\frac{T_1 - T_2}{T_1}$$

the work done

$$= L_1 \left(\frac{T_1 - T_2}{T_1} \right) \text{ heat units per lb. of substance.}$$

By a slight modification this Vapour Carnot cycle becomes the well-known Rankine cycle used for comparison of steam engine and steam turbine performance. The modification is twofold. First, the isothermal compression is not stopped at D but is continued until all the substance is liquid at D_1, its temperature being T_2. Secondly, it is necessary to supply heat directly to raise the temperature of the liquid from T_2 to T_1. The volume of the liquid is supposed constant at all pressures.

48. The Constant Volume Cycle or Otto Cycle. This cycle is the standard of comparison for internal

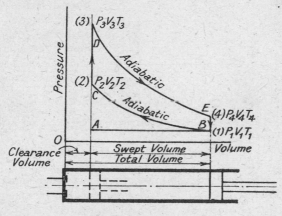

Fig. 32.

combustion engines. The heat is received and rejected at constant volume.

Fig. 32 shows this cycle on the pressure-volume diagram.

The line AB represents the induction of the charge of working substance, and the thermal cycle begins at B.

The charge of fuel and air is compressed adiabatically from B to C. Heat is then liberated by combustion, the temperature rising, but the volume remaining constant.

In this part of the cycle, shown at CD, the pressure and temperature rise to their maximum values. The working stroke, D to E, now takes place, the gas expanding adiabatically. At the end of the stroke heat is removed at constant volume, E to B.

Let C_v = specific heat at constant volume.

T_1 = temperature at B, T_2 = temperature at C,

T_3 = temperature at D, T_4 = temperature at E.

and let 1 lb. of working substance be considered.

Heat supplied from C to D = $C_v (T_3 - T_2)$

,, rejected ,, E to B = $C_v (T_4 - T_1)$

∴ Work done = Heat supplied − heat rejected

$$= C_v(T_3 - T_2) - C_v(T_4 - T_1)$$

∴ Efficiency $= \dfrac{\text{Work done}}{\text{Heat supplied}}$

$$= \frac{C_v(T_3 - T_2) - C_v(T_4 - T_1)}{C_v(T_3 - T_2)}$$

$$= \frac{(T_3 - T_2) - (T_4 - T_1)}{(T_3 - T_2)}$$

$$= 1 - \frac{T_4 - T_1}{T_3 - T_2}$$

The compression ratio $= r = \dfrac{V_B}{V_C}$

$$= \text{the expansion ratio} = \frac{V_E}{V_D}$$

The compression is adiabatic according to the law $PV^\gamma = C$ where $\gamma = \dfrac{C_p}{C_v}$.

$$\therefore P_B V_B{}^\gamma = P_C V_C{}^\gamma$$

$$\therefore P_B V_B V_B{}^{\gamma-1} = P_C V_C V_C{}^{\gamma-1}$$

$$\therefore R T_1 V_B{}^{\gamma-1} = R T_2 V_C{}^{\gamma-1}$$

$$\therefore T_1 V_B{}^{\gamma-1} = T_2 V_C{}^{\gamma-1}$$

$$\therefore \frac{T_1}{T_2} = \left(\frac{V_C}{V_B}\right)^{\gamma-1} = \left(\frac{1}{r}\right)^{\gamma-1}$$

Also the expansion is adiabatic and hence

$$T_3 V_D{}^{\gamma-1} = T_4 V_E{}^{\gamma-1}$$

$$\therefore \frac{T_4}{T_3} = \left(\frac{V_D}{V_E}\right)^{\gamma-1} = \left(\frac{1}{r}\right)^{\gamma-1}$$

$$\therefore \frac{T_4}{T_3} = \frac{T_1}{T_2}. \quad \therefore T_4 = \frac{T_1 T_3}{T_2}$$

$$\therefore \text{Efficiency } \eta = 1 - \frac{T_4 - T_1}{T_3 - T_2} = 1 - \frac{\dfrac{T_1 T_3}{T_2} - T_1}{T_3 - T_2}$$

$$= 1 - \frac{T_1}{T_2}\left(\frac{T_3 - T_2}{T_3 - T_2}\right)$$

$$= 1 - \frac{T_1}{T_2}$$

$$= 1 - \left(\frac{1}{r}\right)^{\gamma-1}$$

This cycle becomes the " air standard cycle " when air is taken in as the working substance.

In this case $\gamma = 1.404$ and thus

$$\text{Air Standard efficiency} = 1 - \left(\frac{1}{r}\right)^{0.404}$$

EXAMPLE. The compression ratio of an internal combustion engine is 4. Find the air standard efficiency.

$$\eta = 1 - \frac{1}{r^{0.404}} = 1 - \frac{1}{4^{0.404}} = 1 - \frac{1}{1.751} = 1 - 0.571$$

$$= 0.429 \text{ or } 42.9 \text{ per cent.}$$

EXAMPLE. A gas engine has a compression ratio of 5 to 1. The charge is taken in at 13 lbs. per sq. in. and 40° C. It is then compressed according to the law $PV^{1.3} = C$, and at the end of compression it receives heat at constant volume to the extent of 150 C.H.U. per lb. of charge. What is the maximum pressure and temperature attained at constant volume ? $C_v = 0.17$.

$$P_2 = P_1\left(\frac{V_1}{V_2}\right)^{1.3}$$

$$= 13 \times 5^{1.3} = 13 \times 8.104$$

$$= 105 \text{ lbs. per sq. in.}$$

$$\text{Temperature } T_2 = \frac{P_2 V_2}{P_1 V_1} T_1$$

$$= \frac{8 \cdot 104}{5} \times 313$$

$$= 507° \text{ C. abs. or } 234° \text{ C. (ordinary).}$$

$$\text{Temperature rise} = \frac{\text{heat added}}{\text{mass} \times \text{sp. heat}}$$

$$= \frac{150}{1 \times 0 \cdot 17}$$

$$= 883° \text{ C.}$$

$$\therefore \text{ Final temperature} = 507 + 883 = 1,390° \text{ C. abs.}$$

$$= 1,117° \text{ C. ordinary.}$$

$$\text{Final pressure} = 105 \times \frac{1,390}{507} = 288 \cdot 5 \text{ lbs. per sq. in. abs.}$$

EXAMPLES VII

1. A gas engine exhausts into an atmosphere at 14° C. and the highest temperature attained in the cylinder immediately after combustion is 1,400° C. If the engine could be made to run without loss and use all the available heat what would be its efficiency ?

2. A steam engine works at 250 lbs. per sq. in. If a river is available for condensing water in such plentiful supply that its temperature is not raised appreciably, what is the maximum possible thermal efficiency if the river temperature is 8° C. ?

3. The compression ratio of a petrol engine is 5·2. What is its ideal efficiency on the air standard cycle ? $\gamma = 1 \cdot 4$.

4. A gas engine charge before compression begins has a pressure of 13·8 lbs. per sq. in. and a temperature of 36° C. At the end of compression the fuel gives 160 C.H.U. to each pound of mixture. Assuming a compression ratio of 4·8, calculate the temperature at the end of compression and after the burning of the fuel. $PV^{1 \cdot 25} = C$ and $C_v = 0 \cdot 17$.

5. Calculate the air standard efficiency of a gas-engine of 16 ins. stroke, 12 ins. diam. of cylinder, and 480 cu. ins. of clearance volume. Take $\gamma = 1 \cdot 4$. Determine also the gas consumption per I.H.P. per hour, assuming the gas to have a calorific value of 300 C.H.U. per cu. ft., and the ratio of the thermal efficiency of the engine to its air standard efficiency to be as 55 : 100.   U.E.I.

CHAPTER VIII

FORMATION AND PROPERTIES OF STEAM

49. Heat Content of Steam. In a steam-raising plant the steam is formed from water under conditions of constant pressure. The lowest temperature at which water can exist naturally is 0° C. Hence, this temperature is chosen from which to measure the quantity of heat in the steam. Water is regarded as incompressible at the pressures generally used in practice, and in the following discussion the mean specific heat is taken as unity.

We will now consider 1 lb. of water pumped into a boiler, heated up, evaporated to the condition of dry steam, and then superheated by being raised in temperature at constant pressure.

There are three distinct stages in the supply of the heat during the above process of generation.

(1) The water is heated up to the boiling temperature.

(2) The state is changed from liquid to vapour.

(3) The dry steam is heated up to the final temperature.

The temperature at which evaporation takes place depends upon the pressure. There is only one value of this temperature for any one pressure.

The temperature of evaporation corresponding to any pressure may be found by consulting a steam table.

Let t_g = temperature of formation of steam in degrees centigrade or Fahrenheit.

t_f = temperature at which the water begins to receive heat.

Then sensible heat added = $(t_g - t_f)$ per lb. of water.
$$= (t_g - t_f) \text{ C.H.U.}$$
When $t_f = 0°$ C., then the sensible heat $= (t_g - 0)$
$$= t_g \text{ C.H.U.}$$
and this value is the one given in the tables.

This sensible heat, or liquid heat, is denoted by h. Thus for Centigrade Heat Units $h = t_g - 0$ and for British Thermal Units $h = t_g - 32$.

The second stage referred to above is that of evaporation, generation or formation. Any of these three terms is used to indicate the change of state from hot water at temperature t_g, to steam at temperature t_g. The heat is supplied at constant temperature, and is the latent heat of the substance when the final state is *dry* steam. This quantity of heat, the latent heat, is denoted by L. If an amount of heat less than L be supplied to 1 lb. of water at this stage, then only part of it will be evaporated.

The latent heat is given approximately by the Regnault Equation

$$L = 606 \cdot 5 - 0 \cdot 695 \ t_g \text{ for C.H.U.}$$
and $\qquad L = 1{,}114 - 0 \cdot 695 \ t_g \text{ for B.T.U.}$

For higher temperatures of formation, the latent heat decreases.

Also the total heat of formation from $0°$ C. $H = h + L$

$$= (t_g - 0) + (606 \cdot 5 - 0 \cdot 695 \ t_g)$$
$$= (606 \cdot 5 + 0 \cdot 305 \ t_g) \text{ C.H.U. } t_g \text{ being } °C.$$
Also $H = (t_g - 32) + (1{,}114 - 0 \cdot 695 \ t_g)$
$$= (1{,}082 + 0 \cdot 305 \ t_g) \text{ B.T.U. } t_g \text{ being } °F.$$

The total heat H in the above is for water starting at $0°$ C. or $32°$ F. and finishing as dry steam.

The third stage commences when the steam has been completely formed. Any further supply of heat to it will cause rise in temperature at constant pressure. This heat supply is connected with the temperature rise by the equation

Heat added = mass $\times$ specific heat $\times$ temperature rise.

Let C_p = specific heat of steam at constant pressure.
     t_s = final temperature of steam.
     t_g = temperature of generation.

then $(t_s - t_g)$ is the superheat, and is merely a temperature difference.

Super-Heat is the term used to denote the *quantity* of heat added to the dry steam.

Hence $h_s = 1 \times C_p \times (t_s - t_g)$
$= C_p(t_s - t_g)$ heat units per lb.

Thus the total heat of superheated steam is

$$h + L + C_p(t_s - t_g).$$

The quantities h (liquid heat), L (latent heat), and H (total heat) are obtained directly from steam tables, but steam table values require some correction when the evaporation is not complete, or when the steam is superheated.   The value of C_p varies from 0·48 to 0·6.

50. Steam Tables or Steam Properties. The collected information contained in steam tables comprises

pressure in lbs. per sq. in. absolute $= p$,
temperature of generation in °C. (by thermometer) $= t_g$,
volume of 1 lb. of steam (specific volume) in cu. ft. $= v_s$,
liquid or sensible heat per lb. reckoned from 0° C. $= h$,
latent heat in C.H.U. per lb. $= L$,
total heat of dry steam in C.H.U. per lb. reckoned
from 0° C. $= H$.

TABLE II

p	t_g	v_s	h	L	H
1	38·78	331·1	38·7	574·3	613
5	72·39	73·4	72·2	555·6	627·8
10	89·57	38·38	89·5	545·6	635·1
14·7	100	26·79	100·0	539·2	639·2
25	115·6	16·29	115·8	529·2	645·0
50	138·3	8·51	139·0	513·8	652·8
100	164·3	4·44	165·7	494·7	660·4

EXAMPLE. Find the heat necessary to raise the temperature of 1 lb. of feed water at 60° C. to a generation temperature of 138·3° C.

From tables liquid heat at 138·3° C. = 139 C.H.U.
,,   ,, in feedwater = 60 ,,
Heat required to raise temperature = 79 ,,
The substance is still liquid at the end of the heat supply.

EXAMPLE. Steam is generated at a pressure of 100 lbs. per sq. in. absolute from feed water at 40° C. Find the heat required to produce 1 lb. of dry steam.

Total heat of 1 lb. dry steam at 100 lbs./sq. in.

$$= h + L$$
$$= 165 \cdot 7 + 494 \cdot 7$$
$$= 660 \cdot 4 \text{ C.H.U. from } 0° \text{ C.}$$

Total heat of 1 lb. of feedwater at 40° C. = 40 C.H.U.

$$\therefore \text{ Heat required } = 660 \cdot 4 - 40$$
$$= 620 \cdot 4 \text{ C.H.U.}$$

EXAMPLE. Find the heat required to produce 1 lb. of super-heated steam, temperature 200° C., at a pressure of 100 lbs. per sq. in. absolute from feed water at 30° C. Take C_p for steam = 0·48.

Total heat of 1 lb. of dry steam from 0° C. = $h + L$

$$= 165 \cdot 7 + 494 \cdot 7$$
$$= 660 \cdot 4 \text{ C.H.U.}$$

Additional heat required to superheat

$$= C_p(t_s - t_g)$$
$$= 0 \cdot 48(200 - 164 \cdot 3)$$
$$= 0 \cdot 48 \times 35 \cdot 7 = 17 \cdot 14 \text{ C.H.U.}$$

Total heat in 1 lb. of superheated steam

$$= 660 \cdot 4 + 17 \cdot 14 = 677 \cdot 54 \text{ C.H.U.}$$

Total heat in 1 lb. of feed water at 30° C. = 30 C.H.U.

$$\therefore \text{ Heat required } = 677 \cdot 54 - 30 = 647 \cdot 54 \text{ C.H.U.}$$

51. Wet Steam. This is steam containing a quantity of water diffused throughout its mass in the form of very fine particles resembling a mist.

Wet steam requires a small addition of heat to dry it (or evaporate the mist), and since the process takes place at constant pressure and temperature the heat required will be latent heat. The heat shortage in wet steam is always latent heat.

Let x = the dryness fraction.

Then x is the weight of dry steam in 1 lb. of the mixture of steam and moisture.

EXAMPLE. How much heat will be required to produce 1 lb. of wet steam of dryness 0·95 at 100° C. from feed water at 100° C. ?

In this case, only latent heat is required, the feed water temperature being that of evaporation.

$$L = 539 \cdot 2 \text{ (at } 100° \text{ C.).}$$
$$\therefore \text{ Heat required } = 0 \cdot 95 \text{ L}$$
$$= 0 \cdot 95 \times 539 \cdot 2 = 512 \cdot 24 \text{ C.H.U.}$$

The addition of 26·96 units of heat would complete the evaporation and give dry steam. No sensible heat can be given to the steam until this is done, after which, addition of heat would produce superheat.

EXAMPLE. The temperature of feed water supplied to a boiler is 45° C., and the working pressure is 100 lbs. per sq. in. absolute. The condition of the steam leaving the boiler is 0·97 dry, and 7·7 lbs. of water are changed into steam of this quality per lb. of coal burned. Find the amount of heat usefully employed for steam raising per lb. of coal.

Total heat in 1 lb. of steam at 100 lbs./sq. in.

$$= h + xL$$
$$= 165·7 + 0·97 \times 494·7$$
$$= 165·7 + 479·86$$
$$= 645·56 \text{ C.H.U. from } 0° \text{ C.}$$

Total heat of 1 lb. of feed water = 45 C.H.U. from 0° C.

∴ Heat required to produce 1 lb. of wet steam

$$= 645·56 - 45$$
$$= 600·56 \text{ C.H.U.}$$

∴ Heat usefully employed for steam raising per lb. of coal burned

$$= 7·7 \times 600·56$$
$$= 4624·3 \text{ C.H.U.}$$

EXAMPLE. The condition of steam entering a surface condenser is, pressure = 5 lbs. per sq. in. absolute and dryness = 0·82. The water resulting from the condensation leaves the condenser at a temperature of 60° C. Find the heat removed from the steam per lb., and also the weight of condensing water required per lb. of steam if the temperature rise of the condensing water is 25° C.

Heat in steam per lb. as it enters condenser

$$= h + xL$$
$$= 72·2 + 0·82 \times 555·6$$
$$= 72·2 + 455·6$$
$$= 527·8 \text{ C.H.U. from } 0° \text{ C.}$$

Heat per lb. remaining in the water formed by condensation

$$= 60 \text{ C.H.U. from } 0° \text{ C.}$$

Heat removed from 1 lb. of steam in condenser

$$= 527·8 - 60$$
$$= 467·8 \text{ C.H.U.}$$

Each lb. of cooling water carries away 25 C.H.U.

∴ Wt. of cooling water required per lb. of steam $= \dfrac{467·8}{25}$

$$= 18·7 \text{ lbs.}$$

52. Division of Energy in 1 lb. of Steam.

Let V_w = volume of 1 lb. of water in cu. ft.

V_s = ,, ,, ,, ,, dry steam in cu. ft.

P = absolute pressure at which steam is formed in lbs. per sq. ft.

L = latent heat corresponding to P.

t_g = temperature of generation at P.

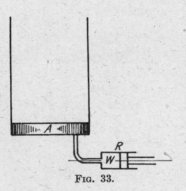

Suppose the generation of 1 lb. of steam to take place in a vertical cylinder fitted with piston, A (fig. 33), which rests initially on the bottom of the cylinder and causes the pressure P.

The force pump R now delivers to the cylinder 1 lb. of water of volume V_w against the pressure of the piston which it lifts.

Fig. 33.

Then work done in forcing in the water =

$$PV_w \text{ ft.-lbs.} = \frac{PV_w}{J} \text{ heat units.}$$

Under ideal conditions this work could be recovered, and thus it is legitimately included in the sum of energy possessed by the fluid.

Next, heat the water, thus adding sensible or liquid heat from 0° C. to temperature t_g° C.

We have,

Heat supplied = work done + gain in internal energy.

or $(t_g - t_f) = 0$ + gain in internal energy.

No external work is done during the heat supply since we suppose the water unchanged in volume. Hence, internal energy of liquid reckoned from 0° C. $= t_g = h$.

∴ Total energy of liquid at $t_g = \left[h + \dfrac{PV_w}{J} \right]$ heat units.

We now have 1 lb. of hot water in the cylinder at the temperature of generation. Further heat supply produces change of state from water to steam at constant pressure P and temperature t_g.

$$\text{Final volume} = V_s.$$
$$\text{Initial} \quad ,, \quad = V_w.$$

∴ Work done in raising piston to accommodate V_s

$$= P(V_s - V_w) \text{ ft.-lbs.}$$
$$= \frac{P}{J}(V_s - V_w) \text{ heat units.}$$

This work is external to the steam and is called the external energy of evaporation.

The heat supplied, however, during this stage = L heat units, also, heat supplied = work done + gain in internal energy.

i.e., $L = \frac{P}{J}(V_s - V_w) + \text{gain in I.E.}$

∴ Gain in I.E. $= L - \frac{P}{J}(V_s - V_w).$

Collecting all the internal energy put into the steam from 0° C. we have

Total internal energy $= h + L - \frac{P}{J}(V_s - V_w)$

$$= h + L + \frac{PV_w}{J} - \frac{PV_s}{J}.$$

But $h + L = \text{total heat} = H$

Also, total liquid energy $= h + \frac{PV_w}{J}$

∴ Total energy in 1 lb. of steam $= h + \frac{PV_w}{J} + L$

$$= h + L + \frac{PV_w}{J}$$
$$= H + \frac{PV_w}{J}$$
$$= H_T$$

∴ Total *Internal* Energy $= H_T - \frac{PV_s}{J}$ heat units.

Note that H_T includes the work done in pumping the feed water into the boiler, whilst H does not.

EXAMPLE. Find the total energy of 1 lb. of steam at 128 lbs. per sq. in. absolute. Also find the total internal energy and the total external work per lb. of steam.

	p	t_g	V_s	h	L
Steam table values	128	174·4	3·522	176·8	488·1

Volume of 1 lb. of water = 0·016 cu. ft.

$$\text{Work done by feed pump} = \frac{PV_w}{J} = \frac{128 \times 144 \times 0 \cdot 016}{1,400}$$

$$= 0 \cdot 2106 \text{ C.H.U.}$$

$$\text{Total energy} = h + L + \frac{PV_w}{J}$$

$$= 176 \cdot 8 + 488 \cdot 1 + 0 \cdot 2106$$

$$= 665 \cdot 1106 \text{ C.H.U.}$$

$$\text{Total external work} = \frac{PV_s}{J} = \frac{144 \times 128 \times 3 \cdot 522}{1,400}$$

$$= 46 \cdot 4 \text{ C.H.U.}$$

$$\text{Total internal energy} = \text{Total Energy} - \text{External work}$$
$$= 665 \cdot 1106 - 46 \cdot 4$$
$$= 618 \cdot 7106 \text{ C.H.U.}$$

The total external work is the sum of the external work done in pumping, and the external work done during evaporation.

EXAMPLE. Using the data of the last example, find the total liquid energy and the internal latent heat.

$$\text{Total liquid energy} = \text{work done in pumping} + \text{liquid heat}$$
$$= 0 \cdot 2106 + 176 \cdot 8$$
$$= 177 \cdot 0106 \text{ C.H.U.}$$

Internal latent heat = heat supplied during evaporation − external work done during evaporation

$$= L - \frac{P(V_s - V_w)}{J}$$

$$= 488 \cdot 1 - \frac{128 \times 144}{1,400} (3 \cdot 522 - 0 \cdot 016)$$

$$= 488 \cdot 1 - (46 \cdot 4 - 0 \cdot 2106)$$

$$= 441 \cdot 9106 \text{ C.H.U.}$$

This is often called the disintegration heat of the steam. It is the amount of latent heat which would be required to evaporate the water at constant volume equal to V_s.

53. Quality of Steam. By this is meant its state as regards dryness or superheat.

If the dryness is 0·9, say, then $\frac{1}{10}$ lb. of water still remains to be evaporated in every pound of wet steam. This condition could be defined by saying that the steam is 90 per cent. dry or 10 per cent. wet.

If the dryness is unity, then the whole is steam without any superheat.

If the steam is superheated 20° C., say, it means that its temperature is 20° C. above the temperature of generation, i.e. $t_g + 20$.

Since steam cannot be wet and superheated at the same time, it follows that in superheated steam, we know that no moisture exists. To determine the amount of superheat it is only necessary to measure the pressure and temperature of the steam. From steam tables we can then find the temperature of generation corresponding to the measured pressure, and, using the equation—

Superheat — temperature of steam generation temperature, find the degree of superheat.

The word superheat is used to denote temperature in excess of generation temperature, and super-heat the amount of heat given to the steam per lb. when superheating it.

If steam is wet, its temperature is that of generation no matter what the degree of wetness may be. Temperature and pressure alone will, therefore, give us no indication of dryness. It is often necessary to know the dryness of steam in use, and this must be determined by actual test.

54. Tests for Dryness Fraction of Steam. These tests are carried out as part of the complete test of a steam plant.

Various methods in use are as follows :
(1) The Barrel Calorimeter.
(2) The Throttling Calorimeter (Peabody).
(3) The Separating Calorimeter (Carpenter).
(4) Combined Separating and Throttling Calorimeter.

55. The Barrel Calorimeter. A suitable vessel (fig. 34) containing a measured quantity of water is placed

G

upon the platform of a weighing machine, and a supply of the steam under test is brought into the vessel. The steam, mixing with the water, gives up some of its heat and raises the temperature of the water.

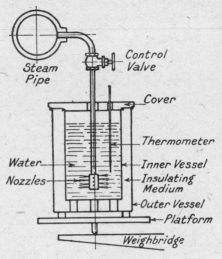

Fig. 34.

The temperature of the water is taken before and after blowing in the steam. The weight of the apparatus is also found before and after the experiment.

Let p = pressure of steam in pipe.

h_1 = liquid heat at temperature corresponding to p.

t_2 = temperature of water and vessel before experiment.

t_3 = temperature of water and vessel after experiment.

h_2 = liquid heat corresponding to t_2.

h_3 = ,, ,, ,, ,, t_3.

L_1 = latent heat of steam corresponding to p.

x = dryness fraction of steam in pipe.

W = equivalent weight of water.

W_w = weight of water at commencement.
W_v = weight of vessel.
W_s = weight of steam blown into vessel.
C = specific heat of material of vessel.

Water equivalent of system = W = $W_w + CW_v$.
Heat lost by steam = heat gained by calorimeter system.

$$W_s(h_1 - h_3 + xL_1) = W(t_3 - t_2)$$
$$= W(h_3 - h_2)$$

$$\therefore (h_1 - h_3) + xL_1 = \frac{W}{W_s}(h_3 - h_2)$$

$$\therefore x = \frac{\dfrac{W}{W_s}(h_3 - h_2) - (h_1 - h_3)}{L_1}.$$

EXAMPLE. In a test of wet steam made by a barrel calorimeter the following observations were made. Calculate the dryness fraction of the steam.

Weight of copper calorimeter $\qquad$ = 2·19 lbs.
,, ,, ,, ,, and water = 8·49 ,,
,, ,, ,, ,, ,, ,, and steam = 8·91
Specific heat of copper = 0·092
Initial temperature of water = 7° C.
Final ,, ,, ,, = 44·5° C.
Temperature of steam = 154° C.

Equivalent weight of water (W) = (8·49 − 2·19) + 2·19 × ·092
$\qquad$ = 6·3 + 0·20 = 6·5 lbs.
$\qquad$ Weight of steam (W_s) = 8·91 − 8·49 = 0·42 lbs.
Latent heat of steam at 154° C. (from tables) (L_1) = 503 C.H.U.
Liquid ,, water at 154° C. (from tables) (h_1) = 155 ,,
,, ,, ,, at 7° C. (h_2) = 7 ,,
,, ,, ,, at 44·5° C. (h_3) = 44·5 ,,

$\qquad$ Heat lost by steam = heat gained by calorimeter system
$$W_s(h_1 - h_3 + xL_1) = W(t_3 - t_2)$$
$$= W(h_3 - h_2)$$
$$0·42(155 - 44·5 + x \times 503) = 6·5(44·5 - 7)$$
$$0·42(110·5 + 503x) = 6·5 \times 37·5$$
$$46·4 + 211·2x = 244$$
$$211·2x = 197·6$$
$$x = \frac{197·6}{211·2}$$
$$= 0·935$$

56. Throttling of Steam. Steam is said to be throttled when it passes through a restricted opening, such as a partially closed valve, or a small hole in a metal plate. Throttled steam is reduced in pressure, but its volume increases. Provided no heat is lost by leakage, the total energy, $H + \dfrac{PV_w}{J}$, (see Art. 52) of the steam is the same before and after throttling, if no work is done external to the steam. Since the total heat of steam is less for lower temperatures and pressures it follows that if steam, originally dry, passes from a higher pressure to a lower, without loss of heat, then it must become superheated. Wet steam, if throttled, becomes drier. If only slightly wet, it may become superheated slightly, due to throttling.

This principle is made use of in the throttling calorimeter. The quantity $\dfrac{PV_w}{J}$ is so small, that in the case of steam it may be neglected in general.

57. The Throttling Calorimeter. In calculating results from the observations taken with a throttling calorimeter we assume

(1) that no work is done by the steam externally,

(2) that the velocity of the steam sinks to zero after throttling, and thus there is no kinetic energy.

(3) No heat is lost to external bodies.

The equations representing the possible changes in the steam then become as follows :

(The suffix (1) denotes the initial and (2) the final state.)

(a) Wet steam throttled and remaining wet.

$$h_1 + x_1 L_1 = h_2 + x_2 L_2.$$

(b) Wet steam throttled and reaching dryness $= 1$.

$$h_1 + x_1 L_1 = h_2 + L_2.$$

(c) Wet steam throttled and becoming superheated.

$$h_1 + x_1 L_1 = h_2 + L_2 + C_p(t_s - t_g).$$

(*d*) Dry steam becoming superheated.

$$h_1 + L_1 = h_2 + L_2 + C_p(t_s - t_g)$$

t_s = temperature of superheated steam.

$t_g =$,, ,, generation.

The Peabody Throttling Calorimeter consists of a vessel into which steam can be admitted through a small opening controlled by a valve. The steam admitted is that under test, and the vessel has inserted in it a ther-

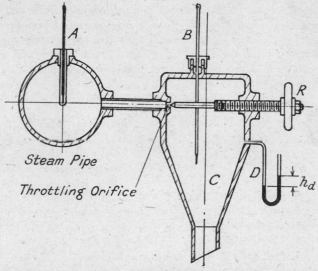

FIG. 35.

mometer. This vessel is large enough for the steam within to be sensibly at rest, and is open to the atmosphere. A (fig. 35) is a thermometer inserted in the steam under test, and B a thermometer in the calorimeter. In order to ascertain the pressure after throttling, a manometer D is fixed to the body of the calorimeter, and its reading shows the difference between the pressure in the calorimeter and the atmospheric pressure. The latter must be obtained at the time of the test by reading the barometer.

Let t_1 = reading of thermometer A.

t_s =   ,,   ,,   ,,   B.

h_a = barometric reading in inches of mercury.

h_d = reading of manometer in inches of mercury.

p_2 = pressure after throttling in lbs. per sq. in.

C_p = specific heat of superheated steam.

t_{g2} = temperature of generation corresponding to p_2.

then $p_2 = (h_a + h_d)\dfrac{14 \cdot 7}{30}$ lbs. per sq. in.

Heat in 1 lb. of steam after throttling
$$= h_2 + L_2 + C_p(t_s - t_{g2})$$

where h_2, L_2 and t_{g2} are taken from steam tables corresponding to p_2.

Heat in 1 lb. of steam before throttling $= h_1 + x_1 L_1$. Values of h_1 and L_1 are taken from tables corresponding to t_1.

$$\therefore \ h_1 + x_1 L_1 = h_2 + L_2 + C_p(t_s - t_{g2})$$
$$\therefore \ x_1 = \frac{h_2 + L_2 + C_p(t_s - t_{g2}) - h_1}{L_1}$$

If no superheat is registered on thermometer B, the method fails. It is generally only applicable if the dryness is greater than $0 \cdot 97$ or thereabout.

58. The Separating Calorimeter. This consists of a device for trapping the water and draining it off. As the steam can only be partially dried it can only give approximate results.

EXAMPLE. In an experimental determination of the dryness of steam by the throttling calorimeter the following results were observed :—Pressure of steam before throttling, 64 lbs. per sq. in. absolute ; temperature after throttling, 102° C. ; pressure after throttling, 14·7 lbs. per sq. in. Calculate the dryness fraction.

Heat in steam before throttling $= 148 \cdot 1 + x \times 508$

Heat in steam after throttling $= 100 \cdot 5 + 539 + 0 \cdot 48(102 - 100)$

$$= 639 \cdot 5 + 0 \cdot 48 \times 2$$
$$= 640 \cdot 46$$
$$\therefore \ 148 \cdot 1 + 508x = 640 \cdot 46$$
$$508x = 492 \cdot 36$$
$$x = \frac{492 \cdot 36}{508}$$
$$= 0 \cdot 969.$$

EXAMPLES VIII

1. Find the quantity of heat necessary to produce, from water at $0°$ C., 1 lb. of superheated steam at a pressure of 180 lbs. per sq. in. absolute and a temperature of $260°$ C. C_p for steam $= 0.48$.

2. Calculate the quantity of heat which must be given to 1 lb. of feed water at $25°$ C. to produce superheated steam at 60 lbs. per sq. in. by gauge.and a temperature of $240°$ C.

3. An engine uses 18·6 lbs. of steam per I.H.P. per hour. The steam is at a pressure of 120 lbs. per sq. in. by gauge and is 0·92 dry. If feed-water is $15°$ C. and the engine develops 26·4 I.H.P., find the number of C.H.U.s supplied to the engine per hour.

4. A boiler produces 4,800 lbs. of steam per hour at a pressure of 195 lbs. per sq. in. absolute and 0·95 dry. The calorific value of the fuel is 8,160 C.H.U.s per lb. and 65 per cent. of this heat passes through the boiler plates. If the feed water is at $28°$ C., find the weight of coal required per hour.

5. Steam at a pressure of 2 lbs. per sq. in. absolute and 80 per cent. dry enters a condenser. The resulting water leaves the condenser at $46°$ C. If the cooling water enters at $9°$ C. and leaves at $34°$ C. find the weight of cooling water required per lb. of steam condensed.

6. The steam which leaves an engine enters the condenser at 1·5 lbs. per sq. in. pressure and 94 per cent. dry. The condensate leaves the condenser at $45°$ C. If the weight of condensate per hour is 2,260 lbs. and the cooling water rises in temperature $24°$ C., find the number of gallons of cooling water required.   1 gallon $= 10$ lbs.

7. Find the internal energy and the external work of 1 lb. of dry steam at 160 lbs. per sq. in. absolute, reckoning from water at the temperature of generation.

8. Find the external work done and the internal energy stored in forming 1 lb. of steam from $0°$ C., 12 per cent. wet at 180 lbs. per sq. in. absolute.

9. The steam in a throttling calorimeter at atmospheric pressure is found to be at a temperature of $103°$ C. If its pressure before passing through the orifice is 120 lbs. per sq. in. by gauge, what is its dryness fraction ?

10. Steam from a steam range where its pressure is 175 lbs. per sq. in. by gauge and its temperature $200°$ C. passes through a small orifice to a throttling calorimeter. A mercury U-tube gauge fitted to the calorimeter shows the pressure within it to be 3 ins. of mercury above atmospheric pressure. What should be the reading on a thermometer inserted in the calorimeter ?

11. One pound of water at $15°$ C. is converted, at constant pressure, into steam at an absolute pressure of 110 lbs. per sq. in. and having a dryness fraction of 0·92. Determine in foot-lbs. :

(a) The total amount of work done.

(b) The internal work done during evaporation.

(c) The external work.

(d) The work done during the rise of temperature of the water. The volume of 1 lb. of water is 0·016 cu. ft. and of 1 lb. of dry saturated steam at 110 lbs. per sq. in. 4·07 cu. ft.   U.L.C.I.

12. One pound of steam at an absolute pressure of 180 lbs. per sq. in. is generated from water at a temperature of 50° C. If the dryness fraction of the steam is 0·94, determine in foot-lbs. :

(a) The total work done.

(b) The internal work done during evaporation.

(c) The external work done.

(d) The work done during the rise of temperature of the water. The volume of 1 lb. of water is 0·016 cu. ft. and of 1 lb. of dry saturated steam at 180 lbs. pressure is 2·562 cu. ft.   U.L.C.I.

13. Describe briefly, with the aid of an outline sketch, a calorimeter for determining the dryness fraction of steam. Steam at an absolute pressure of 115 lbs. per sq. in. flows into a tank containing 300 lbs. of water at 10° C. The final temperature of the water is 27° C. and the increase in weight is 8·5 lbs. Determine the dryness fraction of the steam.   U.L.C.I.

14. How could you tell whether the steam in a throttling calorimeter was superheated or not ? To determine the dryness fraction of the steam supplied to an engine a separating and throttling calorimeter were connected in series, and the following data obtained during a 10 minutes' test :

Pressure in steam main, 110 lbs. per sq. in. absolute.

Pressure in throttling calorimeter, 14·7 lbs. per sq. in. absolute.

Temperature in throttling calorimeter, 108° C.

Water collected at separator, 0·35 lb.

Steam received by throttling calorimeter, 8·1 lbs.

Assuming the mean specific heat of superheated steam to be 0·5, calculate

(a) the dryness fraction of the steam leaving the separating calorimeter ;

(b) the dryness fraction of the steam in the main.   U.E.I.

15. Calculate the internal energy and the work done in formation of 1 lb. of saturated steam at a pressure of 220 lbs. per sq. in. absolute from feed water at 0° C. (a) when the steam is dry, (b) when the dryness fraction is 0·8. Neglect the volume of the water.

    U.E.I.

16. What is meant by the term " wire-drawing " ? If wet steam be wire-drawn, what is the result ? If dry steam be wire-drawn, what happens then ? Steam, which is 0·03 wet, and at a pressure of 380 lbs. per sq. in. absolute, passes through a reducing valve. If the pressure on the reduced side is 200 lbs. per sq. in. absolute, what is then the dryness fraction ?   U.E.I.

CHAPTER IX

STEAM BOILERS

59. Introduction. The function of a steam boiler is to transfer heat yielded by the fuel to the water and thus produce steam.

The mechanical construction and the appearance of the boiler depend upon the arrangements made for burning the fuel and effecting the transfer of heat.

Boilers may be divided into two main classes, (1) Fire-tube boilers, (2) and Water-tube boilers.

60. Fire-tube Boilers. In these boilers the water surrounds tubes through the inside of which the hot gases from the furnace pass. In one of its forms, this type of boiler is constructed with one, two or three large tubes in the ends of which the grates are arranged as in Lancashire and Cornish boilers. Again, the tubes may be smaller but more numerous, as in locomotive boilers ; such boilers are known as multitubular boilers.

61. Water-tube Boilers. Water-tube boilers have a large number of tubes, connecting " drums " or " headers," in and out of which the water flows during the heat supply. The water-tubes traverse the combustion chamber in an inclined direction to assist circulation of the water. This type of boiler requires a large combustion chamber and the construction enables this to be arranged easily. The large combustion space assists in bringing about complete combustion of the fuel.

62. The Lancashire Boiler. Many illustrations of this type of boiler are available and a diagram will be found on page 228 of the Authors' *Mechanics and Applied Heat*.

The boiler consists of a large cylinder through which two large fire-tubes pass. The tubes are large enough to hold the fire-grate at the front end of the boiler. A fire-brick " bridge " is built at the back end of the grate to prevent the fire from being pushed over the end, and to cause the hot gases to impinge on the top of the fire-tube or flue. The sudden cooling of the gases at this point is often the cause of smoke production. Passing on to the end of the boiler, the flue gases descend by the downtake flue to the bottom flue, which extends under the full length

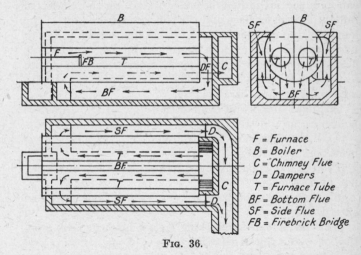

F = Furnace
B = Boiler
C = Chimney Flue
D = Dampers
T = Furnace Tube
BF = Bottom Flue
SF = Side Flue
FB = Firebrick Bridge

FIG. 36.

of the boiler. When they reach the front of the boiler again they divide into two paths and traverse the whole length of the boiler in the side flues, whence they pass on to the chimney.

The hot gases thus traverse the length of the boiler three times : once through the tubes ; once under the boiler ; once along its sides.

When a superheater is fitted to this boiler it is placed in the downtake flue where the gases are still at a very high temperature (see fig. 37).

From the diagram it will be seen that the heating surface is the sum of (a) the internal surface of the fire tubes, (b) the area at the bottom over the bottom flue, (c) the area of the shell in contact with the gases in the side flues. This heating surface is not all equally effective, since that part of it which is more remote from the fire is supplied with gases at lower temperature than that near the fire. That part of the heating surface which receives direct radiant heat from the fire is most effective in producing steam. The amount of steam which a Lancashire boiler can produce is limited because of the small amount of radiant heating surface and the restricted grate area. The length of the grate in a hand-fired boiler is from 6 feet to 9 feet, and the diameter of the tubes from $2\frac{1}{2}$ feet to 3 feet. The grate area thus varies from 30 square feet to 54 square feet for a two-flue boiler. The ratio of heating surface area to grate area is about 24.

The more important characteristics of the Lancashire boiler are as follows :

(1) It is simple in construction and requires simple brickwork mountings.

(2) It has a good efficiency (about 70 per cent.) when not overloaded or " forced."

(3) Most parts can be readily examined, internally and externally.

(4) When at normal working level it holds a large quantity of water compared with its rate of evaporation and thus it can meet large sudden demands for steam. It does so, however, on falling pressure, and if the excessive demand persists this fall will necessitate stoppage of the engines.

(5) It has but little margin of rate of steam production, and cannot meet demands by increased liberation of heat in the furnaces.

(6) Because of its large water content, it is fairly safe from the risk of uncovering the furnace crowns in short periods of time. If the crowns are uncovered they become overheated and may collapse altogether, with disastrous results.

(7) It is simple to manage.

(8) The shell, having a large diameter, is subject to fairly heavy stresses at moderate pressures. Thus the boiler is not suitable for pressures much above 250 lbs. per square inch.

(9) The circulation of water, upon which the rate of steam production depends, is not good, especially at starting. It is most vigorous near the fires.

63. The Superheater. The steam leaves the boiler at the top and is taken to a header immediately over the downtake flue. It is then compelled to flow down through a series of U-tubes, and up into a second header alongside

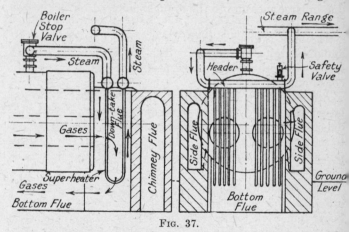

Fig. 37.

the first. When it reaches the second header, it is much hotter than on leaving the first header, because it has taken in a considerable quantity of heat. The amount of heat thus absorbed depends upon the time taken to pass from header to header. The amount of superheat thus depends upon the rate at which steam flows from boiler to engine. When the engine takes a small quantity of steam the superheat will be higher than when greater quantities are required.

A diagram of a superheater for a Lancashire boiler is given in fig. 37.

In order to prevent the superheater tubes from becoming overheated when the engines are stopped, the boiler should be "damped down," that is, the amount of air entering the furnaces is reduced by partially closing the dampers. When the pressure reaches blowing-off point, a safety-valve on the discharge side of the superheater discharges steam which must traverse the superheater tubes.

64. The Locomotive Boiler. The principal feature of this boiler is its power to meet the demand for steam in large quantities compared with its dimensions. This is due in large measure to the draught induced by the engine exhaust blast.

The blast is greater when the engine is doing more work and discharging more steam. The rate of combustion then increases approximately in proportion to the rate of steam consumption.

Attempts have been made to improve the water circulation at the fire-box end of locomotive boilers by introducing water tubes in the fire-box. Mr. Gresley, Engineer to the London and North-Eastern Railway Co., has recently put an engine into service, which uses a modified Yarrow water-tube boiler.

Fig. 38 shows the outline of a locomotive boiler of ordinary type. The superheater tubes in the locomotive boiler run back towards the firebox inside the fire tubes. Only a limited number of these tubes are so used and they are made larger in diameter than the rest to permit the flow and return tubes of the superheater to be inserted. The headers are in the smoke-box.

Fig. 39 shows a large detail of the superheater for a locomotive.

The amount of coal, which can be burned per square foot of grate surface per hour, varies from 60 lbs. to 200 lbs. in modern locomotive boilers, but the latter figure is not an economical one. The boilers are often designed on the assumption that about 130 lbs. per square foot per hour is the limit of economical combustion.

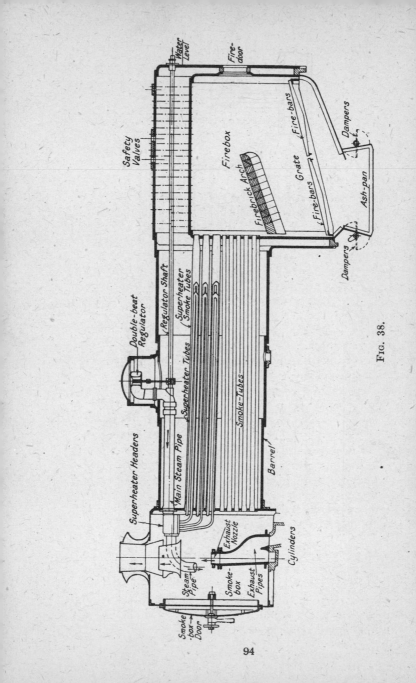

FIG. 38.

94

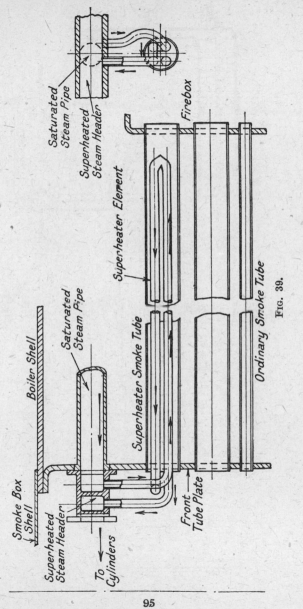

Saturated Steam Pipe

Superheated Steam Header

Superheater Element

Firebox

Ordinary Smoke Tube

Boiler Shell

Saturated Steam Pipe

Superheater Smoke Tube

Smoke Box Shell

Superheated Steam Header

To Cylinders

Front Tube Plate

FIG. 39.

95

65. The Water-tube Boiler.   Fig. 40 shows the well-known Babcock and Wilcox boiler.

FIG. 40.

The bank of inclined tubes is placed directly in the furnace, and the result is that a large amount of heat is transmitted through the tubes to the water, in proportion to the area exposed. In these water-tube boilers the movement of the water is very rapid, and vigorous circulation results. This is due to the reduction in density when water is heated, and to the lifting effect of small bubbles of steam. Water does not conduct heat very readily, and when the water near the tube is partially evaporated, it is necessary to replace it quickly to ensure rapid steam raising. The water-tube boiler does this by the positive circulation which is the chief feature of this type of boiler. The tubes are inclined for the special purpose of promoting circulation.

The superheater in this boiler is placed under the top steam drum and is very close to the furnace.

The chief features of the water-tube boiler are :

(1) High rate of evaporation in proportion to size.

(2) Large combustion spaces and therefore very good combustion. The combustion is complete before the gases reach the boiler plates.

(3) Great mechanical strength due to small diameter of steam drums and tubes. Boilers are now being built for 1,600 lbs. per square inch working pressure, in actual industrial service.

(4) Occupation of small floor space with considerable height.

(5) Suitability for mechanical, pulverized fuel, and oil fuel firing.

(6) Greater safety as regards damage to life and property due to small diameter of drums and tubes.

(7) Small tubes tend to scale up, and types of boilers with bent tubes are difficult to clean. A silted tube may cause a stoppage of the boiler.

(8) If very sudden demands come upon the boiler, the water-level may fall quickly to a dangerous degree, and damage be done before it is observed. Automatic feed regulating devices minimize this danger considerably.

66. Evaporation. The evaporation of a boiler is stated in lbs. per hour and this is known as the capacity of the boiler. This boiler rating fixes the grate area, the heating surface, and the storage capacity. The designer, to obtain a stated evaporation capacity, uses experimental data with regard to the consumption of coal per square foot per hour. This quantity is greatly influenced by the draught.

Large water-tube boilers are now built to evaporate 150,000 lbs. of water per hour, whilst Lancashire boilers range up to 11,000 lbs. per hour.

67. Boiler Performance. This may be regarded as the steam produced per lb. of coal, or the efficiency may be used as a measure of performance. The comparison of two boilers can only be made on the basis of weight of steam produced per hour, when both use the same fuel, have the same feed-water temperature, and the same working pressure. Actual feed temperatures and working pressures vary widely, and it is necessary to adopt a standard feed temperature and standard working pressure. The feed temperature adopted is 100° C. or 212° F. and the working pressure 14·7 lbs. per square inch, i.e. atmospheric pressure. This condition requires the latent heat of 1 lb. of steam at atmospheric pressure to evaporate 1 lb. of the water. This latent heat is 539 C.H.U., and since this heat produces 1 lb. of steam under the standard conditions it is called the Standard Evaporation Unit.

EXAMPLE. The heat passing through the plates of a certain boiler per lb. of coal burned is 4,380 C.H.U. Find the number of standard evaporation units equivalent to this heat.

This is the useful heat, since all of it must enter the water.

∴ Weight of water evaporated by 4,380 C.H.U. "*from* feed water at 100° C. *and* formed into dry steam *at* 100° C. " = $\frac{4,380}{539}$ lbs.

$$= 8\cdot13 \text{ lbs.}$$

This is the standard evaporation produced by this heat. The statement in inverted commas is usually abbreviated to "from and at 100° C."

68. Equivalent Evaporation. If a given weight of steam is produced, from feed water at a certain temperature, and at a certain working pressure, then the equivalent evaporation is the weight of steam which would be produced, from and at 100° C., by the same amount of heat which produces the steam under the actual conditions.

The heat producing the steam is the heat passing through the boiler-plates. This can be obtained if we know the actual weight of water evaporated, its feed temperature, its working pressure and quality.

Let t_f = feed temperature and h_f = its liquid heat.

t_g = temperature of generation and h_g = corresponding liquid heat.

L = latent heat of steam.

x = dryness fraction.

W = weight of water actually evaporated.

E = equivalent evaporation (from and at 100° C.).

Then heat required to produce 1 lb. of steam

$$= (h_g' - h_f) + xL$$

and heat required to produce W lbs. of steam

$$= W[h_g - h_f + xL].$$

This is the amount of heat available for evaporation under standard conditions.

$$\therefore E = \frac{W[h_g - h_f + xL]}{539} \text{ lbs.}$$

W may be 1 lb. if we require to find the evaporation equivalent to 1 lb. actual evaporation, or it may be, as is more usual, the weight of water evaporated per lb. of coal.

If two boilers use the same coal the boiler which has the higher equivalent evaporation is the better boiler for steam raising. If the fuels are different, then the only accurate way to compare performances is by calculating efficiencies.

69. Boiler Efficiency. This is defined as the ratio

$$\frac{\text{Heat actually producing steam}}{\text{Heat liberated in the furnace}},$$

both quantities being measured in the same units and relating to the same duration of time. Compared in this way, two boilers are judged on their abilities to utilize the heat liberated in the furnaces.

Let W_1 = wt. of steam actually evaporated in a given time.

C = wt. of coal or oil burned in same time.

H = higher calorific value of fuel in heat units per lb.

h_f = liquid heat in feed.

h_g =   ,,   ,, at generation temperature.

L = latent heat of steam.

x = dryness fraction of steam.

η = efficiency of boiler.

Then heat used in producing steam = $W_1[(h_g - h_f) + xL]$

Heat liberated in furnace = $C \times H$.

$$\text{Boiler efficiency} = \frac{W_1[(h_g - h_f) + xL]}{C \times H}.$$

If W = evaporation per lb. of fuel

$$\eta = \frac{W[(h_g - h_f) + xL]}{H}.$$

If the loss of heat due to unburnt fuel is considerable, this loss should be subtracted from the denominator.

The important difference between this equation and that for the equivalent evaporation is in the denominator. In the efficiency equation it is the higher calorific value of the fuel, and in the equivalent evaporation it is the latent heat at 100° C.

If the steam is superheated, then the additional heat must be included within the brackets in the numerator.

EXAMPLE. A boiler evaporates $8\frac{1}{4}$ lbs. of water per lb. of coal burned. The pressure is 128 lbs. per sq. in. absolute, and the feed temperature is 60° C. Find the equivalent evaporation if the steam is dry as it leaves the boiler.

From steam tables total heat of 1 lb. of dry steam 128 lbs. per sq. in.
                                                                    = 664·9 C.H.U.

From steam tables liquid heat of 1 lb. feed at 60° C.   =   60·1   ,,

Heat which must pass into boiler to produce 1 lb.

                                                    steam = 604·8   ,,

Heat actually passing into boiler per lb. of coal   = 604·8 × $8\frac{1}{4}$

                                                    = 4,990 C.H.U.

Equivalent evaporation per lb. of coal   = $\dfrac{4,990}{539}$

                                                    = 9·25 lbs.

EXAMPLE. Find the boiler efficiency in the above case if the calorific value of the coal is 7,800 C.H.U. per lb.

The calorific value is the heat which 1 lb. of coal can generate in the furnace.

$$\text{Boiler efficiency} = \frac{\text{Heat actually used in producing steam}}{\text{Heat supplied by combustion}}.$$

We may make 1 lb. of coal the basis of comparison independently of time.

$$\therefore \text{Boiler efficiency} = \frac{4,990}{7,800}$$

$$= 0.64 \text{ or } 64 \text{ per cent.}$$

EXAMPLE. Compare the performance of the boilers A and B, first, on the equivalent evaporation basis, second, on the efficiency basis.

Test Results.

	Boiler A.	Boiler B.
Weight of coal used in lbs. per hour	2,080	2,740
Weight of steam generated in lbs. per hour	11,800	17,500
Feed water temperature, ° C.	10	20
Absolute pressure of steam in lbs. per sq. in.	145	165
Temperature of steam leaving boiler, ° C.	252	278
Calorific value of coal in C.H.U.	7,900	8,050

Take specific heat of steam as 0.5.

BOILER A

From steam tables, temperature of dry steam at 145 lbs. per sq. in. = 179.8; and total heat of dry steam at 145 lbs. per sq. in. = 666.1.

Heat required to superheat = $(252 - 179.8) \times 0.5$
$$= 72.2 \times 0.5 = 36.1 \text{ C.H.U.}$$

Total heat per lb. of superheated steam = $666.1 + 36.1 = 702.2$ C.H.U.

Heat supplied to 1 lb. of steam = $702.2 - 10 = 692.2$ C.H.U.

$$\text{Steam produced per lb. of coal} = \frac{11,800}{2,080} = 5.675 \text{ lbs.}$$

$$\therefore \text{Equivalent evaporation} = \frac{5.675 \times 692.2}{539} = 7.28 \text{ lbs.}$$

$$\text{Boiler efficiency} = \eta = \frac{5.675 \times 692.2}{7,900}$$

$$= 0.497 \text{ or } 49.7 \text{ per cent.}$$

BOILER B

Temperature of dry steam at 165 lbs. per sq. in. $= 185 \cdot 5°$ C.

Total heat ,, ,, ,, ,, ,, $= 667 \cdot 6$ C.H.U.

Heat required to superheat $= 0 \cdot 5(278 - 185 \cdot 5)$

$$= 46 \cdot 25 \text{ C.H.U.}$$

Total heat per lb. of superheated steam $= 667 \cdot 6 + 46 \cdot 25$

$$= 713 \cdot 85 \text{ C.H.U.}$$

Heat supplied to 1 lb. of steam $= 713 \cdot 85 - 20$

$$= 693 \cdot 85 \text{ C.H.U.}$$

Steam produced per lb. of coal $= \dfrac{17,500}{2,740} = 6 \cdot 4$ lbs.

$\therefore$ Equivalent evaporation $= \dfrac{6 \cdot 4 \times 693 \cdot 85}{539} = 8 \cdot 23$ lbs.

Boiler efficiency $= \eta = \dfrac{6 \cdot 4 \times 693 \cdot 85}{8,050}$

$$= 0 \cdot 552 \text{ or } 55 \cdot 2 \text{ per cent.}$$

Ratio $\dfrac{\text{Equiv. Evap. B}}{\text{Equiv. Evap. A}} = \dfrac{8 \cdot 23}{7 \cdot 28} = 1 \cdot 13.$

Ratio $\dfrac{\text{Efficiency of B}}{\text{Efficiency of A}} = \dfrac{0 \cdot 552}{0 \cdot 497} = 1 \cdot 11.$

70. Heat Flow. The heat produced is all developed in the furnace and may be divided into sections as follows :

(1) Heat leaving in steam.

(2) Heat leaving in gases.

(3) Heat leaving in ashes, including unburnt fuel.

(4) Radiation losses.

These four items can be arranged in the form of a balance-sheet.

The heat leaving in gases = weight of gas × temperature rise × specific heat of gas.

Weight of the gas = weight of air required + weight of fuel.

Heat leaving in ashes = weight of ashes × specific heat × temperature excess above datum temperature + weight of unburnt fuel in ashes × calorific value.

The datum temperature is conveniently taken as that of the boiler house, because the air and fuel are at that temperature.

TABLE III

COMBUSTION PER SQUARE FOOT OF GRATE PER HOUR

Combustion.	Draught.
22 lbs.	0·73 inches of water
30	0·95
40	1·1
60	3·0
70	4·0
120	8·0
130	10·0

(The last four values refer to locomotive boilers.)

TABLE IV

RATIO OF HEATING SURFACE TO GRATE AREA

Type of Boiler.	Ratio $\dfrac{\text{Heating Surface}}{\text{Grate Area}}$.
Lancashire	24 Average values
Water tube . . .	55
Water tube (Marine) .	35
Loco.	65
Scotch	35
American . . .	65

Superheating surface is about 25 per cent. of heating surface.

TABLE V

BOILER EFFICIENCIES

Type of Boiler.	Efficiency.
Small Lancashire . .	50% without economizer.
Large Lancashire . .	70% with economizer.
Small water tube . .	55% without economizer.
Large water tube . .	80% with preheater and economizer.
Loco. . . .	70%
Marine . . .	65%

EXAMPLES IX

1. State the advantages and disadvantages of water-tube boilers as compared with fire-tube boilers. Make a neat proportional sketch of any type of boiler with which you are acquainted, indicating clearly the various accessories and mountings. The accessories are not to be sketched, only positioned. U.E.I.

2. A steam boiler is found to evaporate 8·4 lbs. of water at 20° C. into saturated steam, 95 per cent. dry, at 215 lbs. per sq. in. for each pound of coal consumed. The calorific value of the coal

is 8,020 C.H.U. per lb. Eighteen lbs. of air enter the furnace for every lb. of coal burned. The temperature of the boiler room is 20° C., and of the gases at the base of the chimney 260° C. Determine :

(a) The efficiency of the boiler ;
(b) The equivalent evaporation per pound of coal ;
(c) The proportion of the heat of the coal passing up the chimney.

You may assume the mean specific heat of the flue gases to be 0·24.

U.E.I.

3. Sketch and describe either (a) a Scotch type marine boiler, or (b) a Babcock and Wilcox water-tube boiler. N.C.T.E.C.

4. A boiler plant supplies steam at 220 lbs. per sq. in. absolute 0·96 dry, to a turbine of 2,000 horse-power, with a steam consumption of 11·2 lbs. per horse power per hour. The feed temperature is 60° C. Calculate the boiler efficiency if the calorific value of the coal is 7,500 C.H.U. per lb., and the consumption 1·25 tons per hour. For dry steam at 220 lbs. per sq. in. : $h = 202$ C.H.U. per lb. ; $L = 468$ C.H.U. per lb. N.C.T.E.C.

5. What do you understand by " equivalent evaporation from and at 100° C. " ? A boiler generated 8½ lbs. of steam per lb. of coal burned from feed water at 21° C. The steam pressure was 145 lbs. per sq. in. absolute, and the dryness fraction of the steam was 0·95. Find the equivalent evaporation from and at 100° C. and the efficiency of the boiler, the calorific value of the fuel being 7,600 C.H.U. per lb. U.L.C.I.

6. During a boiler test the following data were observed :

Duration of test	2 hours.
Average steam pressure by gauge .	175 lbs. per sq. in.
Temperature of steam leaving boiler .	320° C.
Total steam generated . . .	18,200 lbs.
Calorific value of coal as fired . .	7,029 C.H.U. per lb.
Coal fired	2,260 lbs.
Average feed water temperature .	60° C.
Total heating surface . . .	2,320 sq. ft.
Total grate surface	73·2 sq. ft.

Find (a) The efficiency of the boiler ;
(b) The coal fired per square foot of grate area per hour ;
(c) The steam generated per square foot of heating surface per hour.

The specific heat of the superheated steam is to be taken as 0·56.

U.L.C.I.

7. A test of a steam generating plant gave the following data :

Total weight of steam generated per hour .	12,000 lbs.
Absolute pressure of steam generated . .	170 lbs. per sq. in.
Temperature of feed water entering economizer	65° C.
Temperature of feed water leaving economizer	166° C.

Find (a) the percentage saving of heat due to the economizer ;

(b) the evaporation of the boiler in lbs. per hour at 170 lbs. per sq. in. absolute under the same conditions of firing, but without the economizer ;

(c) the equivalent of the economizer in percentage increase of boiler power.　　　　　U.L.C.I.

8. Two tests of a boiler gave evaporations of 8 lbs. and 14·5 lbs. of steam from and at 100° C. per lb. of coal and per lb. of oil fuel respectively. How many barrels of oil, each weighing 325 lbs., are equivalent in heat value to 1 ton of coal ? If the calorific value of the oil is 10,280 C.H.U. per lb., what is the calorific value of 1 lb. of the coal ? Find also the efficiency of the boiler.

NOTE.—The boiler, which originally burned coal, was converted so as to burn oil fuel. The above data are from tests taken before and after conversion, and it is to be assumed that the efficiency of the boiler was the same in each case.　　　　　U.L.C.I.

9. The following data were recorded during a boiler test :

Duration of trial	8 hours.
Boiler pressure, in lbs. per sq. in. absolute . .	183
Temperature of air in boiler house . . .	31° C.
Temperature of gases in chimney . . .	272° C.
Temperature of feed water	15·5° C.
Total feed water	102,600 lbs.
Total coal	10,738 lbs.
Contents of ash pans	148 lbs.
Combustibles percentage of ash pans contents .	42·7
Air used, per lb. of coal	17 lbs.

Determine :

(a) The heat units used in generating steam from feed water per lb. of coal.

(b) The number of heat units passing away up the chimney per lb. of coal.

(c) The heat units represented by unburnt fuel per lb. of coal.

(d) The thermal efficiency per cent.

(e) By difference the heat units lost by radiation, imperfect combustion, etc., per lb. of coal.

Given—The calorific value of the coal 7,944 C.H.U. and the specific heat of the products of combustion 0·24.　　　　　U.L.C.I.

CHAPTER X

THE STEAM ENGINE PLANT

71. Essentials of a Steam Plant. In most of the preceding chapters, we have been dealing with the fundamental properties of gases and vapours in relation to the action of heat upon them.

In the last chapter we have treated of boilers for steam raising, since that subject followed naturally upon the question of steam generation.

It is proposed now to deal in a general way with the equipment which is used in connection with a heat engine, using water vapour or steam as the working substance.

The component parts of a modern plant are :
(1) the feed pump, (2) the steam generator or boiler, (3) the engine and (4) the condenser.

In addition to these there are auxiliaries which assist these parts in better performing their respective functions.

The engine mentioned in (3) above may be a reciprocating engine or a turbine.

The relative arrangement of the components is shown in fig. 41, and it will be noted it is divided into three sections :

(*a*) The high pressure section on the left of OX.

(*b*) The low pressure section between O'Y and O'Y'.

(*c*) The engine section, between OX and OY, where the work is done and where the pressure falls.

The condenser will generally need, as accessories, an extraction pump to remove condensed water from the condenser, an air ejector to remove air which accumulates, and a circulating pump to maintain a supply of condensing water. In greater detail, then, the functions of the principal parts are as follows :

106

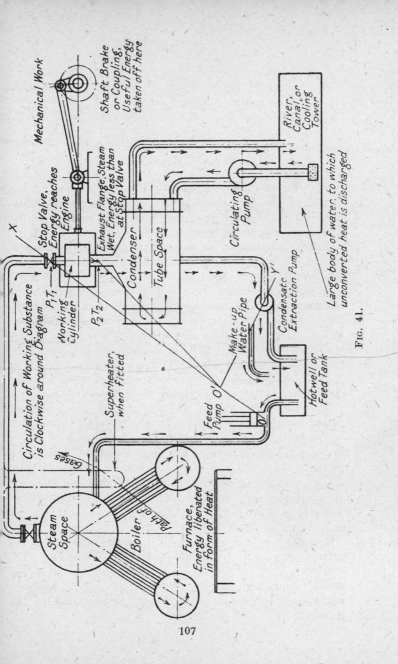

Fig. 41.

107

(1) The extraction pump and feed pump remove water from the low pressure section and force it into the boiler which is at high pressure.

(2) The boiler produces steam with its high energy content.

(3) The engine receives heat for the purpose of converting it into mechanical work.

(4) The condenser is to maintain a low temperature and low pressure, thus increasing the amount of work which may be obtained per pound of steam.

(5) The air ejector removes air from the condenser as fast as it enters.

(6) The hot-well receives hot water discharged from the condenser, and serves as feed-water tank.

To make allowance for losses due to blowing at the safety-valve and leakage into the atmosphere, it is necessary to add a small amount of water to the boiler supply. This is called the make-up feed, and is a very small quantity compared to the amount circulating in a well-controlled up-to-date plant. It is now the practice to close the feed system and de-aerate the make-up water before introducing it. This assists in reducing corrosion and in maintaining a high vacuum.

72. The Reciprocating Engine. At this stage the student is expected to be familiar with the general arrangement of a reciprocating steam engine, and the details are best studied in connection with Engineering Drawing and Design.

It is necessary to grasp, however, that it is in the cylinder of such an engine that the heat is converted into work. The rest of the engine is concerned mainly with changing the reciprocating motion of the piston into rotary motion, working the necessary valves, and controlling the speed by means of the governor.

The steam is distributed to the cylinder by means of the admission valves which admit steam during an appropriate interval, and the exhaust valves which permit it to escape at the end of the useful stroke. There must be one admission and one exhaust valve for each side of the piston in a double-acting engine. This is quite apparent in the case of drop valves, Corliss valves and similar types, but the common slide valve is really four valves in one casting. Each edge corresponds to one single purpose valve.

In the uniflow engine the faces of the piston act as exhaust valves.

The student at this stage is recommended to take any available opportunity of studying technical journals and makers' catalogues, with a view to becoming familiar with different types of engines and their details.

73. Steam Movements. The events occurring for *one side of the piston* are as follows :

(1) Admission of steam by opening inlet valve.

(2) Cessation of steam supply, or " cut-off " by closing inlet valve.

(3) Release of steam by opening the exhaust valve.

(4) Compression of steam in the clearance space, after closing of the exhaust valve.

These events are arranged so that there is appreciable movement of the piston between events (2) and (3).

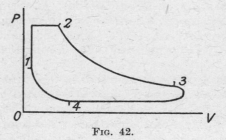

Fig. 42.

Here expansion occurs, when the steam gives up some of its internal energy. These events are shown by corresponding numbers on the diagram of fig. 42.

When the steam is exhausted it is passed to the atmosphere in the case of a non-condensing engine, or to the condenser in a condensing engine. In the former type the whole of the indicator diagram lies above the atmospheric line as shown in fig. 43.

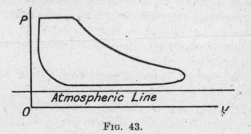

FIG. 43.

A condensing engine diagram will lie partly below the atmospheric line as indicated in fig. 44, and in the low pressure cylinder of a compound engine, the whole diagram is sometimes below this line.

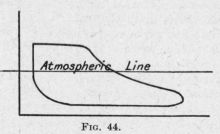

FIG. 44.

74. Condenser Function and Types. The function of the condenser is to maintain a low temperature. This is necessary to obtain the maximum possible energy from the steam and to secure high efficiency. This fact will be seen at once if the student has grasped the principle involved in Carnot's Cycle. The condenser is the cold body to which heat is rejected. Low pressure accompanies the low temperature, and thus all condensers maintain a vacuum under normal conditions. The lowest temperature ideally possible is that of the available water supply for condensing purposes. This is called the condensing water, or sometimes the circulating water. The condensed steam itself is called the *condensate*. The temperature of the condensate is higher on leaving the condenser than that of the circulating water at inlet. The condensate thus has a considerable liquid heat reckoned from 0° C. It is discharged into the hot-well, whence the feed pump transfers it to the boiler.

There are several types of condenser in use but only the surface and jet types will be described.

75. The Surface Condenser. This is used where large quantities of inferior water are available for cooling, and where the better quality of water for boiler feed purposes is to be economized. This latter water passes through the boiler, engine, condenser and hot-well in a continuous cycle, and only a small quantity of make-up water is needed. The circulating water is kept quite separate and is often taken from a canal, river, or, in the case of ships and seaside plants, from the sea.

When the surface condenser is used with a reciprocating engine it is liable to become very dirty due to the oil which passes through the cylinders. Oil separators are often fitted to entrap a large portion of the oil leaving the engine in the exhaust steam. The oil is deposited on the outside of the tubes, and seriously interferes with the rate of heat transmission through the tubes. The effect is to reduce the condensation rate per square foot of condensing surface. This difficulty does not arise in the case of the steam turbine, because there is no internal lubrication.

The condenser consists of a vessel more or less cylindrical in form. A good example is shown in fig. 45. It is provided with a steam inlet I of large area and outlets O and O' for the air. The condensate leaves at the bottom of the condenser at L. The ends of the main vessel are closed by means of perforated tube plates P, into which the tubes are fixed in such a manner that water leakage through the tube-plates into the main condensing space is prevented. A detail of the packing arrangement is

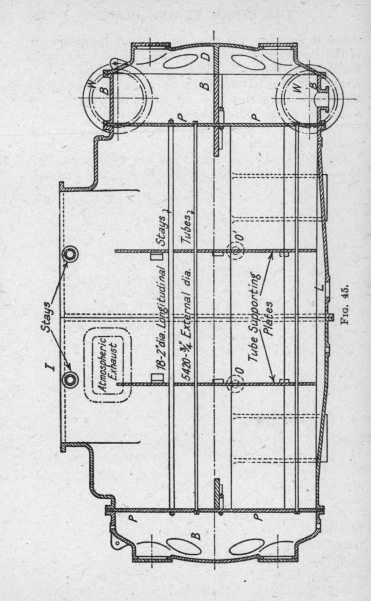

FIG. 45.

shown in fig. 45A. The tubes pass through the main body
of the condenser between the tube-plates, and the steam
impinges on the outer surface of the tubes where it is
condensed. The water thus formed drips to the bottom of
the condenser, whence it is withdrawn at L by the wet
extraction pump. The sectional elevation shows two tubes
only, but actually some 5,420 tubes are fitted in the condenser shown in fig. 45.

The ends of the condenser tubes are enclosed in water
boxes B, which follow the general shape of the condenser

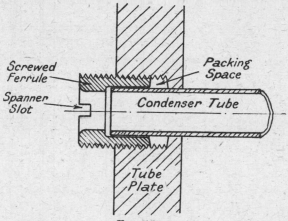

FIG. 45A.

body, and are themselves closed by large doors or covers
D. The water boxes are provided with inlet and outlet
water pipes W. Baffles or stop-plates are arranged in the
water boxes for the purpose of directing the circulating
water through the tubes.

The circulating water flows through banks or " passes "
of tubes in alternate directions. In the condenser illustrated there are two passes with 2,710 tubes in each. The
single baffle plate is clearly shown in the right hand of the
view (fig. 45). The whole of the 5,420 tubes must be
taken in calculating the surface area upon which conden-

I

sation takes place, but only the tubes in one "pass" must be taken into account when calculating the area of water flow.

The inlet and outlet water pipes are arranged so that the coolest water meets the coolest vapour and condensate. The water thus enters at the bottom and passes through the lowest tubes first, then through the upper tubes to the exit. This is known as the contraflow principle, and is adopted to maintain a temperature difference throughout the whole length of water flow. The designer has to compromise between cooler condensate, with lower temperature of feed but better vacuum, and warmer condensate, with hotter boiler feed and poorer vacuum.

The condenser is most effective when the quantity of air in it is as small as possible. Air enters the condenser system (1) with the feed water when this is drawn from an open tank or reservoir, (2) by leakage at glands and joints in the portion of the plant which is under vacuum. Its effect is threefold : (a) it exerts a pressure just as if it were present without vapour ; (b) being a poor heat conductor, particularly at low densities, it reduces the heat transmission rate ; (c) it increases the size of air pump necessary, and thus the power required to drive it is increased.

If not removed the air would accumulate in the condenser and ultimately destroy the vacuum. It will be understood that the condenser produces the state of vacuum, but the air pump or ejector is necessary to maintain it. The air pump may be either a " dry " or a " wet " pump. A dry pump removes the air and mixed vapour alone, and must be supplemented by a wet pump to extract the condensate. With many reciprocating engines the wet pump deals with both the air and condensate, but the vacuum which results is only moderate.

If high vacuum, say $28\frac{1}{2}$ to 29 inches, be required, some modern form of steam air-ejector is needed, for air removal, and the condensate must be dealt with separately. This arrangement is shown in the next article on the jet condenser, but it will operate equally well with a surface condenser.

There is, however, this difference, that in the surface condenser the wet pump deals only with condensate, whilst in the jet type it must remove both condensate and injection water since they are intimately mixed.

Fig. 46A shows the air ejector which, in a modern plant, takes the place of the dry air pump. It is of the two-stage type, and is fitted with intermediate condenser, C, between the stages, to render the last stage more effective. The steam enters the ejector through the valve in the top right-hand corner of the figure, and flows through the nozzles just above the throats B and E at high velocity. The jets are arranged in such a way that the air is entrained (dragged into the jet) at a rapid rate. This produces and maintains a vacuum at the flange " A," which is connected to the condenser, and through this passage the air is drawn from the condenser.

The mixture then passes on to the diverging portion of the first stage ejector tube below B, where it slows down in speed and builds up in pressure, entering the inter-condenser at the bottom left-hand side of the vessel. Here the water from the jet D cools the air and increases its density, any vapour, together with the steam from nozzles at B, being condensed. The air then passes out of the inter-condenser, just over the letter D, to the second stage ejector, where its pressure is built up to atmospheric value and from which the steam from the nozzles E passes to the hot-well or feed heaters. The bottom flange is connected to the extraction pump suction pipe, and thus establishes a balance between the inter-condenser and the main condenser. Thus the water entering at D is drained back to the wet extraction pump. This ejector is a good example of a modern high efficiency extractor for the maintenance of a high vacuum. The auxiliary water jet D enables the ejector to deal with a greater quantity of air in a given time, and with a given weight of steam passing through the nozzles. It is used with the surface condenser described above and also with the jet condenser now to be described.

76. The Jet Condenser. Fig. 46 shows a condenser of the jet type. The cooling water is sprayed amongst the incoming steam with the result that rapid and effective condensation occurs.

The supply of water is usually under a slight pressure at the spray nozzles to initiate the flow of the water, but when the engine begins to discharge steam a vacuum is quickly formed, which induces the injection water in large quantities. The quantity is regulated by the injection valve. The temperature of the condensate is equal to that of the condensing water, as it leaves the condenser. The jet condenser is used where large quantities of good water are available, particularly where the injection water is suitable for boiler feed purposes. It occupies much less space than a surface condenser, and is sometimes fitted to the engine above the engine-room floor level. Often the extraction pump is accommodated in the condenser casting.

In fig. 46, E is the centrifugal type extraction pump, situated in the base of the condenser. The steam enters the condenser at the top and descends into the body A. A belt B, passing round the top portion of the condenser body, forms a water service pipe into which spray nozzles, C, are fitted. These nozzles are arranged completely to spray the space A below the level of the belt B, with the result that all the steam is quickly condensed.

The valve V is the injection valve which controls the supply of injection water. The condensate and injection water, now mixed together, fall to the bottom of the condenser, whence the water passes behind and in front of the section plane shown in the illustration, into the eye of the pump impeller, which forces the water through the non-return valve N. The extraction pump deals only with the water, whilst the air goes through the passage J to the air ejector H of the type described above.

The float G operates the valve F, by means of the levers shown, when the water level rises to it. This opens the condenser to the atmosphere and immediately destroys the vacuum. For this reason the arrangement is known as a

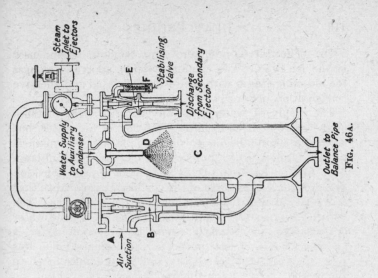

Steam
Inlet to
Ejectors

Stabilising
Valve

E
F

Discharge
from Secondary
Ejector

Water Supply
to Auxiliary
Condenser

D

C

Air
Suction

B

Outlet to
Balance Pipe

FIG. 46A.

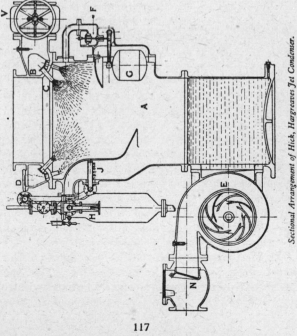

V

F

B

C

G

A

D

J

H

E

N

Sectional Arrangement of Hick, Hargreaves Jet Condenser.

FIG. 46

vacuum breaker. It is fitted to prevent flooding of the condenser body with consequent damage to the engine, if the extraction pump should fail.

The condenser illustrated is of the parallel flow type, because both steam and water flow in the same direction after meeting.

For permission to reproduce figs. 45, 46 and 46A, the authors are indebted to Messrs. Hick, Hargreaves & Co., who have kindly placed these illustrations at their disposal.

77. Condenser Efficiency. There is no generally accepted definition of condenser efficiency, but a method adopted by the well-known makers of turbines, Messrs. C. A. Parsons & Co., has been widely used.

By this method it is stated

Condenser efficiency

$$= \frac{\text{Temperature rise of cooling water}}{\text{Vacuum temperature} - \text{Inlet cooling water temperature}}$$

EXAMPLE. The inlet cooling water for a condenser has a temperature of 25° C. and the outlet is 32° C. The vacuum is 28 ins. with the barometer at 30 ins. Find the condenser efficiency.

Absolute pressure in condenser = 30 − 28

$$= 2 \text{ ins. of mercury}$$
$$= 0·98 \text{ lbs. per sq. in.}$$

Corresponding steam temperature = 38° C.

$$\therefore \text{ Condenser efficiency} = \frac{32 - 25}{38 - 25} = \frac{7}{13}$$

$$= 53·8 \text{ per cent.}$$

78. Elementary Calculation on Surface Condenser. The number of tubes in the surface condenser depends upon the area of surface required to condense the steam, and upon the length of the condenser.

Let W = total weight of steam to be condensed per hour.

A = area of condensing surface in sq. ft.

C = steam condensed per hour per sq. ft. (C varies from 6 to 12 lbs. per hour).

l = length between tube plates.

d = outside diameter of each tube in feet.

Now $A = \dfrac{W}{C}$

Surface area of one tube $= \pi d l$

$\therefore$ Number of tubes $= \dfrac{A}{\pi d l} = \dfrac{W}{C \pi d l}$.

Let $n_c =$ number of tubes in condenser.

$n_p =$,, ,, ,, per pass.

$P =$,, ,, passes.

Then $n_p = \dfrac{n_c}{P}$.

Area of flow for circulating water $= \dfrac{\pi d_i^2}{4} \times n_p$ where $d_i =$ inside diameter of tube.

EXAMPLE. Calculate the number of tubes required in a surface condenser to condense 120,000 lbs. of steam per hour. Distance between tube plates $= 10$ ft. Inside diameter of tubes $= \frac{5}{8}$ ins. Outside diameter $= \frac{3}{4}$ ins. Condensation rate $= 12$ lbs. per sq. ft. per hour.

Also find the quantity of circulating water if the velocity of flow is 6 ft. per sec. through the tubes and the number of passes $= 2$.

$$\text{Area of tubes} = \frac{120,000}{12} = 10,000 \text{ sq. ft.}$$

$$\text{Area of one tube (outside)} = \pi d l = \pi \times \tfrac{3}{4} \times \tfrac{1}{12} \times 10 \text{ sq. ft.}$$

$$= \frac{31 \cdot 4}{16} = 1 \cdot 96 \text{ sq. ft.}$$

$$\therefore \text{ Number of tubes} = \frac{10,000}{1 \cdot 96} = 5,102.$$

$$\text{Number of tubes per pass} = \frac{5,102}{2} = 2,551.$$

Area of flow for circulating water $= 2,551 \times 0 \cdot 7854 \times (\tfrac{5}{8} \times \tfrac{1}{12})^2$
$= 5 \cdot 41$ sq. ft.

Quantity of water $= 5 \cdot 41 \times 6 \times 60 \times 60 \times 62 \cdot 4$ lbs. per hour.
$= 7,292,000$ lbs. per hour.

79. Vacuum Efficiency of a Condenser. The lowest pressure which can exist in a given condenser is that of the vapour corresponding to the condensate temperature. This would be the pressure in a perfect condensing plant. The pressure in the actual condenser is greater than the ideal pressure by an amount equal to the pressure of the air present in the condenser.

Let p_i = ideal pressure in inches of mercury.

p_a = actual ,, ,, ,, ,,

The actual vacuum = Barometric pressure − p_a

ideal ,, = Barometric pressure − p_i

The latter quantity is the greater and is the perfect vacuum.

The ratio $\dfrac{\text{actual vacuum}}{\text{ideal vacuum}}$ is called the vacuum efficiency.

It will be noted that the vacuum efficiency depends on the effectiveness of the air extractor.

EXAMPLE. The temperature of the condensate in a condenser is 30° C., and the vacuum is 28 ins. of mercury, with the barometer at 30 ins. Find the vacuum efficiency.

Back pressure of vapour corresponding to 30° C. = 0·61 lbs. per sq. in.

$$= 0·61 \times \frac{30}{14·7}$$

$$= 1·242 \text{ ins. of mercury.}$$

$$\therefore \text{ Ideal vacuum} = 30 - 1·242$$

$$= 28·758 \text{ ins.}$$

$$\therefore \text{ Vacuum efficiency} = \frac{28}{28·758} = 0·974$$

$$= 97·4 \text{ per cent.}$$

EXAMPLES X

1. A steam engine uses 13·5 lbs. of steam per I.H.P. per hour. The boiler feed pump has an efficiency of 60 per cent. Find what percentage of the indicated work is expended in driving the feed pump if the boiler pressure by gauge is 180 lbs. per sq. in. Is all this energy wasted ?

2. The above engine exhausts into a jet condenser where the pressure is 1·5 lbs. per sq. in. absolute. For every pound of steam condensed 32 lbs. of cooling water are used. Find the percentage of the indicated work used by the extraction pump if the atmospheric pressure is 15 lbs. per sq. in. and the pump has an efficiency of 68 per cent.

3. The steam exhausted to a jet condenser by a steam turbine is at a pressure of 1·5 lbs. per sq. in. and 84 per cent. dry. If the injection water per lb. of steam is 28 lbs. and is supplied at 8° C.,

find the temperature of the water removed by the extraction pump.

4. Calculate the number of tubes in a condenser required to condense 80,000 lbs. of steam per hour.

Length of tubes = 8 ft. Inside diam. = $\frac{5}{8}$ in. Outside diam. = $\frac{3}{4}$ in. Condensation rate, 12 lbs. per sq. ft. No. of passes = 2.

If 30 lbs. of circulating water are used per lb. of condensate, find the velocity of flow through the tubes.

5. A steam turbine, using 12 lbs. of steam per horse power hour, develops 1,500 horse power. The steam passes thence to a condenser at a pressure of 1 lb. per square inch absolute with dryness fraction 0·88. Determine the circulating water required, in gallons per hour, assuming a rise in temperature from 15° C. to 30° C. and a hot-well temperature of 30° C.

At a pressure of 1 lb. per sq. in. absolute, the temperature is 38·7° C., the heat of the liquid is 38·7 C.H.U. per lb., and the total heat of evaporation is 612·5 C.H.U. per lb. Assume the heat of the liquid at 15° C. and 30° C. to be 15 and 30 C.H.U. per lb. respectively. U.E.I.

6. A test of a surface condensing plant gave the following results :

Steam condensed per hour	2,520 lbs.
Temperature of exhaust steam entering condenser .	44·4° C.
Weight of circulating water used per min. . .	3,740 lbs.
Revolutions per min. of air pump	67
Temperature of air pump discharge . . .	43·7° C.
Vacuum recorded	27·18 ins.
Barometer reading	30 ins.

The air pump (single acting) is 10 ins. diameter and has a stroke of 7 ins. Determine :

(a) The increase of temperature of the circulating water ;
(b) The vacuum efficiency of the condenser ;
(c) The volumetric capacity of the air pump per lb. of steam condensed. U.L.C.I.

7. Briefly explain how the condensate is removed from and a vacuum is obtained in a surface condenser.

The vacuum in a surface condenser is 29 ins. with a barometer reading of 30 ins. (15 lbs. per sq. in.). The quantity of steam to be condensed per hour is 150,000 lbs. The temperature difference between that of the entering steam and that of the cooling water at outlet is 5° C. The temperature of the condensate leaving the condenser is 22° C., and that of the cooling water at inlet is 13° C. Find the number of lbs. of cooling water required per min. U.L.C.I.

8. In a test of a surface condenser the average weight of steam condensed per hour was 48,600 lbs. The pressure of the steam entering the condenser was 1·25 lbs. per sq. in. absolute, and the

temperature of the condensed steam leaving the condenser was 39° C. The temperatures of the condensing water at inlet and outlet were 23·4° C. and 38° C. respectively. Find the number of gallons of condensing water passing through the condenser per minute, assuming the steam enters the condenser in a dry saturated condition. If the average velocity of flow of the water through the condenser tubes was 7 ft. per sec., find the number of condenser tubes of $\frac{3}{4}$-in. internal diameter required, assuming that the condenser is of the two-flow type. U.L.C.I.

9. The weight of steam condensed in an hour in a surface condenser is 29,100 lbs. The pressure of the steam entering the condenser is 1·45 lbs. per sq. in. absolute, and its dryness fraction is 0·91. The temperatures of the cooling water at inlet and outlet are respectively 28·8° C. and 38·4° C. and the temperature of the hot-well is 44° C. The area of the cooling surface in the condenser is 2,120 sq. ft., and the cooling water passes through two nests of tubes in series, each nest containing 640 tubes of $\frac{5}{8}$-in. internal diameter. Find :

(a) The number of gallons of cooling water required per minute ;
(b) The weight of steam condensed per hour per square foot of cooling surface ;
(c) The velocity in feet per second of the cooling water through the tubes. U.L.C.I.

CHAPTER XI

HYPOTHETICAL INDICATOR DIAGRAM

80. Hypothetical Diagram. In preliminary calculations connected with engine design, it is customary to use
an imaginary diagram, which would result if the engine
worked in accordance with certain assumptions or hypo-
theses. Such a diagram is called a hypothetical indicator
diagram. The results obtained from it can then be
modified to suit known practical conditions.

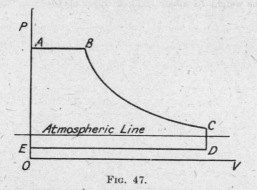

Fig. 47.

The assumptions made are :
(1) There is no clearance.
(2) Steam is supplied to the cylinder at a constant
      pressure equal to boiler pressure shown by the
      line AB (fig. 47).
(3) Cut-off is instantaneous, thus giving a sharp change
      of direction at B.
(4) The expansion, BC, is hyperbolic, i.e. $PV = C$.
(5) Expansion is carried to the end of the stroke.

(6) Release takes place at the end of the stroke, and pressure falls instantly to exhaust pressure, shown by the line CD.

(7) Exhaust takes place at constant pressure and continues throughout the whole stroke.

It should be noted that the length ED does not now represent the stroke or volume of the engine. This quantity is represented by the horizontal length of the inner diagram.

In addition to the above, exhaust pressures are assumed, (*a*) in the case of a condensing engine to be the designed condenser pressure, (*b*) in a non-condensing engine to be 2 or 3 lbs. per sq. in. above atmospheric pressure.

In actual engines the hypothetical conditions are departed from in a manner given below.

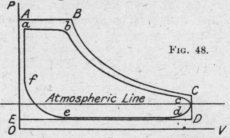

Fig. 48.

(1) All engines have clearance space for mechanical reasons, see fig. 48.

(2) Steam is supplied at a pressure which rapidly rises, but is finally less than boiler pressure (*f* to *a*). It then falls slightly, due to piston acceleration, inertia and friction in steam pipe (*a* to *b*).

(3) At *b* the cut-off is more or less sluggish and gives a rounded corner.

(4) The expansion line is not hyperbolic but falls below and to the left of it (*b* to *c*). This is due to condensation in the cylinder.

(5) The exhaust valve opens and expansion is stopped before the end of the stroke, in order to allow the pressure to drop before the piston begins its return stroke.

(6) In spite of early release the line showing how pressure falls is curved as shown by portion *cd*, indicating that pressure fall is not complete at the commencement of the back stroke.

(7) The exhaust line often lies above the assumed back-pressure line.

81. Diagram Factor. The general effect of these modifications is to make the actual indicator diagram, taken from an engine, less than the hypothetical diagram.

The ratio $\dfrac{\text{area of actual diagram}}{\text{area of hypothetical diagram}}$ is called the Diagram Factor.

The mean effective pressure in a cylinder is the difference between the average pressures during the forward stroke and back stroke of the piston.

For example, if the average absolute pressure during the forward stroke is 45 lbs. per sq. in., and the average absolute pressure on the same side of the piston during the return stroke is 18 lbs. per sq. in., then the mean effective pressure

$$= (45 - 18) = 27 \text{ lbs. per sq. in.}$$

In order to compare the areas of the actual and hypothetical indicator diagrams, it is necessary for both to be set down to the same scale of pressure and volume.

Then $\dfrac{\text{Area of actual indicator diagram}}{\text{Area of hypothetical indicator diagram}}$

$$= \dfrac{\text{Mean height of actual diagram}}{\text{Mean height of hypothetical diagram}}$$

$$= \dfrac{\text{Mean effective pressure from actual diagram}}{\text{Mean effective pressure from hypothetical diagram}}.$$

Let D = diagram factor for an engine.

P_{mH} = Hypothetical mean effective pressure in lbs. per square foot.

P_{mA} = Actual mean effective pressure in lbs. per square foot.

Then $P_{mA} = P_{mH} \times D.$

The real diagram factor can only be found when the engine is built and tested, but it is taken as having the same value for different engines of the same type.

Values of D vary between 0·6 and 0·9.

82. Determination of Mean Effective Pressure. The M.E.P. may be found from the diagram, hypothetical or actual, in several ways.

(1) By mid-ordinates taken from end to end.

(2) By finding areas, counting squares.

(3) By finding areas with a planimeter.

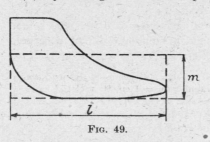

FIG. 49.

All methods aim at the determination of the height of a rectangle of equal area to the diagram.

In fig. 49 the full line shows the actual diagram, and the dotted lines the equivalent rectangular diagram.

The area of the rectangle is the same as that of the actual figure traced by the indicator.

Let s = scale of pressures in lbs. per square inch per inch.

a = area of diagram in square inches.

l = length of diagram in inches.

m = mean height of diagram.

Then $m = \dfrac{a}{l}$ and M.E.P. $= sm$.

$\therefore$ M.E.P. $= s\dfrac{a}{l}$ lbs. per sq. in.

The above shows how the M.E.P. may be calculated, if methods (2) and (3) are adopted.

When method (1) is used the area need not be calculated. In this case divide the diagram into a number of strips of equal width. Ten is a convenient number, though more may be taken if greater accuracy is required. At the centre of each strip set down the " mid "-ordinate. Measure all mid-ordinates, add their lengths together to find the total length, and divide by the number of mid-ordinates to find the mean height of the diagram, m.

Then M.E.P. $= sm$.

The mid-ordinates are shown in fig. 50 with arrow-heads. The ordinates are without arrowheads and need not necessarily be drawn. In measuring mid-ordinates care must be taken to measure from boundary to boundary of the diagram, and not from the atmospheric line or the zero pressure line.

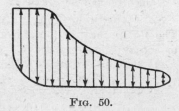

Fig. 50.

EXAMPLE. A hypothetical indicator diagram set down to scales of 1 in. = 25 lbs. per sq. in. and 1 in. = 1 cu. ft. enclosed an area of 4·5 sq. ins. The swept volume of the cylinder is 3 cu. ft. Find the probable mean effective pressure if the diagram factor is 0·7.

Length of diagram = 3 ins.

$$\therefore \text{ Mean height} = \frac{4·5}{3} = 1·5 \text{ ins.}$$

Hence Hypothetical M.E.P. = 1·5 × 25
= 37·5 lbs. per sq. in.
∴ Probable M.E.P. = 37·5 × 0·7
= 26·25 lbs. per sq. in.

EXAMPLE. The total length of 10 mid-ordinates on a gas engine indicator diagram is 5·63 ins. The spring scale is 120 lbs. per sq. in. per in. Find the M.E.P.

$$\text{Mean height of diagram} = \frac{5·63}{10} = 0·563 \text{ in.}$$

$$\therefore \text{ M.E.P.} = 0·563 \times 120$$
= 67·56 lbs. per sq. in.

EXAMPLE. The area of an indicator diagram for the L.P. cylinder of a compound engine was 3·5 sq. ins. The length of diagram was 2·3 ins. The spring scale was $\frac{1}{20}$. Find the M.E.P. in the cylinder.

$$\text{Mean height} = \frac{3·5}{2·3}$$
= 1·52 in.
∴ M.E.P. = 1·52 × 20
= 30·4 lbs. per sq. in.

83. Work done in Hypothetical Cycle.

Let P_1 = absolute initial pressure in lbs. per square foot.

V_1 = volume at cut-off in cubic feet.

V_2 = volume swept by piston during working stroke in cubic feet.

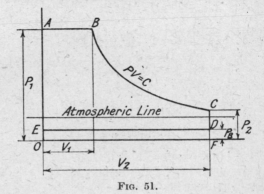

Fig. 51.

P_2 = pressure at end of expansion in lbs. per square foot absolute.

P_B = back pressure in lbs. per square foot absolute.

Work done during admission at P_1 (A to B)

$$= P_1V_1 \text{ ft.-lbs.}$$

Work done during expansion (B to C)

$$= P_1V_1 \log_e \frac{V_2}{V_1} \text{ ft.-lbs. (see Art. 40)}$$

Work done during exhaust at P_B(D to E)

$$= P_BV_2 \text{ ft.-lbs.}$$

The last-named quantity of work is done on the steam and not by the steam. Hence it is of opposite sign to the first and second quantities.

∴ Net work done per cycle

$$= P_1V_1 + P_1V_1 \log_e \frac{V_2}{V_1} - P_BV_2$$

$$= P_1V_1\left(1 + \log_e\frac{V_2}{V_1}\right) - P_BV_2$$

We may now derive a formula for the mean effective pressure.

Let P_m = mean effective pressure.

The work done by a constant pressure P_m acting through the stroke volume, V_2, must equal the net work done per cycle.

$$\therefore P_m V_2 = P_1 V_1 \left(1 + \log_e \frac{V_2}{V_1}\right) - P_B V_2$$

$$\therefore P_m = P_1 \frac{V_1}{V_2} \left(1 + \log_e \frac{V_2}{V_1}\right) - \frac{P_B V_2}{V_2}$$

$$= \frac{P_1(1 + \log_e r)}{r} - P_B$$

where r = ratio of expansion = $\dfrac{V_2}{V_1}$.

The M.E.P. thus obtained is in lbs. per square foot. To convert to lbs. per square inch it is only necessary to divide by 144, and we then have

$$p_m = \frac{p_1(1 + \log_e r)}{r} - p_B$$

where p_m, p_1, and p_B are in lbs. per square inch.

The actual M.E.P. in the engine will then be $p_m \times$ diagram factor

$$= p_m \times D.$$

The ratio of expansion is the reciprocal of the cut-off fraction when clearance is neglected.

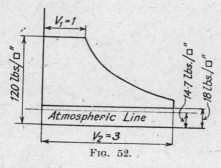

FIG. 52.

Thus with cut-off at $\frac{1}{4}$ stroke the ratio of expansion is 4.

EXAMPLE. Find the probable mean effective pressure for an engine supplied with steam at 120 lbs. per sq. in. absolute, cut-off $\frac{1}{4}$ stroke, hyperbolic expansion, back pressure 18 lbs. per sq. in. absolute, and diagram factor = 0·75. (See fig. 52.)

K

Hypothetical M.E.P. $= \dfrac{p_1(1 + \log_e r)}{r} - p_B$

$$= \dfrac{120(1 + 2 \cdot 3026 \times \log_{10} 3)}{3} - 18$$

$$= 40(1 + 2 \cdot 3026 \times 0 \cdot 4771) - 18$$
$$= 40(1 + 1 \cdot 098) - 18 = 83 \cdot 92 - 18$$
$$= 65 \cdot 92 \text{ lbs. per sq. in.}$$
$\therefore$ Probable M.E.P. $= 65 \cdot 92 \times \cdot 75$
$$= 49 \cdot 4 \text{ lbs. per sq. in.}$$

EXAMPLE. Find the dimensions of a steam engine cylinder to develop 120 I.H.P. The steam supply is at 100 lbs. per sq. in. absolute. The engine makes 80 r.p.m. and is double-acting. Cut-off is at $\frac{1}{4}$ stroke, diagram factor $= 0 \cdot 7$ and back pressure $= 16$ lbs. per sq. in. The stroke is twice the diameter of the cylinder. Neglect clearance.

Hypothetical M.E.P. $= \dfrac{p_1(1 + \log_e r)}{r} - p_b$

$$= \dfrac{100(1 + 2 \cdot 3026 \times \log_{10} 4)}{4} - 16$$

$$= 25(1 + 2 \cdot 3026 \times 0 \cdot 6021) - 16$$
$$= 25(1 + 1 \cdot 386) - 16$$
$$= 59 \cdot 6 - 16 = 43 \cdot 6 \text{ lbs. per sq. in.}$$
Probable M.E.P. $= 43 \cdot 6 \times 0 \cdot 7 = 30 \cdot 52$ lbs. per sq. in.

Work to be done per min. $= 33,000 \times 120$ ft.-lbs.

,, ,, ,, stroke $= \dfrac{33,000 \times 120}{2 \times 80} = 24,750$ ft.-lbs.

Also work done per stroke $= 144 \times 30 \cdot 52 \times \dfrac{\pi d^2}{4} \times 2d$

$$= 72 \times 30 \cdot 52 \pi d^3 \text{ ft.-lbs.}$$

$\therefore 72 \times 30 \cdot 52 \times \pi d^3 = 24,750$

$$d^3 = \dfrac{24,750}{72 \times 30 \cdot 52 \times \pi}$$

$$= 3 \cdot 6.$$

$\therefore d = 1 \cdot 53$ ft.
$$= 18 \cdot 36 \text{ ins.}$$
Stroke $= 2d = 2 \times 18 \cdot 36 = 36 \cdot 72$ ins.

84. The Compound Engine.

In the compound engine the expansion is divided up into two or more stages. The first stage in the expansion occurs in the high pressure cylinder, and the last stage in the low pressure cylinder.

If there are more than two stages in the expansion the intermediate stages take place in the intermediate pressure cylinders. The steam entering the high pressure cylinder passes through the successive cylinders. Suppose the cut-off in the first cylinder is at $\frac{1}{4}$ stroke, and that the second cylinder of a two-stage compound engine is three times the volume of the first, then the total expansion in the whole engine

$$= \frac{1}{\frac{1}{4}} \times 3 = 4 \times 3 = 12.$$

The total expansion in a compound engine

$$= \frac{\text{Volume at end of L.P. stroke}}{\text{Volume at cut-off in H.P. cylinder}}$$

The ratio $\dfrac{\text{Volume swept by piston in L.P. cylinder}}{\text{Volume swept by piston in H.P. cylinder}}$ is known as the cylinder ratio.

Thus, total expansions = Expansion ratio in H.P. cylinder × cylinder ratio.

In calculating the sizes of the cylinders of a compound engine, it is assumed that all the expansions occur in the L.P. cylinder, and this cylinder must be large enough to permit this expansion ratio and to develop the whole power. When this L.P. volume has been determined, it is divided by a chosen cylinder ratio in order to find the H.P. volume. The strokes and diameters are then chosen to satisfy these volumes.

The hypothetical M.E.P. is calculated in the same manner as for a simple engine, using the total expansions and not the L.P. expansion ratio. This M.E.P. is known as the *hypothetical referred mean effective pressure*.

EXAMPLE. Find the sizes of the cylinders of a two-stage compound engine to develop 300 I.H.P. at a speed of 75 revolutions per minute. Cylinder ratio = 3. Cut-off in H.P. cylinder at $\frac{1}{4}$ stroke. Pressure of steam supply = 120 lbs. per sq. in. absolute. Back pressure 3 lbs. per sq. in. absolute. Diagram factor = 0·65. Stroke in both cylinders = the L.P. cylinder diameter.

Total expansion ratio $= 4 \times 3 = 12$

Referred hyp. M.E.P. $= \dfrac{p_1(1 + \log_e r)}{r} - p_B$

$\qquad = \dfrac{120(1 + \log_e 12)}{12} - 3$

$\qquad = 10(1 + 2 \cdot 3026 \times 1 \cdot 0792) - 3$
$\qquad = 34 \cdot 9 - 3 = 31 \cdot 9$ lbs. per sq. in.

Probable referred M.E.P. $= 31 \cdot 9 \times 0 \cdot 65 = 20 \cdot 7$ lbs. per sq. in.

Volume of L.P. cylinder $\times$ M.E.P. referred $\times$ strokes per min. $=$
Work done per min.

Vol. of L.P. $\times 20 \cdot 7 \times 144 \times 2 \times 75 = 300 \times 33,000$.

$\qquad \therefore$ Vol. of L.P. $= \dfrac{300 \times 33,000}{2 \times 75 \times 20 \cdot 7 \times 144}$

$\qquad\qquad = \dfrac{33,000}{20 \cdot 7 \times 72} = 22 \cdot 1$ cu. ft.

Let $D =$ diameter in ft. of L.P. cylinder.

Then $\qquad 0 \cdot 7854 D^2 \times D = 22 \cdot 1$

$\qquad\qquad D^3 = \dfrac{22 \cdot 1}{0 \cdot 7854} = 28 \cdot 15$

$\qquad\qquad \therefore D = 3 \cdot 05$ ft.

and $\qquad\qquad$ Stroke $= 3 \cdot 05$ ft.

$\qquad$ Vol. of H.P. cylinder $= \dfrac{22 \cdot 1}{3} = 7 \cdot 36$ cu. ft.

If $d =$ diam. of H.P. cylinder

then $\qquad 0 \cdot 7854 d^2 \times D = 7 \cdot 36$

$\qquad\qquad d^2 = \dfrac{7 \cdot 36}{0 \cdot 7854 \times 3 \cdot 05} = 3 \cdot 07$

$\qquad\qquad \therefore d = 1 \cdot 75$.

Cylinder sizes are H.P. $1 \cdot 75$ ft. dia., $3 \cdot 05$ ft. stroke.
L.P. $3 \cdot 05$ ft. dia., $3 \cdot 05$ ft. stroke.

EXAMPLES XI

1. Using the method of Article 41, draw to scale a hypothetical indicator diagram for a steam engine whose stop-valve pressure is 120 lbs. per sq. in. absolute, back pressure 17 lbs. per sq. in., and cut-off $\frac{1}{3}$ stroke. Find the mean effective pressure on this diagram. Use a pressure scale of 50 lbs. per sq. in. per in. height of diagram, and let 3 ins. represent the full stroke.

2. By the same method as in example 1 draw a hypothetical indicator diagram for an expansion ratio of 12. Steam pressure is 180 lbs. per sq. in. absolute and back pressure is 2 lbs. per sq. in. Choose your own scale (not too small) and find the mean effective pressure.

3. Assume that example 2 applies to a cylinder of 20 ins. diam. and 36 ins. stroke. Take a diagram factor of 0·8 and 120 revs. per min. as the speed of the engine, double acting, and calculate the probable I.H.P.

4. Check the results of examples 1 and 2 by calculation.

5. A two-cylinder double-acting steam engine has to develop 280 I.H.P. at a speed of 160 revs. per min. The pressure is 180 lbs. per sq. in. absolute, and the back pressure is 2 lbs. per sq. in. absolute. Cut-off occurs at ⅔ stroke and the diagram factor is 0·75. If the stroke is 1½ times the diameter, find the cylinder sizes.

6. Assume the particulars in example 2 to apply to a compound double-acting engine of 75 I.H.P. with diagram factor 0·7, and speed 120 revs. per min. The cylinder ratio is 3 and the diameter and stroke of the low-pressure cylinder are equal. The strokes of both cylinders are equal. Calculate the cylinder sizes.

7. Determine the size of the cylinder for an engine which is required to develop 200 I.H.P. at 250 revs. per min., when the initial pressure is 180 lbs. per sq. in. absolute and the back pressure is 16 lbs. per sq. in. Assume a hyperbolic expansion curve, and a cut-off of 25 per cent. of the stroke. Assume a diagram factor of 0·8. Proportion of stroke to piston diameter = 4 : 3.

N.C.T.E.C.

8. Calculate the cylinder diameters and stroke of a compound engine to develop 600 I.H.P. under the following conditions :— Admission pressure 170 lbs. per sq. in. absolute ; back pressure 2 lbs. per sq. in. absolute ; revolutions per min. 120 ; mean piston speed 720 ft. per min. ; number of expansions 15 ; diagram factor 0·85 ; cylinder ratio 3·5.

N.C.T.E.C.

9. Calculate the cylinder diameter and stroke of a four-stroke gas engine to develop 25 B.H.P. at 400 revs. per min. ; assuming a mechanical efficiency of 80 per cent., mean effective pressure 80 lbs. per sq. in., ratio of stroke to cylinder diameter 1·5.

N.C.T.E.C.

10. Steam at an absolute pressure of 240 lbs. per sq. in. is to be supplied to a triple-expansion engine having a total expansion ratio of 24. Assuming that the whole of the work is done in the low pressure cylinder, find the diameter of this cylinder in order that the engine may develop 3,000 horse power at a speed of 105 revs. per min. Length of stroke 3 ft., back pressure 3 lbs. per sq. in. absolute, and diagram factor 0·6.

U.L.C.I.

11. A double-acting single-cylinder steam engine is to develop 50 I.H.P. at a speed of 120 revs. per min. Steam pressure at admission 65 lbs. per sq. in. absolute, cut-off 0·4 stroke. Stroke 18 ins. Assuming a back pressure of 16 lbs. per sq. in. absolute and a diagram factor of 0·85, find the diameter of the cylinder. What would you expect the B.H.P. to be ?

U.L.C.I.

12. Explain the term " diagram factor."

In a double-acting single-cylinder steam engine, the cylinder diameter is 15 ins. and the stroke 20 ins. Steam is admitted at an absolute pressure of 70 lbs. per sq. in., and is cut off at 0·35 stroke, and the back pressure is 15·5 lbs. per sq. in. absolute. The B.H.P. at a speed of 150 revs. per min. is 60, and the mechanical efficiency is 81 per cent. Find the diagram factor for the engine. U.L.C.I.

13. Write down the formula for the determination of the mean effective pressure obtained from the theoretical (steam engine) indicator diagram. State the meaning of each symbol used and the assumptions upon which the formula is based.

A single-cylinder double-acting steam engine develops 50 I.H.P. when running at 230 revs. per min. The cylinder is 9 ins. diam., and the stroke $13\frac{1}{2}$ ins. The steam is supplied at 75 lbs. per sq. in. gauge, and the condenser pressure is 5 lbs. per sq. in. The cut-off takes place at 0·625 stroke. Determine the value of the diagram factor. U.E.I.

14. A two-cylinder compound double-acting steam engine is required to develop 180 I.H.P. in each cylinder. The average piston speed must not exceed 750 ft. per min. Given the following further data, find the stroke of the engine and the requisite diameter of the H.P. cylinder. Boiler pressure 80 lbs. per sq. in. absolute. Pressure in L.P. steam chest 16 lbs. per sq. in. absolute. Revs. per min. = 125. Cut-off in H.P. cylinder at $\frac{1}{2}$ stroke. Diagram factor, 0·85. U.E.I.

15. If the ratio of volumes of the cylinders in a compound engine be $1 : 3\frac{1}{2}$, the boiler pressure 90 lbs. per sq. in. by gauge, the terminal pressure 10 lbs. per sq. in. absolute, and there is a drop in pressure of 5 lbs. per sq. in. between the boiler and the engine, determine the point of cut-off in the H.P. cylinder. U.E.I.

16. A locomotive has two cylinders each 20 ins. diam. by 2 ft. stroke. The initial pressure of the steam is 250 lbs. per sq. in. absolute, and the back pressure is 20 lbs. per sq. in. absolute. The clearance volume is 7 per cent. of the volume swept by the piston. Use a diagram factor of 0·85 and calculate the indicated horse power developed by the engine when cut-off occurs at $\frac{5}{8}$ stroke, and the driving wheels are making 120 R.P.M. U.E.I.

CHAPTER XII

ENTROPY AND ENTROPY DIAGRAMS

85. Entropy. Entropy is a very useful conception in heat engine theory. When understood it leads us to important results which, by other methods, can only be obtained much more laboriously.

Entropy cannot be readily defined in physical terms, and hence the student is advised to follow carefully what is said concerning entropy, and the examples given in this chapter, with confidence that his conception of it will become clearer.

All heat is not equally valuable for converting into work. Heat that is put into a substance at a high temperature has a greater possibility of conversion into work than heat put into the substance at a lower temperature. Entropy is a function of a quantity of heat which indicates the possibility of converting that heat into work. When heat is added at a high temperature entropy increase is small; when heat is added at a low temperature entropy is greater. Thus, for maximum entropy, we have minimum availability for conversion into work. For minimum entropy, we have maximum availability for conversion into work.

Carnot's cycle shows us that the higher the temperature of supply of the heat, the greater will be the efficiency, and hence, the greater will be the work done. Entropy can indicate this availability of the heat.

If entropy be plotted horizontally, and absolute temperature be plotted vertically on a diagram during the addition of heat to a body, then we have the area of this diagram representing heat.

Thus, Entropy change $= \dfrac{\text{Heat change}}{\text{Absolute temperature}}$.

Another way of defining entropy is to say that it is that thermal property of a substance which remains constant when the substance expands or is compressed adiabatically in a cylinder.

86. Behaviour of Entropy. Entropy increases when heat is supplied whether temperature changes or not.

Entropy decreases when heat is removed whether temperature changes or not.

Entropy remains constant in all adiabatic frictionless processes.

Entropy increases if heat is lowered in temperature without work being done, as in a throttling process.

Entropy increases if heat is degraded or reduced in availability by friction.

The unit of Entropy is called the " Rank."

EXAMPLE.   50 C.H.U. of heat are supplied to a substance at a constant temperature of 300° C. absolute. Find the increase in entropy.

$$\text{Increase in entropy} = \frac{50}{300}$$

$$= 0\cdot166 \text{ Ranks.}$$

This gives a working form for the definition of entropy.

Entropy, like quantities of heat, must be reckoned from some specified datum of temperature, and for unit mass of substance.

We are not often concerned with absolute units of entropy, but we require to calculate changes in entropy very frequently.

Let ϕ_1 = final entropy.

ϕ_2 = initial entropy.

H = heat supplied in C.H.U.

T = absolute temperature in ° C. during the supply.

Then when T is constant $\phi_1 - \phi_2 = \dfrac{H}{T}$ ranks.

The number of units of entropy will be the same whether C.H.U. and ° C. are used or B.Th.U. and ° F., thus showing that the entropy depends only on the state of the heat supplied, as regards temperature. The actual quantity of heat and the actual temperature will be the same no matter in what units they are expressed.

EXAMPLE. Calculate the increase in entropy when 100 C.H.U. are supplied (a) at 500° C. absolute and (b) at 1,500° C. abs.

(a) $\phi_1 - \phi_2 = \dfrac{100}{500} = 0 \cdot 2$ ranks.

(b) $\phi_1 - \phi_2 = \dfrac{100}{1,500} = 0 \cdot 067$ ranks.

It is useful to note here the Carnot efficiency of this heat in the two cases, assuming the lowest temperature limit of the cycle to be 300° C. absolute in both cases.

(a) Carnot efficiency $= \dfrac{500 - 300}{500} = 0 \cdot 4.$

(b)   ,,   ,, $= \dfrac{1,500 - 300}{1,500} = 0 \cdot 8.$

Thus work available in case (a) $= 0 \cdot 4 \times 100 = 40$ C.H.U. and   ,,   ,,   ,,   ,,   (b) $= 0 \cdot 8 \times 100 = 80$ C.H.U.

87. Case of Isothermal Expansion. With isothermal expansion or compression the temperature is constant, and the heat supplied or removed is equal to the work done by or on the gas.

$$\therefore \; \phi_1 - \phi_2 = \frac{RT \log_e r}{T}$$

for a perfect gas, R being in heat units per lb. in this case.

Isothermal expansion in a vapour, when in the presence of the liquid, is always evaporation and then

$$\phi_1 - \phi_2 = \frac{\text{Amount of latent heat supplied}}{\text{Absolute temperature of evaporation}}.$$

Thus entropy increase during evaporation of unit weight

$$= \frac{L}{T} \text{ ranks.}$$

The work done here is not equal to the heat supplied, because of the large amount of heat required to change the state from liquid to vapour.

The cases of entropy dealt with are very simple ones since temperature has been constant. It is now necessary to consider the change in entropy, when the temperature is changing during the supply or removal of heat.

88. Change of Entropy. Let 1 lb. of substance be considered.

Let ϕ_1 = final entropy, ϕ_2 = initial entropy.

T_1 = final temperature, T_2 = initial temperature.

C = specific heat.

The value of C will depend upon the nature of the substance and its state. It will be different for different substances and for different states.

Let δH = a small increment of heat supplied whilst the temperature remains sensibly constant at T.

$\delta\phi$ = corresponding increment of entropy.

Then
$$\delta\phi = \frac{\delta H}{T}$$

but
$$\delta H = C.\delta T$$

$$\therefore \quad \delta\phi = C\frac{\delta T}{T}$$

The total change of entropy from T_2 to T_1 becomes

$$\phi_1 - \phi_2 = C \int_{T_2}^{T_1} \frac{dT}{T}$$

$$= C\left[\log_e T\right]_{T_2}^{T_1} = C \log_e \frac{T_1}{T_2}.$$

The two forms of entropy expression, viz.

$$\frac{H}{T} \text{ and } C \log_e \frac{T_1}{T_2},$$

are the only forms met with and are very important.

89. Entropy of Steam. In this case entropy is reckoned from $0°$ C. This means that the entropy in water at 0° C. is regarded as zero, but it is necessary to use absolute temperatures in entropy calculation.

Let T_s = absolute temperature of superheated steam.

$\quad$ T = $\quad$,, $\quad\quad\quad$,, $\quad\quad$,, generation of steam.

$\quad \phi_{ss}$ = entropy of superheated steam.

Entropy added to water in raising it from 0° C. (273° absolute) to T° absolute $= C \log_e \dfrac{T}{273}$.

C for water is unity.

Entropy added to steam during evaporation $= \dfrac{L}{T}$.

Entropy added to steam during superheating $= C_p \log_e \dfrac{T_s}{T}$

where C_p = specific heat at constant pressure. Thus the total entropy added in all three stages

$$= \phi_{ss} = C \log_e \frac{T}{273} + \frac{L}{T} + C_p \log_e \frac{T_s}{T}.$$

EXAMPLE.   Calculate the entropy of 1 lb. of water at 50° C.

Zero entropy is at 0° C. or 273° absolute,

$$\therefore \; \phi_{w50} = C \log_e \frac{T}{273}$$

$$= 1 \times 2 \cdot 3026 \times \log_{10} \frac{323}{273}$$

$$= 2 \cdot 3026 \times \log_{10} 1 \cdot 182$$
$$= 2 \cdot 3026 \times 0 \cdot 0726$$
$$= 0 \cdot 1672 \text{ ranks.}$$

EXAMPLE.   Calculate the change in entropy when water is heated from 50° C. to 150° C.

$$\phi_{w50} = C \log_e \frac{323}{273} = 0 \cdot 1672 \text{ ranks.}$$

$$\phi_{w150} = C \log_e \frac{423}{273} = 2 \cdot 3026 \times \log_{10} 1 \cdot 55$$

$$= 2 \cdot 3026 \times 0 \cdot 1903$$
$$= 0 \cdot 438 \text{ ranks.}$$

Change in entropy $= \phi_{w150} - \phi_{w50} = 0 \cdot 438 - 0 \cdot 1672 = 0 \cdot 2708.$

The change could be calculated directly from

$$C \log_e \frac{T_1}{T_2}$$

$$= 2 \cdot 3026 \log_{10} \frac{423}{323}$$

$$= 2 \cdot 3026 \log_{10} 1 \cdot 308$$

$$= 2 \cdot 3026 \times 0 \cdot 117$$

$$= 0 \cdot 270 \text{ ranks.}$$

EXAMPLE. Steam is produced at a temperature of 150° C. Find the increase in entropy of 1 lb. of steam during evaporation.

$$\text{Evaporation Entropy} = \frac{L}{T}.$$

From tables, $L = 506 \cdot 2$.

$$\therefore \phi_{incr.} = \frac{506 \cdot 2}{423} = 1 \cdot 194 \text{ ranks.}$$

This is the entropy of evaporation at 150° C., the corresponding pressure being 69·24 lbs. per sq. in.

EXAMPLE. Find the evaporation entropy of wet steam at 150° C. Dryness fraction 0·95.

Here the latent heat supplied to 1 lb. $= 0 \cdot 95 \times 506 \cdot 2$.

$$\therefore \text{Evaporation entropy} = \frac{0 \cdot 95 \times 506 \cdot 2}{423}$$

$$= 0 \cdot 95 \times 1 \cdot 194$$

$$= 1 \cdot 134 \text{ ranks.}$$

Note that $x = \dfrac{\text{Actual evaporation entropy per lb.}}{\text{Maximum evaporation entropy per lb.}}$

$$= \text{dryness fraction.}$$

This is useful in determining the dryness fraction from the temperature entropy diagram.

EXAMPLE. Find the change in entropy when 1 lb. of feed water at 30° C. is made into superheated steam at 99·56 lbs. per sq. in. and 220° C. C_p for steam $= 0 \cdot 5$.

Latent heat at this pressure $= 495 \cdot 9$ C.H.U.
Evaporation temperature $= 164°$ C.

Total entropy of 1 lb. of water at 30° C. $= \log_e \dfrac{303}{273}$

$$= 2 \cdot 3026 \times \log_{10} 1 \cdot 109$$

$$= 2 \cdot 3026 \times 0 \cdot 0449$$

$$= 0 \cdot 1035 \text{ ranks.}$$

Entropy of 1 lb. of water at 164° C. $= \log_e \dfrac{437}{273}$

$$= 2 \cdot 3026 \times \log_{10} 1 \cdot 598$$
$$= 2 \cdot 3026 \times 0 \cdot 2036$$
$$= 0 \cdot 469 \text{ ranks.}$$

Evaporation entropy $= \dfrac{495 \cdot 9}{437} = 1 \cdot 134$ ranks.

Entropy increase during superheat $= C_p \log_e \dfrac{493}{437}$

$$= 0 \cdot 5 \times 2 \cdot 3026 \times \log_{10} 1 \cdot 129$$
$$= 0 \cdot 5 \times 2 \cdot 3026 \times 0 \cdot 0527$$
$$= 0 \cdot 0607 \text{ ranks.}$$

Total entropy of superheated steam $= 0 \cdot 469 + 1 \cdot 134 + 0 \cdot 0607$
$$= 1 \cdot 6637 \text{ ranks.}$$

Entropy of 1 lb. feed water $= 0 \cdot 1032$.

∴ Change in entropy per lb. $= 1 \cdot 5605$ ranks.

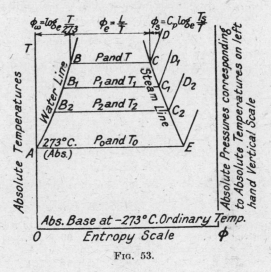

Fig. 53.

90. The Temperature-Entropy Diagram for Water and Steam.

This diagram is often known as the T – φ (Tee-Phi) diagram and is shown in fig. 53. A reproduction of the Board of Education T – φ diagram is also shown in fig. 58, and is copied by permission of the

Controller of His Majesty's Stationery Office. The base of the diagram is drawn at a temperature of $-273°$ C., or $0°$ C. absolute. The entropy of water is reckoned from $0°$ C., the ordinary freezing-point of water.

Consequently, all lines constructed on this diagram lie above this level of temperature, i.e. above the line AE. The point A is the starting point of the diagram and the line AB is the entropy-temperature line for water. It is called the *water line*. This line is the curve plotted from the equation $\phi_w = \log_e \dfrac{T}{273}$, assuming the specific heat of water to be constant and equal to unity. The highest point is fixed by the highest pressure for which the diagram is likely to be used.

The three points B_2, B_1 and B have values of temperature T_2, T_1 and T respectively, and these temperatures, when substituted in the above equation, give the corresponding entropies of water.

The steam line, CE, lies towards the right hand of the diagram, and slopes in the opposite direction to that of the water line. It can only be plotted when the water line has been set down. If evaporation be permitted to take place at temperature T, the latent heat at this temperature being L, then the length of the line BC will represent the evaporation entropy $\dfrac{L}{T}$, which is the change in entropy during evaporation at the temperature T. Similarly, the lengths B_1C_1 and B_2C_2 will represent $\dfrac{L_1}{T_1}$ and $\dfrac{L_2}{T_2}$ respectively.

The several lengths are set out from B, B_1 and B_2 and thus points C, C_1 and C_2 are obtained. A smooth curve drawn through these points is the *steam line*.

The diagram may now be divided into three parts or fields.

(1) The liquid or water field to the left of the water line.

(2) The saturation field between the water and steam lines.

(3) The superheat field on the right of the steam line.

91. Constant Pressure Lines in the Superheat Field. These lines are plotted with entropy and temperature as co-ordinates, the pressure being constant whilst the steam is superheated. The constant pressure superheat lines start from points on the steam line such as C, C_1 and C_2. The lines, such as CD, fig. 54, are plotted from the equation

$$\phi_s = C_{\bar{p}} \log_e \frac{T_s}{T},$$

using C as origin, and ϕ_s and $(T_s - T)$ as co-ordinates.

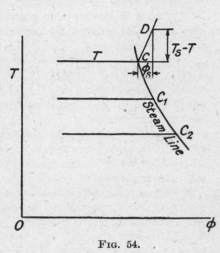

Fig. 54.

One point D is shown, and similar points can be found up to any degree of superheat likely to be needed. The whole line ABCD, in fig. 53, is a complete constant pressure line.

AB represents the supply of liquid heat.

BC   ,,   ,,   ,,   ,, latent heat.

CD   ,,   ,,   ,,   ,, additional heat for super-heating.

92. Lines of Constant Dryness and Constant Superheat. If the evaporation is not complete, the steam will be wet and the entropy less than that of dry steam. The shortage of entropy is proportional to the shortage of latent heat. The actual evaporation entropy is now $\frac{xL}{T}$, where x is the dryness fraction. Suppose that F, in fig. 55, represents the state of the wet steam, then length BF is

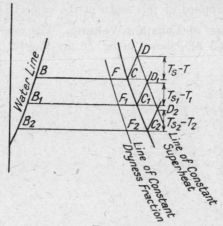

FIG. 55.

proportional to the actual evaporation entropy. Hence

$$\frac{BF}{BC} = \frac{\dfrac{xL}{T}}{\dfrac{L}{T}} = x.$$

Thus, the point F lies on the line BC such that

$$\frac{BF}{BC} = \frac{\text{amount of latent heat supplied}}{\text{latent heat of the steam (dry)}} = \frac{xL}{L} = x.$$

If points F_1 and F_2 divide the lines B_1C_1 and B_2C_2 in the same ratio $\dfrac{BF}{BC}$, then the points F, F_1, and F_2 are all state points for steam with the same dryness fraction, but at different pressures.

A smooth curve drawn through such points is a line of constant dryness.

The lines of constant superheat are plotted by locating points D, D_1 and D_2 on the constant pressure lines in the superheat field, starting from C, C_1 and C_2, by making $T_s - T = T_{s1} - T_1 = T_{s2} - T_2$. These lines are not often required, and consequently are not printed on the diagrams supplied at this stage of the subject.

93. Lines of Constant Volume. The curved lines AC, AC_1 and AC_2 shown in fig. 56 are lines of constant volume.

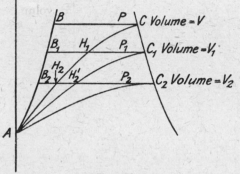

FIG. 56.

Let the specific volumes at P, P_1 and P_2 be V, V_1 and V_2 respectively.

Then the volume represented by any point on the line through C must be V, that is, the volumes at C, H_1 and H_2 are equal to V.

During the evaporation of 1 lb. of water, at a given moment, the proportion of the 1 lb. of water, which has become steam, is the same as the proportion of the latent heat which has been given to the water. Thus, if a point H_1 on B_1C_1 be taken, $\dfrac{B_1H_1}{B_1C_1}$ of the latent heat has been given to the water and thus $\dfrac{B_1H_1}{B_1C_1}$ of a pound of water has become steam. If, then, 1 lb. of steam at pressure P_1 occupies V_1 cu. ft., the volume of steam represented by the position of H_1 is $\dfrac{B_1H_1}{B_1C_1} \times V_1$.

L

Make this equal to V, that is, let

$$V = \frac{B_1 H_1}{B_1 C_1} \times V_1$$

then

$$\frac{B_1 H_1}{B_1 C_1} = \frac{V}{V_1}$$

∴ if $B_1 C_1$ represents V_1, $B_1 H_1$ represents V.

H_2 may be chosen in a similar way to represent volume V at pressure P_2. Points thus located, when joined by a smooth curve, give a line of constant volume. Also for volume V_1, H_2' may be chosen on the pressure line P_2.

Note that the volume of the unevaporated water is neglected, but it is relatively very small. The completed diagram is shown in fig. 57.

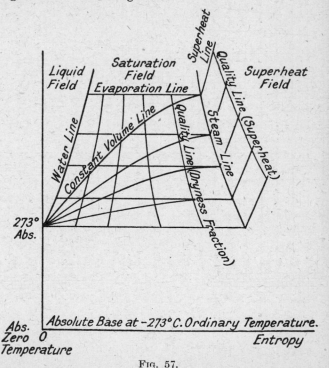

FIG. 57.

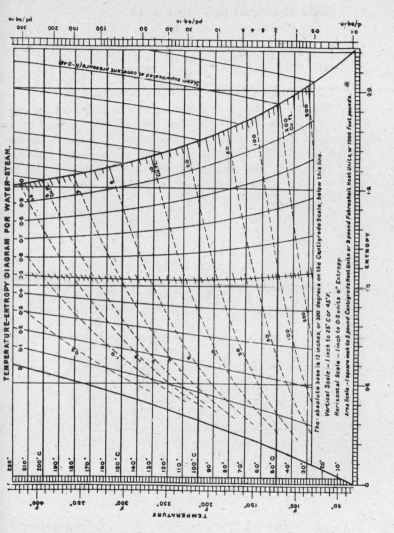

FIG. 58.

94. Scale of Diagram. Let

S_T = temperature scale in ° C. per inch vertical.

S_ϕ = entropy scale in Ranks per inch horizontal.

Then 1 square inch area = $S_T \times S_\phi$ heat units.

The area of the diagram represents energy in heat units, and work quantities may be found by measuring areas on this diagram, as in the case of the P – V diagram, but with this difference; in the P – V diagram the area must be multiplied by a work scale in foot-lbs., whilst in the T – ϕ diagram the area must be multiplied by a heat scale in heat units.

The scales of the T – ϕ diagram generally in use are

entropy, 1 in. = 0·2 ranks.

temperature, 1 in. = 25° C. intervals or 45° F. intervals.

Thus 1 sq. in. = 0·2 × 25 = 5 C.H.U.

or „ „   „ = 0·2 × 45 = 9 B.T.U.

EXAMPLE. The area of the diagram, representing a cycle plotted on the T-ϕ chart, is measured and found to be 14½ sq. ins. Find the ideal work thus represented.

Work represented = 5 × 14·5 = 72·5 C.H.U.

or   = 9 × 14·5 = 130·5 B.T.U.

or   = 5 × 14·5 × 1,400 = 101,500 ft.-lbs.

EXAMPLES XII

1. One pound of water at 100° C. is changed into dry steam at 100° C. Calculate the increase in entropy.

2. Find the increase in entropy during the evaporation of 1 lb. of water at 180° C.

3. What is the increase in entropy during the evaporation of 1 lb. of water at a pressure of 200 lbs. per sq. in. absolute ?

4. Calculate the increase in entropy when 1 lb. of water at 15° C. is heated to a temperature of 180° C.

5. Determine the entropy, reckoned from 0° C., when 1 lb. of water is changed into steam at 180° C.

6. Steam has a pressure of 160 lbs. per sq. in. absolute and 85 per cent. dry. If it was formed from feed water at 40° C., what was the entropy added to it per lb. ?

7. Reckoned from 0° C., what is the entropy in 1 lb. of steam at 60 lbs. per sq. in. absolute with 100 degrees Centigrade of superheat ?

8. One pound of wet steam at 14·7 lbs. per sq. in. has 1·6 ranks of

entropy reckoned from 0° C.   Find the dryness fraction and the volume of 1 lb. of the wet steam.

9. Starting from a pressure of 130 lbs. per sq. in. absolute, read off from an entropy chart the dryness fraction of 3 cu. ft. of steam at pressures descending by 20 lbs. per sq. in. to 30 lbs. per sq. in. What is the line thus followed on the entropy chart called ?

CHAPTER XIII

ENTROPY APPLICATIONS

95. Ideal Steam Cycle. This is known as the Rankine Cycle and is the standard of comparison for all steam engines. It is carried out as follows :

    (1) One lb. of water is pumped into the cylinder or boiler at pressure P_1.

    (2) Heat is supplied to raise the temperature of the water from feed temperature T_2 to boiling temperature T_1.

    (3) Latent heat is now supplied at T_1 and evaporation takes place, shown by line BD, fig. 59.

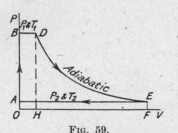

FIG. 59.

    (4) Heat supply is discontinued and the steam expands adiabatically until the pressure falls to the back pressure. This is known as complete expansion to distinguish it from the expansion of the hypothetical diagram, which has a terminal pressure higher than the back pressure. This is represented by the line DE and at E the steam is wet.

    (5) The wet steam is condensed at pressure P_2 until it is all water. The volume diminishes to that of 1 lb. of water and this stage is shown by EA.

The cycle is now complete.

The feed temperature in the ideal cycle is that of the condensing steam in stage (5).

The pressures P_1 and P_2 are the upper and lower limits respectively, and the corresponding temperatures are T_1 and T_2. Comparing the Rankine Cycle with the Carnot Cycle for steam, it will be seen that the supply of heat to the water replaces the supply of energy to the wet steam by means of the adiabatic compression (see Art. 47) and that the isothermal compression is completed.

96. Work done per Pound of Steam from the P – V Diagram.

Let $V_1 =$ volume of 1 lb. of steam at P_1 shown at D.

$\quad V_2 = \quad$,, ,, ,, as shown at E.

$\quad n =$ index in the expansion law $PV^n = C$.

Work done in pumping and generation of steam is represented by OBDH,

$$= P_1 V_1 \text{ ft.-lbs.}$$

Work done in adiabatic expansion is represented by DEFH,

$$= \frac{P_1 V_1 - P_2 V_2}{n - 1} \text{ ft.-lbs.}$$

Work done by piston in condensation and compression is represented by EFOA $= P_2 V_2$ ft.-lbs.

Work done in cycle per lb. of steam

$$= P_1 V_1 + \frac{P_1 V_1 - P_2 V_2}{n - 1} - P_2 V_2$$

$$= \frac{(n - 1) P_1 V_1 + P_1 V_1 - P_2 V_2 - (n - 1) P_2 V_2}{n - 1}$$

$$= \frac{n}{n - 1} (P_1 V_1 - P_2 V_2)$$

$$= \frac{n}{n - 1} \times P_1 V_1 \left(1 - \frac{P_2 V_2}{P_1 V_1} \right)$$

But $P_1 V_1{}^n = P_2 V_2{}^n$

$$\therefore \frac{V_2{}^n}{V_1{}^n} = \frac{P_1}{P_2} \qquad \therefore \frac{V_2}{V_1} = \left(\frac{P_1}{P_2} \right)^{\frac{1}{n}}$$

$\therefore$ Work done per lb. of steam

$$= \frac{n}{n-1} \times P_1 V_1 \left(1 - \frac{P_2 \, P_1^{\frac{1}{n}}}{P_1 \, P_2^{\frac{1}{n}}} \right)$$

$$= \frac{n}{n-1} P_1 V_1 \left\{ 1 - \left(\frac{P_2}{P_1} \right)^{\frac{n-1}{n}} \right\}$$

The values of n for adiabatic expansion of steam are given in Article 38.

If the above work is divided by V_1 we obtain the work done per cubic foot of steam used. Thus

Work done per cubic foot

$$= \frac{n}{n-1} P_1 \left\{ 1 - \left(\frac{P_2}{P_1} \right)^{\frac{n-1}{n}} \right\}$$

$$= \frac{n}{n-1} \left(P_1 - P_1^{\frac{1}{n}} P_2^{\frac{n-1}{n}} \right) \text{ ft.-lbs.}$$

97. The Rankine Cycle on the $T-\phi$ Diagram.

The superheated steam cycle is dealt with here because it is now the most common. If dry steam is used the result is easily modified (see example worked in Chapter XIX p. 256).

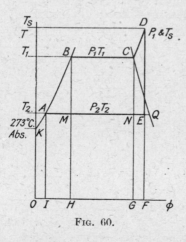

FIG. 60.

Starting with feed water at T_2 and remembering that the diagram is drawn for 1 lb. of steam we have the initial state point at A (fig. 60).

The liquid heat contained in this state is represented by the area OIAK, and in the ideal cycle the liquid heat is never less than this value.

The stages in the cycle are:

Stage (i). Liquid heat is supplied to raise the temperature from T_2 to T_1. The state point moves from A to B and the heat supplied is $h_1 - h_2$. The area ABHI represents this heat.

Stage (ii). Evaporation now takes place. Latent heat is supplied at the temperature T_1 and the state point moves from B to C. This heat is represented by the area HBCG. To superheat the steam, further heat is added and is represented by the area CDFG.

The total energy at D is represented by the area of the diagram under the line KABCD, and the energy at A is represented by the area of the diagram under the short length of the water line KA ; both areas being measured down to the absolute temperature base.

Thus the area under ABCD, down to the absolute base, measures to scale the heat supplied, and is

$$(h_1 - h_2) + L_1 + C_p(T_s - T_1).$$

Stage (iii). The steam in condition D expands adiabatically in the engine cylinder to the pressure P_2. As no heat passes into or out of the steam during this process, the entropy is not changed, and hence, the process is represented by a vertical line on the diagram. The state point moves from D to E. The energy in the steam at E is represented by the area KAEFO and is less than the energy at D. The steam, too, is generally wet and has a dryness fraction $\dfrac{AE}{AQ}$, see Article 92.

Stage (iv). Condensation or Isothermal compression now occurs when the steam is condensed at constant temperature T_2 and constant pressure P_2 until it is all liquid, the liquid also being at T_2. The heat removed from it is $x_2 L_2$, where $x_2 = \dfrac{AE}{AQ}$.

The heat now remaining in the substance is that represented by the area OIAK, and is just the same as that contained at the commencement of the cycle.

Work done in the cycle = Heat supplied − Heat rejected

$$= [(h_1 - h_2) + L_1 + C_p(T_s - T_1)] - [x_2 L_2]$$
$$= [h_1 + L_1 + C_p(T_s - T_1)] - [h_2 + x_2 L_2]$$
$$= H_1' - H_2'$$

where $H_1' =$ total heat in steam in condition D.
and $\quad H_2' = \qquad , \qquad , \qquad , \qquad ,$ E.

Note that neither H_1' nor H_2' can be taken directly from the tables. The steam table values must be corrected for superheat or wetness as the case may be.

If the steam is dry, having no superheat, when expansion begins, H_1' will be the total heat as given in the tables. H_2' will still need to have the wetness taken into account.

When the steam is wet at the beginning of the expansion, it will also be wet after expansion.

In this case, both H_1' and H_2' will require correction.

Total heat supplied in the cycle = heat at D — heat at A

$$= H_1' - h_2.$$

Thermal efficiency on Rankine cycle

$$= \frac{\text{work done in cycle}}{\text{heat supplied in cycle}}$$

$$= \frac{H_1' - H_2'}{H_1' - h_2}$$

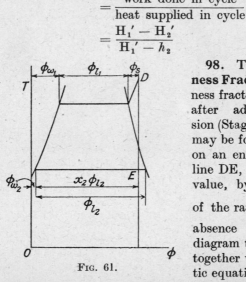

FIG. 61.

98. To Find the Dryness Fraction. The dryness fraction of the steam after adiabatic expansion (Stage iii, Article 97) may be found by drawing on an entropy chart the line DE, and finding the value, by measurement of the ratio $\dfrac{\text{AE}}{\text{AQ}}$. In the absence of an entropy diagram the steam tables together with the adiabatic equation may be used. This equation is readily derived from the entropy chart.

Let ϕ_{l_1} = entropy of latent heat at T_1
ϕ_s = ,, ,, superheat at T_s
ϕ_{l_2} = ,, ,, latent heat at T_2
ϕ_{w_2} = ,, ,, water at beginning of the cycle.

Entropy at E = Entropy at D

$$x_2\phi_{l_2} + \phi_{w_2} = \phi_{w_1} + \phi_{l_1} + \phi_s$$

$$x_2 = \frac{\phi_{w_1} - \phi_{w_2} + \phi_{l_1} + \phi_s}{\phi_{l_2}}$$

$$= \frac{\log_e \frac{T_1}{T_2} + \frac{L_1}{T_1} + C_p \log_e \frac{T_s}{T_1}}{\frac{L_2}{T_2}}$$

$$= \frac{T_2}{L_2}\left[\log_e \frac{T_1}{T_2} + \frac{L_1}{T_1} + C_p \log_e \frac{T_s}{T_1}\right]$$

When there is no superheat and no wetness, the last term disappears and

$$x_2 = \frac{T_2}{L_2}\left[\log_e \frac{T_1}{T_2} + \frac{L_1}{T_1}\right]$$

When the steam at T_1 has dryness fraction = x_1

$$x_2 = \frac{T_2}{L_2}\left[\log_e \frac{T_1}{T_2} + \frac{x_1 L_1}{T_1}\right]$$

(See also p. 276)

EXAMPLE. Find the work done per lb. of steam on the Rankine Cycle between pressure limits of 100 lbs. per sq. in. and 14·7 lbs. per sq. in. Take $n = 1·135$. Also find the work done per cubic foot supplied.

Values from steam tables are:

p	t_g	V_s	L	h	H	ϕ_w	ϕ_s
100	164	4·45	495·8	166·1	661·9	0·4753	1·6101
14·7	100	26·75	539·1	100·5	639·6	0·3136	1·7589

$$V_2 = \left(\frac{P_1}{P_2}\right)^{\frac{1}{1·135}} V_1 = \left(\frac{100}{14·7}\right)^{0·881} \times 4·45$$

$$= 6·81^{0·881} \times 4·45$$
$$= 5·42 \times 4·45 = 24·08 \text{ cu. ft.}$$

Work done $= \dfrac{n}{n-1}(P_1V_1 - P_2V_2)$

$\qquad = \dfrac{1 \cdot 135}{0 \cdot 135}(100 \times 144 \times 4 \cdot 45 - 14 \cdot 7 \times 144 \times 24 \cdot 08)$

$\qquad = 8 \cdot 42 \times 144(445 - 354)$
$\qquad = 8 \cdot 42 \times 144 \times 91 = 110{,}292$ ft.-lbs.

Work done per cu. ft. supplied $= \dfrac{110{,}292}{4 \cdot 45}$

$\qquad\qquad\qquad\qquad\qquad = 24{,}800$ ft.-lbs.

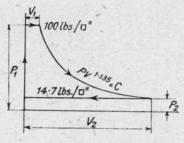

FIG. 62.

Alternative Method I.

Work done per cu. ft. of steam supplied

$$= \dfrac{n}{n-1}\left[P_1 - P_1^{\frac{1}{n}} P_2^{\frac{n-1}{n}} \right]$$

$= 8 \cdot 42\left[14{,}400 - 14{,}400^{\frac{1}{1 \cdot 135}} \times 2{,}116^{\frac{0 \cdot 135}{1 \cdot 135}}\right]$
$= 8 \cdot 42(14{,}400 - 4{,}608 \times 2 \cdot 487)$
$= 8 \cdot 42 \ (14{,}400 - 11{,}460)$
$= 8 \cdot 42 \times 2{,}940$
$= 24{,}750$ ft.-lbs.

(This is close agreement for slide rule values.)
Work done per cubic foot of volume swept.
This is the final volume, since there is no clearance.

Work done per cu. ft. $= \dfrac{110{,}292}{24 \cdot 08}$

$\qquad\qquad\qquad = 4{,}580$ ft.-lbs.

Note that this result is numerically the same as the mean effective pressure expressed in lbs. per square foot.

Alternative Method II.

By heat given up during cycle. Heat in 1 lb. of steam at C. (from tables) = 661·9 C.H.U.

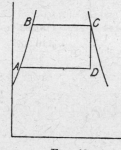

Fig. 63.

Final dryness fraction at D

$$x_D = \frac{T_2}{L_2}\left[\frac{x_1 L_1}{T_1} + \log_e \frac{T_1}{T_2}\right]$$

$$= \frac{373}{539\cdot1}\left[\frac{495\cdot8}{437} + 2\cdot3026 \times \log_{10}\frac{437}{373}\right]$$

$$= 0\cdot693\,(1\cdot132 + 2\cdot3026\,\log\,1\cdot17)$$

$$= 0\cdot693\,(1\cdot132 + 0\cdot157)$$

$$= 0\cdot693 \times 1\cdot289$$

$$= 0\cdot895.$$

Heat in 1 lb. of steam at D $= 100\cdot5 + 0\cdot895 \times 539\cdot1$

$$= 100\cdot5 + 482\cdot5$$

$$= 583.$$

Total work done $= (661\cdot9 - 583)$ C.H.U.

$$= 78\cdot9$$

$$= (78\cdot9 \times 1{,}400) \text{ ft.-lbs.}$$

$$= 110{,}300 \text{ ft.-lbs.}$$

99. Rankine Cycle in terms of Temperature.

An expression for the Rankine Cycle work and efficiency may be obtained by consideration of the $T-\phi$ diagram.

Consider heat supplied (See fig. 60).

$$\text{Area ABHI} = h_1 - h_2 = T_1 - T_2$$

$$\text{,,}\quad \text{BCGH} = L_1 \quad\quad = \phi_{l_1} T_1$$

$$\text{,,}\quad \text{CDFG} = C_p(T_s - T_1).$$

Consider heat rejected.

Heat rejected $= x_2 L_2 =$ area AEFI

$$= T_2 \left[\log_e \frac{T_1}{T_2} + \frac{L_1}{T_1} + C_p \log_e \frac{T_s}{T_1} \right]$$

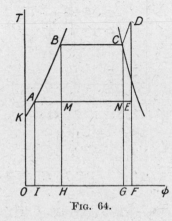

Fig. 64.

∴ Work done on the cycle

$$= T_1 - T_2 + L_1 + C_p(T_s - T_1) - T_2 \left(\log_e \frac{T_1}{T_2} + \frac{L_1}{T_1} + C_p \log_e \frac{T_s}{T_1} \right)$$

$$= T_1 - T_2 + \frac{T_1 L_1}{T_1} - \frac{T_2 L_1}{T_1}$$

$$\qquad\qquad + C_p(T_s - T_1) - T_2 \left(\log_e \frac{T_1}{T_2} + C_p \log_e \frac{T_s}{T_1} \right)$$

$$= (T_1 - T_2)\left(1 + \frac{L_1}{T_1} \right) + C_p(T_s - T_1) - T_2 \left(\log_e \frac{T_1}{T_2} + C_p \log_e \frac{T_s}{T_1} \right)$$

Dividing by the heat supplied gives the efficiency of the cycle.

This is a rather cumbersome expression and is only given here to enable the reader to recognize it as work done in heat units.

EXAMPLE. Find, from the T-ϕ diagram, the ideal work per lb. of dry steam and the Rankine efficiency between pressure limits of 120 lbs. per sq. in. and 1 lb. per sq. in. absolute.   This example is intended to illustrate the use of the entropy diagram for finding work by areas.

Sketch and dimension a T-ϕ diagram as shown in fig. 65, taking the dimensions from a Board of Education chart.

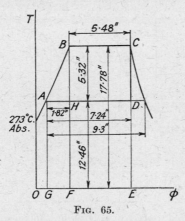

FIG. 65.

The work done is proportional to the area ABCD and in finding this area AB may be taken as a straight line.

For a more correct estimate a number of ordinates may be taken along AB.

$$\text{Area ABH} = \tfrac{1}{2} \times 1 \cdot 82 \times 5 \cdot 32 = 4 \cdot 84 \text{ sq. ins.}$$
$$\text{,, BCDH} = 5 \cdot 32 \times 5 \cdot 48 = 29 \cdot 15 \text{ ,,}$$
$$\text{Total area} = 33 \cdot 99 \text{ ,,}$$

The scale of this diagram is such that 1 square inch represents 5 C.H.U.

$$\therefore \text{ Work done} = 33 \cdot 99 \times 5 \text{ C.H.U.}$$
$$= 169 \cdot 95 \text{ C.H.U.}$$

Alternative Method.

Note that the work could be obtained very quickly by the use of the diagram and steam tables as follows.

$$\text{Final dryness at D} = \frac{7 \cdot 24}{9 \cdot 3} = 0 \cdot 779$$

Heat in steam at C (from 0° C.) = 664 C.H.U.

,,   ,,   ,,   D (,,   ,,   ) = 40 + 0·779 × 573·6
$$= 40 + 447$$
$$= 487 \text{ C.H.U.}$$

$$\therefore \text{ Ideal work} = 664 - 487$$
$$= 177 \text{ C.H.U.}$$

Rankine Efficiency.

Heat supplied is proportional to area ABCEG

$$= 33·99 \text{ sq. in.} + (7·24 \times 12·46) \text{ sq. ins.}$$
$$= 33·99 + 90·2$$
$$= 124·19 \text{ sq. ins.}$$
$$= 621 \text{ C.H.U.}$$

$$\therefore \eta_R = \frac{169·95}{621} = 0·274 \text{ or } 27·4 \text{ per cent.}$$

From the tables heat supplied = 624 C.H.U.

$$\therefore \eta_R = \frac{177}{624} = 28·35 \text{ per cent.}$$

The steam tables used are more modern than the T-ϕ diagram. This accounts for the discrepancies.

100.   Various cycles on P – V and T – ϕ diagrams compared.

Carnot Cycle (fig. 66):

AB shows isothermal expansion.

BC   ,,   adiabatic   ,,

CD   ,,   isothermal compression.

DA   ,,   adiabatic   ,,

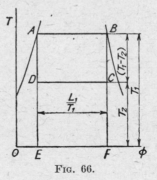

Fig. 66.

The diagram thus becomes a rectangle.

The work done is represented by area ABCD and heat supplied by ABFE.

$$\text{Efficiency} = \frac{\text{area ABCD}}{\text{area ABFE}} = \frac{T_1 - T_2}{T_1}$$

In actual steam engines it is impracticable to expand the steam completely as in the Rankine Cycle. Expansion is stopped at such a point as C and the steam exhausted. Assuming that the pressure falls to exhaust or back pressure whilst the piston is stationary, the P – V diagram becomes ABCDE, fig. 67. The line CD is evidently a constant

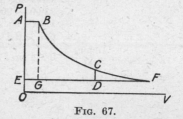

FIG. 67.

volume line. Fig. 68 shows this modification on the T – φ diagram. CD is the constant volume line passing through C, the point where adiabatic expansion is stopped.

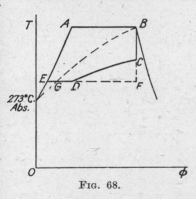

FIG. 68.

In both figures ABCDE represents the work and also CFD shows by how much this cycle falls short of the Rankine Cycle.

When the steam is not expanded at all, the constant volume line follows the course BG. In this case, the area ABGE simply represents the external work done during formation of the steam.

101. Effect of Back Pressure. From fig. 69 it will be seen that, if the back pressure rises from P_3 to P_2 with P_1 remaining constant, a reduction in work will result.

If expansion was complete to pressure P_3, then increase in back pressure to P_2 causes loss at the widest part of the diagram. The reduction of work is proportional to the area shown shaded. This is the effect of decrease in the vacuum in a steam turbine. The steam turbine

M

permits complete expansion. With a reciprocating engine, stopping its expansion at the terminal pressure P_T, the diagram follows a constant volume line from this pressure to the back pressure. The reduction in work, due to raising the back pressure, is then shown by the double shaded area.

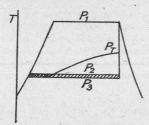

FIG. 69.

Fig. 69 shows (a) that the work done per lb. of steam in a reciprocating engine is less than in a turbine, (b) that a slight variation in condenser pressure is not very serious in the reciprocating engine, but becomes a very important factor in the efficient operation of a turbine.

EXAMPLES XIII

1. Steam is admitted to a cylinder at 160 lbs. per sq. in. absolute and expanded down to the back pressure of 17 lbs. per sq. in. at which it is exhausted. Find the work done per lb. of steam, assuming the law of expansion to be $PV^{1.135} = C$.

2. What would be the work done per lb. of steam if it were expanded to and exhausted at a back pressure of 2 lbs. per sq. in. ?

3. State clearly the processes of the Rankine Cycle.

4. An engine receives dry saturated steam at 180 lbs. per sq. in. absolute, and rejects its exhaust to the condenser at 2 lbs. per sq. in. It works on the Rankine Cycle. Calculate the work done per lb. of steam and the efficiency.

5. Steam at a pressure of 200 lbs. per sq. in. absolute and a temperature of 260° C. passes through an engine working on the Rankine Cycle. The condenser pressure is 1·5 lbs. per sq. in. Find the work done per lb. of steam and the efficiency on this cycle.

6. Steam at a pressure of 120 lbs. per sq. in. absolute and 90 per cent. dry is expanded adiabatically to 16 lbs. per sq. in. absolute. Find both from the entropy chart and by calculation the dryness fraction after expanding.

7. Steam at 100 lbs. per sq. in. absolute with 50° C. of superheat is expanded adiabatically to 2 lbs. per sq. in. absolute. Find the dryness fraction after expansion both by calculation and from the diagram. At what pressure will this steam be dry and saturated during the expansion ?

8. On the temperature-entropy chart with which you are supplied mark with the letters A, B and C the points which show the following states of 1 lb. of water-steam :

A at 190° C. and 95 per cent. dry.

B at 100 lbs. per sq. in. absolute and 60 per cent. dry.

C at 50 lbs. per sq. in. absolute and superheated to 220° C.

If a pound of water-steam receives 3 centigrade pound units of heat, its temperature remaining constant at 150° C., what is its gain of entropy ?   Steam at 109° C. 95 per cent. dry expands adiabatically to 80° C.   What is the condition of the steam at this temperature ?   N.C.T.E.C.

9. Mark on the temperature-entropy chart a line showing the expansion with constant entropy of steam from 120 lbs. per sq. in., 95 per cent. dry, to 5 lbs. per sq. in.   Measure off and write down the dryness and volume per lb. at the latter pressure.

                                            N.C.T.E.C.

CHAPTER XIV

VALVES AND VALVE GEAR

102. Eccentric and Eccentric-rod Motion. The admission of steam to an engine cylinder, and its release to exhaust at the proper moment, are of great importance in the efficient working of a steam engine. Many different types of valves have been used for this purpose, and a large number of these types still survive. The slide valve, with its modification the piston valve, is the most important arrangement used in reciprocating engines for controlling the movement of the steam, and only this type will be dealt with in this chapter. The knowledge gained in a study of the slide valve should make it possible for the student to understand, from a simple description, the working of almost any other type.

The slide valve is generally driven by a crank or eccentric, on the main shaft of the engine, through a connecting rod or eccentric rod. It is necessary to see what connection exists between the position of the crank or eccentric and the crosshead or valve.

Let the eccentricity or " throw " of the eccentric be OA (fig. 70), and let AB be the length of the eccentric rod. As OA rotates about O, B will move backwards and forwards along the direction OB through a distance equal to $2 \times OA = AA' = BB'$.

Take an intermediate position such as OC, then, if CD = AB, the distance moved by the valve attached to D will be BD. With centre D and radius DC draw the arc CM, then AM = BD = the distance moved by the valve. Now the eccentric rod is usually very long compared with the throw of the eccentric, and the curvature in the arc CM is consequently small, so small, in fact, that it may generally be taken as coinciding with the straight line CN, which is a perpendicular dropped from C on AA'.

In studying the motion of a slide valve, we shall find it sufficiently accurate to treat AN as the movement of

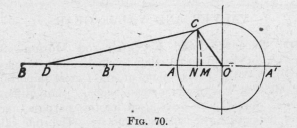

Fig. 70.

the valve whilst OA turns through the angle AOC, but when we are concerned with the movement of a piston or crosshead driven by a crank on the engine shaft, the more accurate value AM will be necessary, because CD is relatively shortened and the curvature of arc CM is greater.

103. Slide Valve and Piston Valve. Figs. 71 and 72 may be taken as representing in diagrammatic form

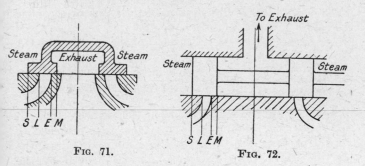

Fig. 71.   Fig. 72.

the essentials of a slide valve and piston valve respectively, both being in their mean positions, that is, at the middle of their strokes.

In each case SL is called the steam lap or outside lap, and EM the exhaust lap or inside lap. The former name in each case is the better one. LE is the width of the port. It will be seen that as far as the control of the steam is concerned, there are no essential differences between a slide valve and a piston valve.

104. Valve Movements. We may now consider the main points in the motion of a valve as in fig. 71, when actuated by an eccentric and rod.

The eccentric throw is OA, and therefore the total valve travel is AA'. Applying the reasoning of Article 102, we see that when the valve is in its mid-position, the eccentric will occupy the position OB or OB'. Let us take it in the position OB, and rotating in a clockwise direction. When OC is reached, so that OP = SL (fig. 71),

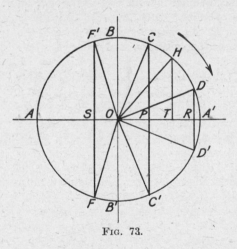

FIG. 73.

the valve will have moved to the right by an amount equal to the steam lap, and hence will be on the point of uncovering the steam port to admit steam to the cylinder. At OD, when PR = LE, the steam port is completely open, and in rotating to OA' the valve does not admit any more steam. The steam edge of the valve thus overruns the exhaust edge of the port. As the eccentric passes OA', the return stroke of the valve begins, and at OD' it begins to close the steam port. When the eccentric reaches OC' the port is just closed, and the steam supply to the cylinder is cut off.

This is called " cut-off." At OB′ the valve is in mid-position, but when the eccentric reaches OF such that OS = EM, the exhaust lap, the valve begins to uncover the port again, but now it opens it to the exhaust space.

This is known as exhaust opening. From eccentric positions OF to OF′ the steam is exhausting, and at F′ the port is again closed. On reaching the position OB, the eccentric, and also the engine, has made a complete revolution and it will be seen that from C to C′ steam is being admitted to the cylinder ; from C′ to F the steam is expanding in the cylinder ; from F to F′ it is being exhausted ; and from F′ to C any steam remaining in the cylinder is trapped, and is being compressed in the clearance space.

105. Positions of Engine Crank. We have now seen what positions are occupied by the eccentric when the chief events in the cycle of operations occur, but our greatest concern is with the positions of the crank and piston of the engine, when these events take place. Theoretically we want the admission of steam to begin when the piston is about to begin its forward stroke, but in practice it is found that, for smooth and efficient working, the port must be opened a little earlier than this. Hence the engine crank must occupy a position a little below OA when the eccentric is at OC. Thus, when the engine crank is actually at OA the eccentric will occupy a position such as OH, and the valve will have opened the port by an amount PT.

This amount of the port opening to steam when the crank is in the dead-centre position and the piston just beginning its stroke is very important, and is called the *lead*. Thus PT is the lead in this particular case. It is obvious, then, that the eccentric must always be in advance of the main crank by an angle AOH, known as the *angular advance*, whilst the excess of this angle over a right angle is called the *angle of advance*. Thus BOH is the angle of advance.

106. Reuleaux Valve Diagram. In order more easily to interpret the results obtained by the diagram explained in the last two articles, it is convenient to regard all the lines turned in a counter-clockwise direction through an angle AOH. Then OH will occupy the position OA, or the position which the main crank occupies at the beginning of the piston stroke.

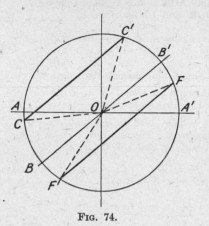

FIG. 74.

We have now the following results from fig. 74. Main crank is in position OC when steam is admitted, in position OC' when cut-off occurs, in position OF when exhaust opens, and in position OF' when exhaust closes. The perpendicular distance from A to the line CC' is the lead, and the angle AOB is the angle of advance. The diagram in this form is known as the Reuleaux Valve Diagram, and is useful for the solving of problems on the slide valve.

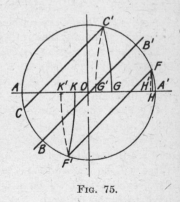

FIG. 75.

EXAMPLE. The travel of a slide valve is 4 ins. The steam lap is 1·2 ins. and the exhaust lap 0·8 in. The angle of advance of the eccentric is 45°. If the connecting rod is four times as long as the main crank, find the position of the piston at cut-off, exhaust opening and exhaust closing. Find also the lead of the valve.

Draw a circle of diameter = 4 ins. and take AOA′ as centre line.
Draw BOB′ making angle AOB = 45° (Angle of advance).
Draw CC′ parallel to BOB′ and 1·2 ins. from it.
Draw FF′   ,,   ,,   ,,'   ,,   0·8 ,,   ,,
At cut-off the main crank is in the direction OC′.
,, exhaust opening ,,   ,,   ,,   ,,   ,,   OF.
,,   ,,   closing   ,,   ,,   ,,   ,,   ,,   OF′.
To find the positions of the piston, imagine the length of crank

= OA and ABA′ to be the crank-pin circle. With radius = 4.$\overline{OA}$
and centre on OA produced, draw arcs of a circle passing through

C′, F and F′. The radius is 4.$\overline{OA}$ because the connecting rod is
four times the length of the crank. The arcs intersect AA′, which
represents the stroke to a suitable scale, in G, H, and K.
The required results are :

$$\text{Cut-off } \frac{AG}{AA'} = 0\cdot63 \text{ of the stroke.}$$

$$\text{Exhaust opening} = \frac{AH}{AA'} = 0\cdot97 \text{ stroke.}$$

$$\text{Exhaust closing} = \frac{A'K}{AA'} = 0\cdot625 \text{ of return stroke.}$$

$$\text{Lead of valve} = \text{perpendicular distance of A from CC}'$$
$$= 0\cdot214 \text{ inch.}$$

Note.—(1) That the circle ABA′ represents both the
eccentric circle and the crank-pin circle to different scales.

(2) That AA′ represents both the valve travel and piston
stroke to different scales.

(3) That the engine is regarded as rotating in a clockwise direction.

(4) That these results apply only to one end of the
valve and therefore to one side of the piston.

If the student understands the foregoing principles, he
will readily see that the diagram for the other end of the
valve will be the same as that shown but turned through
180°, except that the arcs C′G, F′K and FH would not
have to be so treated. Another diagram, however, need
not be drawn, for the results may be obtained by striking
the arcs through C′, F, and F′ from OA′ produced instead
of OA produced.

Then cut-off is $\frac{AG'}{AA'} = 0\cdot52$ of the stroke.

Exhaust opening is at $\dfrac{AH'}{AA'} = 0.96$ stroke.

Exhaust closing is at $\dfrac{AK'}{AA'} = 0.27$ stroke.

The lead remains unaltered.

EXAMPLE. The travel of a slide valve is 3 ins., the lead is $\frac{1}{4}$ in.,

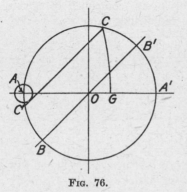

FIG. 76.

and the cut-off is to take place at $\frac{2}{3}$ stroke. Find the steam lap and the angle of advance, when the connecting rod is four times as long as the crank.

Draw a circle 3 ins. diam. With centre A, draw a circle $\frac{1}{4}$ in. radius as shown in fig. 76.

Find the point G so that $AG = \frac{2}{3}AA'$. Draw the arc GC with centre on OA produced and radius $= 4.\overline{OA}$.

Draw a straight line through C touching the circle with centre at A. Then

Angle of advance $= AOB = 43°$.

Outside or steam lap = perpendicular distance between BB' and CC' $= 0.81$ in.

107. Reversing an Engine.

If OB is the crank of an engine, and the eccentric occupies a position such as OA, it should be obvious to the student that the engine will rotate in a clockwise direction. If the eccentric is in the position OC, then the engine will rotate in an anti-clockwise direction. To reverse the direction of rotation of an engine, therefore, it will be sufficient if we can

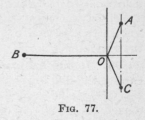

FIG. 77.

arrange at will, so that either OA or OC shall operate the slide valve.

The Stephenson link motion is one of a number of devices for performing this. OB is the crank in fig. 78, OA and OC are eccentrics attached to eccentric rods CD and AF. The rods operate upon the ends of a radial link DF which is slotted for the greater part of its length. In the slot, a block E fits, which is fastened to the valve rod EV.

A suitable arrangement of levers, controlled from the driving platform, allows the radial link to be raised until

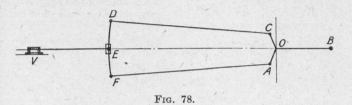

FIG. 78.

F practically coincides with E. The engine shown will then rotate clockwise.

Alternatively, the radial link may be dropped so that D comes down to E, when the eccentric OC will operate the valve and the engine will rotate anti-clockwise. In the mid-position shown, the valve has travel = 2 (lap + lead) which is insufficient to permit the engine to work at all, but for other intermediate positions the engine works with earlier cut-off and smaller valve travel. This is very useful in locomotives and some other types of engines, as it affords a method of controlling steam supply according to load. This method is more efficient than throttling the steam at the regulator.

108. Inside Admission. What has been written regarding the slide valve, piston valve, and eccentric assumes that the steam is admitted at the outside of the valve. Sometimes, especially with piston valves, the steam is admitted on the inside of the valve. If this is the case, an engine which would normally have its eccentric placed at OA′ will have it turned through 180° to the position

OA. With crank at OB and eccentric at OA, fig. 79, the

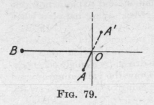

Fig. 79.

engine will rotate in a clockwise direction. The student should have no difficulty in reasoning this case out for himself. The Reuleaux diagram may be used to solve problems in the ordinary way, and when the eccentric position has been found, it can be advanced through 180°.

EXAMPLES XIV

1. The distance between the extreme edges of the steam ports of a steam cylinder is $4\frac{7}{8}$ ins., and the widths of the steam and exhaust ports are respectively 1 in. and $1\frac{7}{8}$ ins. The slide valve is $5\frac{7}{8}$ ins. long in the direction of motion, and is of the ordinary D type. Its travel is $2\frac{1}{2}$ ins., and the distance between the inner edges of the valve is $2\frac{5}{8}$ ins.

Draw to scale a simple sectional sketch of the cylinder ports, with the valve in correct position when the steam port of the cylinder is open to its maximum extent for the admission of steam.

If the lead be $\frac{3}{16}$ in., what is the angle of advance of the eccentric ?

U.L.C.I.

2. What do you understand by the " angle of advance " of an eccentric ?

The travel of a slide valve is $3\frac{3}{4}$ ins., what should be the " eccentricity," or the distance between the centre of the shaft and the centre of the eccentric ?

If the steam lap of the valve is $\frac{7}{8}$ in. and the angle of advance of the eccentric is 30°, what will be the magnitude of the " lead " ? Determine the maximum port opening to steam, and the opening when the piston is at the middle of the stroke.   U.L.C.I.

3. The travel of a slide valve is 4 ins. ; angle of advance 30° ; lead $\frac{1}{16}$ in. ; exhaust lap $\frac{1}{4}$ in. At what fractions of the stroke do cut-off take place and exhaust begin ? Draw an approximate indicator diagram, assuming an initial pressure of 60 lbs. per sq. in. absolute, and a back pressure of 16 lbs. per sq. in. absolute.

U.L.C.I.

4. Show the effect on an indicator diagram of :
(a) Too large an angle of advance.
(b) Too small an angle of advance of the eccentric.
(c) The angle of advance being correct, but the valve incorrectly adjusted on the valve rod.
(d) The effect of the exhaust openings being too small.   U.L.C.I.

5. Sketch in outline and describe the construction of any type of reversing gear with which you are familiar, and explain how the reversal is effected by the gear you describe. What happens when the gear is in an intermediate position ? U.L.C.I.

6. A slide valve has a travel of 6·5 ins. and cuts off steam at 0·64 of the stroke. The outside lap is 1·3 in. and release takes place at 0·94 of the stroke. If this valve were driven by a single eccentric, what would be its angle of advance ? Draw the valve diagram and find the exhaust lap, the maximum opening of the port to steam, and the crank angle at admission. U.L.C.I.

7. The travel of a slide valve is $4\frac{1}{2}$ ins. and the steam lap is 1 in. What is the lead of the valve when the angle of advance of the eccentric is 35° ? Determine the maximum port opening to steam and the fraction of the stroke completed at cut-off, release, and compression. The exhaust lap is $\frac{1}{2}$ inch. U.L.C.I.

8. Describe with the aid of sketches :

(a) Any type of reversing gear for a steam engine and explain its action ; or

(b) The general outline of any form of water-tube boiler, showing in detail the jointing of a tube with the steam drum.

N.C.T.E.C.

9. The travel of a slide valve is $3\frac{1}{2}$ ins. and the lead $\frac{1}{4}$ in. At the crank end steam is cut off at 0·75 and released at 0·95 of the stroke. Find for the crank end (a) the angle of advance, (b) the maximum opening for steam, (c) the exhaust lap. The connecting rod is 6 cranks long. N.C.T.E.C.

10. With the aid of sketches explain the terms steam lap, exhaust lap, and lead, as applied to a slide valve.

The travel of a slide valve is $3\frac{1}{2}$ ins. ; steam lap $\frac{3}{4}$ in. ; exhaust lap $\frac{5}{8}$ in. ; lead, $\frac{1}{8}$ in. Determine the angle of advance and the crank positions at admission, cut-off, release, and compression.

N.C.T.E.C.

11. Explain, by reference to an outline diagram, the construction and action of Stephenson's link motion. N.C.T.E.C.

12. Explain carefully, with the aid of a sketch in each case, the effect on an indicator diagram of the following : (a) an increase of steam lap ; (b) a decrease of exhaust lap ; (c) an increase of lead.

N.C.T.E.C.

13. A simple slide valve is required to give a maximum port opening of $1\frac{1}{2}$ ins. ; the angle of lead is 6° and the cut-off is to occur at $\frac{3}{4}$ stroke. Determine the travel of the valve necessary, also the outside lap and the angle of advance. If compression is to occur at 90 per cent. of the return stroke, what must be the inside lap ?

[You may assume that the connecting rod is infinitely long.]

U.E.I.

14. The slide valve of a vertical engine has a travel of 4 ins.

The lead at the crank end is 0·4 in., and the steam and exhaust laps at this end are 1 in. and 0·4 in. respectively.

The steam ports in the cylinder face are 1½ in. wide in the direction of the travel. The length of the connecting-rod is four times that of the crank. Find from these data :

(a) The angle of advance.

(b) Where cut-off occurs on the up-stroke.

(c) Where release occurs on the up-stroke.

(d) During what fraction of a revolution exhaust is open.

(e) The maximum port-opening to steam at the crank end of the cylinder.

(f) The maximum port-opening to exhaust at the crank end of the cylinder.

And, by projection from your Valve Diagram, sketch the form of Indicator Diagram you would expect to get. U.E.I.

15. The travel of a simple slide valve is 4 ins. ; the steam ports in the cylinder face are each 1½ in. wide in the direction of the travel, and the connecting rod is three times as long as the crank. Draw up, and complete, a table similar to the following :

Event.	Head End.	Crank End.
Cut-off	0·7 stroke	0·7 stroke
Release	0·9 ,,	0·9 ,,
Outside lap		
Inside lap		
Maximum opening to steam . .		
Maximum opening to exhaust . .		
Lead	0·1 in.	
Angle of advance		

How have the equal cut-offs probably been effected ? Is this satisfactory ? U.E.I.

CHAPTER XV

COMBUSTION

109. Source of Heat. There are vast quantities of heat in nature, as in the sun and the interior of the earth.

For practical engineering purposes, however, heat is produced as required by the combustion or burning of some material known as a fuel. Combustion is a chemical process, and for the benefit of the student with no chemical knowledge it is necessary to begin the treatment of combustion by the introduction of the requisite facts.

110. Chemical Combination. The vast variety of substances we see around us is produced by the combination of two or more of a comparatively few substances, known as elements. The special property of an element is that no chemical means are known whereby it may be reduced, or divided, into more elementary constituents. Only about one hundred such elements have been found. Typical elements are iron, copper, gold, carbon, hydrogen.

In this part of our subject we are concerned with only a few, viz. carbon, hydrogen, oxygen, sulphur and nitrogen.

On being ignited in an atmosphere containing a sufficient proportion of oxygen, carbon will combine with oxygen to form new substances, and in doing so, heat is evolved. Hydrogen and sulphur behave in a similar way. Air is an atmosphere with sufficient oxygen in it to support combustion in this way.

The new substances thus formed are called *compounds*, and they are formed according to very definite laws.

As an example, let us consider the case of hydrogen.

One pound weight of hydrogen occupies 178·2 cu. ft. at 0° C. and normal atmospheric pressure. It is convenient to regard this as a standard volume. The weight of one standard volume of any other element, under the same conditions of temperature and pressure, and in the form of a gas, is the atomic weight of that element. A few atomic weights are : Oxygen 16, Carbon 12, Sulphur 32, Nitrogen 14, Hydrogen 1. Only elements have atomic weights, but both elements and compounds have molecular weights.

The molecular weight in lb. of a substance is the weight, when in the form of a gas, of two standard volumes under the above conditions of temperature and pressure.

Molecular weights of a few substances are : Hydrogen 2, Oxygen 32, Nitrogen 28, Water 18, Carbon dioxide 44.

It is useful to note that, since two standard volumes equal $178 \cdot 2 \times 2 = 356 \cdot 4$ cu. ft., the density of a gas is its molecular weight divided by $356 \cdot 4$. Thus the density of hydrogen $= \dfrac{2}{356 \cdot 4} = 0 \cdot 00561$ lbs. per cu. ft., and the density of oxygen $= \dfrac{32}{356 \cdot 4} = 0 \cdot 0897$ lbs. per cu. ft.

The most careful experiments have shown that two volumes of hydrogen combine always with one volume of oxygen, to form two volumes of water gas, i.e. water in the form of a gas. Thus 2 lbs. of hydrogen combine with 16 lbs. of oxygen and form 18 lbs. of water. Or, 1 lb. of hydrogen with 8 lbs. of oxygen form 9 lbs. of water. Moreover, 33,830 C.H.U. of heat are generated.

Thus three important facts may be noted :

(1) Two volumes of hydrogen always combine with one of oxygen.

(2) 1 lb. of hydrogen combines with 8 lbs. of oxygen.

(3) The combustion of 1 lb. of hydrogen in oxygen generates 33,830 C.H.U. of heat.

This last value is known as the " higher " calorific value of hydrogen, because a part of it, corresponding to the latent heat of the steam, is generally lost, so that the " lower " calorific value of 29,000 C.H.U. is more generally useful.

Carbon is the most important element in the fuels commonly used. In its usual forms it is a solid, and is most commonly seen as coke' or charcoal.

Carbon burns in oxygen with the generation of heat, and is capable of forming either carbon monoxide or carbon dioxide. In the latter case, exactly twice as much oxygen per lb. of carbon is required as in the former.

Let H represent 1 lb. of hydrogen or 1 standard volume.

O   „   16 lbs. of oxygen   „ 1   „   „
N   „   14 lbs. of nitrogen „ 1   „   „
C   „   12 lbs. of carbon.   .
S   „   32 lbs. of sulphur.

As carbon and sulphur cannot exist in the form of a gas at 0° C. and atmospheric pressure, we need not be concerned with the volumes. In chemical equations it is convenient for us to deal with not less than two standard volumes. This is because the elements generally have two atoms to a molecule and the single letter, H, for example, is used to represent an atom. Then H_2 represents 2 lbs. of hydrogen or 2 standard volumes. It is also used to represent a molecule, the smallest part which can exist alone. A gas like H_2 is said to have diatomic molecules, because the atoms move about in pairs. Similarly, with O_2 and N_2, which represent 32 lbs. and 28 lbs. respectively.

111. Use of Symbols. These chemical symbols are useful for representing chemical changes. When hydrogen burns in oxygen, steam results. We may represent that change as follows :

$$2H_2 + O_2 = 2H_2O$$
$$4 \text{ lbs.} + 32 \text{ lbs.} = 36 \text{ lbs.}$$

Hence, 4 lbs. of hydrogen and 32 lbs. of oxygen form 36 lbs. of water or steam ; or, 1 lb. of hydrogen and 8 lbs. of oxygen form 9 lbs. of water. This is an important result.

Also, we see that 4 volumes of hydrogen and 2 volumes of oxygen have combined to form 4 volumes of water (in form of gas). Note that there has been a shrinkage because a molecule of H_2O is only the same size as a molecule of hydrogen or oxygen.

N

Let us now take the case of carbon.

$$2C + O_2 = 2CO$$
$$24 \text{ lbs.} + 32 \text{ lbs.} = 56 \text{ lbs.}$$

Here 1 lb. of carbon combines with $1\frac{1}{3}$ lb. of oxygen to form $2\frac{1}{3}$ lbs. of carbon monoxide. Also, whilst we are not concerned with the volume of carbon, we find that two volumes of oxygen have given four volumes of carbon monoxide. Note that the number of CO molecules is twice that of O_2 molecules and, therefore, the volume is twice as great.

But carbon, when completely burnt, forms carbon dioxide.

$$C + O_2 = CO_2$$
$$12 \text{ lbs.} + 32 \text{ lbs.} = 44 \text{ lbs.}$$

Here we have, 1 lb. of carbon combines with $2\frac{2}{3}$ lbs. of oxygen to form $3\frac{2}{3}$ lbs. of carbon dioxide, which has the same volume as that of the oxygen used.

Sulphur, when burnt, forms sulphur dioxide.

$$S + O_2 = SO_2$$
$$32 \text{ lbs.} + 32 \text{ lbs.} = 64 \text{ lbs.}$$

Thus 1 lb. of sulphur combines with 1 lb. of oxygen to form 2 lbs. of sulphur dioxide. The volume of the SO_2 is the same as that of the oxygen (O_2) used.

The conclusions with regard to volume stated above are based upon Avogadro's Law, stated by him in 1811, which is as follows : " Equal volumes of all the different gases, both elementary and compound, contain the same number of molecules." This means that the volume of all molecules is the same at the same pressure and temperature. The student should carefully note, that in all the above equations, the sum of the weights on one side equals the sum of the weights on the other side, but the relationship between the volumes must be reasoned from Avogadro's Law.

112. Heat Generated. We have already stated the higher and lower calorific values of hydrogen as 33,830 and 29,000 respectively. Carbon, burning to carbon monoxide (CO), has a calorific value of 2,450 C.H.U. per lb. of carbon, and when burning to carbon dioxide (CO_2), has the value 8,080 C.H.U. per lb. of carbon. Sulphur has a calorific value of 2,200 C.H.U. per lb. of sulphur.

EXAMPLE. A sample of fuel on analysis is found to contain carbon 87 per cent., hydrogen 10 per cent., ash 3 per cent. Find the calorific value of this fuel per lb., assuming the carbon to be completely burned and taking the lower calorific value of hydrogen.

Heat per lb. of carbon burned = 8,080 C.H.U.

,,   ,,   ,, hydrogen ,,   = 29,000 C.H.U.

Wt. of carbon in 1 lb. of fuel = 0·87 lb.

,, ,, hydrogen   ,,   ,,   = 0·10 lb.

Heat generated per lb. of fuel burned

$$= 0·87 \times 8,080 + 0·10 \times 29,000$$
$$= 7,030 + 2,900$$
$$= 9,930 \text{ C.H.U.}$$

EXAMPLE. Taking the analysis in the previous example, find the weight and volume of oxygen required.

1 lb. of carbon requires $2\frac{2}{3}$ lbs. of oxygen.

1 lb. of hydrogen   ,,   8 lbs.   ,,

0·87 lb. of carbon   ,,   ($0·87 \times 2\frac{2}{3}$) lbs. of oxygen = 2·32

0·10 ,, hydrogen   ,,   ($0·10 \times 8$)   ,,   ,,   = 0·80

Total oxygen = 3·12 lbs.

1 lb. of oxygen occupies 11·2 cu. ft., i.e. $\dfrac{356·4}{32}$.

3·12 lbs. of oxygen occupies $11·2 \times 3·12 = 34·95$ cu. ft.

Note. This is the volume at 0° C. and normal pressure.

113. Nitrogen and Air. Oxygen alone is not available for the purposes of combustion. It exists, in plentiful supply, associated with nitrogen in the air. The effect of the nitrogen is to make combustion less vigorous than it would be with pure oxygen, and also to carry away some of the heat produced. The oxygen and nitrogen of the air are simply mixed together and are not chemically combined.

We may take the composition of air as being,

(1) Oxygen 23% Nitrogen 77% by weight.

(2)   ,,   21%   ,,   79% by volume.

This neglects a number of other gases in the air, which, for our purposes, are not important.

EXAMPLE. A sample of oil contains 85 per cent. carbon and 15 per cent. hydrogen. Find the weight and the volume of air required for complete combustion.

Oxygen required for the carbon $= 0.85 \times 2.66 = 2.26$ lbs.

,,   ,,   ,, ,, hydrogen $= 0.15 \times 8 \quad = 1.20$,,

Total $= 3.46$ lbs.

$\therefore$ Wt. of air required $= 3.46 \times \dfrac{100}{23} = 15$ lbs.

Density of oxygen $= \dfrac{\text{Molec. Wt.}}{356.4} = \dfrac{32}{356.4} = 0.0897$ lb. per cu. ft.

$\therefore$ Volume of oxygen required $= \dfrac{3.46}{0.0897} = 38.55$ cu. ft.

$\therefore$ Volume of air required $= 38.55 \times \dfrac{100}{21}$

$= 183.3$ cu. ft.

Note that this is the volume of air at $0°$ C. and 14.7 lbs. per sq. in. It is also the minimum amount of air which is theoretically required. To ensure the complete combustion of any fuel it is necessary to supply air in excess of this amount.

EXAMPLE. A sample of anthracite gave the following analysis : carbon 92.5 per cent., hydrogen 3.4 per cent., oxygen 2.6 per cent., ash 1.5 per cent. Assuming that 20 per cent. of excess air is supplied, find the required volume of air per lb. of fuel. Also find the calorific value of the coal.

Oxygen required by the carbon $= 0.925 \times 2.66$ lbs. $= 2.46$ lbs.

,,   ,,   ,, hydrogen $= 0.034 \times 8$ lbs. $= 0.276$,,

Total oxygen $= 2.736$,,

Less oxygen already present in fuel $= 0.026$,,

2.710 lbs.

Theoretical volume of oxygen $= \dfrac{2.710}{0.0897} = 30.2$ cu. ft.

Theoretical volume of air $= 30.2 \times \dfrac{100}{21} = 143.6$ cu. ft.

$\therefore$ Air actually supplied $= 143.6 \times \dfrac{120}{100} = 172.4$ cu. ft

In calculating the calorific value it is assumed that the oxygen is already combined with the hydrogen. Hydrogen already combined with oxygen $= \dfrac{0 \cdot 026}{8} = 0 \cdot 0032$ lbs.

$\therefore$ Hydrogen to be burned $= 0 \cdot 034 - 0 \cdot 0032 = 0 \cdot 0308$ lbs.

Heat generated by burning carbon $= 0 \cdot 925 \times 8{,}080 = 7{,}480$ C.H.U

Heat generated by burning hydrogen

$$= 0 \cdot 0308 \times 29{,}000 = \underline{\quad 893 \quad} \; ;$$

$\therefore$ Calorific value of fuel $= 8{,}373$,,

114. Products of Combustion.

It is sometimes useful to calculate the composition of the mixture of gases which result from the combustion of a quantity of some specified fuel.

EXAMPLE. Acetylene has the chemical formula C_2H_2. Find the volume of air required for its complete combustion, and, assuming the actual air supply to be 80 per cent. in excess, calculate the composition by volume of the resulting products. Take 1 cu. ft. of the acetylene.

The chemical equation is

$$2C_2H_2 \quad + \quad 5\,O_2 \quad = 4CO_2 \quad + 2H_2O$$
$$4 \text{ vols.} \quad + \quad 10 \text{ vols.} \quad = 8 \text{ vols.} \quad + 4 \text{ vols.}$$

or $\quad$ 1 cu. ft. $+$ 2·5 cu. ft. $=$ 2 cu. ft. $+$ 1 cu. ft.

From this it appears that 1 cu. ft. of acetylene requires 2·5 cu. ft. of oxygen.

$\therefore$ Volume of air required $= 2 \cdot 5 \times \dfrac{100}{21} = 11 \cdot 9$ cu. ft.

$\therefore$ Volume of air supplied $= 11 \cdot 9 \times \dfrac{180}{100} = 21 \cdot 42$ cu. ft.

Volume of products of combustion :

Vol. of CO_2 $\qquad$ from chemical equation $\quad = 2$ cu. ft.

,, ,, H_2O (steam) $\quad$,, $\qquad$,, $\qquad$,, $\quad = 1$,,

Unused oxygen $= \dfrac{21 \cdot 42 \times 21}{100} - 2 \cdot 5 = 4 \cdot 5 - 2 \cdot 5 = 2$ cu. ft.

Nitrogen $= \dfrac{21 \cdot 42 \times 79}{100} = 16 \cdot 92$ cu. ft.

If a sample of this mixture of products of combustion were taken for analysis, the steam would condense, and thus there would be left :

2 cu. ft. CO_2 + 2 cu. ft. oxygen + 16·92 cu. ft. nitrogen

$$= 20 \cdot 92 \text{ cu. ft.}$$

Percentages :

$$CO_2 = \frac{2 \times 100}{20 \cdot 92} = 9 \cdot 56 \text{ per cent.}$$

$$O_2 = \frac{2 \times 100}{20 \cdot 92} = 9 \cdot 56 \quad ,,$$

$$N_2 = \frac{16 \cdot 92 \times 100}{20 \cdot 92} = 80 \cdot 88 \quad ,,$$

Two points are worthy of note :

(1) The products of combustion are less in volume than the marsh gas and air.

(2) The large proportion of nitrogen present.

EXAMPLE. The analysis of a sample of Scotch coal was as follows :—Carbon 80·63 per cent. ; hydrogen 5·16 per cent. ; oxygen 10·61 per cent. ; sulphur 0·84 per cent. ; ash, etc. 2·76 per cent.

If 18 lbs. of air are supplied per lb. of coal, calculate the composition by weight of the flue gases if the combustion is complete.

Wt. of CO_2 in flue gas = $0 \cdot 8063 \times 3\frac{2}{3}$ = 2·96 lbs.

,,   ,, H_2O ,,   ,,   = $0 \cdot 0516 \times 9$ = 0·46 ,,

,,   ,, SO_2 ,,   ,,   = $0 \cdot 0084 \times 2$ = 0·017,,

,,   ,, N_2 ,,   ,,   = $18 \times \frac{77}{100}$ = 13·86 ,,

The ash does not enter into the problem.

Total weight of flue gases

= wt. of air supplied + wt. of fuel − wt. of ash

= 18 + 1 − 0·0276

= 18·972 lbs.

Wt. of oxygen = 18·972 − (2·96 + ·46 + ·017 + 13·86)

= 18·972 − 17·297

= 1·675 lbs.

These values may be converted into percentages if we so desire

EXAMPLE. Taking the data and results of the last example, calculate the composition, in volume percentages, of the flue gas.

$$\text{Density of a gas} = \frac{\text{molecular weight}}{356 \cdot 4} \text{ lbs. per cu. ft.}$$

Molecular weight of CO_2 = $12 + 16 \times 2 = 44$

,,   ,,   ,, H_2O = $2 + 16$ = 18

,,   ,,   ,, SO_2 = $32 + 16 \times 2 = 64$

,,   ,,   ,, N_2 = 14×2 = 28

,,   ,,   ,, O_2 = 16×2 = 32

The H_2O is omitted as it would condense and occupy negligible volume.

Vol. of $CO_2 = 2 \cdot 96 \div$ density $= \dfrac{2 \cdot 96 \times 356 \cdot 4}{44} = 24 \cdot 0$ cu. ft.

,, ,, $SO_2 = \dfrac{0 \cdot 017 \times 356 \cdot 4}{64} = 0 \cdot 95$,,

,, ,, $N_2 = \dfrac{13 \cdot 86 \times 356 \cdot 4}{28} = 176 \cdot 8$,,

,, ,, $O_2 = \dfrac{1 \cdot 675 \times 356 \cdot 4}{32} = 18 \cdot 7$,,

Total volume $= 220 \cdot 45$,,

CO_2 per cent. $= \dfrac{24 \times 100}{222 \cdot 1} = 10 \cdot 87$ per cent.

SO_2 ,, ,, $= \dfrac{2 \cdot 6 \times 100}{222 \cdot 1} = 0 \cdot 43$,,

N_2 ,, ,, $= \dfrac{176 \cdot 8 \times 100}{222 \cdot 1} = 80 \cdot 21$,,

O_2 ,, ,, $= \dfrac{18 \cdot 7 \times 100}{222 \cdot 1} = 8 \cdot 49$,,

100·00

Sometimes carbon monoxide is present amongst the products of combustion. This is to be avoided as far as practicable for two reasons. In the first place, it is a highly poisonous gas, and if discharged in confined spaces or where it is likely to be inhaled, it may cause the death of human beings or animals. In the second place, it denotes inefficient combustion. We have seen that when carbon burns to form CO_2 its calorific value is 8,080 C.H.U., but when burnt to CO, this value is only 2,450 C.H.U. The loss per lb. of carbon burnt to form CO is therefore $8,080 - 2,450 = 5,630$ C.H.U. The waste is therefore obvious.

115. Efficient Stoking. The method of applying the fuel in the furnace of a boiler has a great bearing upon its efficient use. The main principles are : (a) There must be a supply of air sufficient to ensure complete combustion. (b) The combustion must be sufficiently rapid to maintain a high temperature.

If the supply of air is short, complete combustion is

impossible, and CO is found amongst the flue gases. Moreover, black smoke may be produced.

The fuel should be applied so that the back portion of the fire remains bright. In this case, the gases which are emitted from the fresh fuel, will be ignited if sufficient air is present. On the next application of coal a portion of the burning fuel should be pushed to the back of the grate. If the air supply is excessive, then the unused oxygen, and all the nitrogen will absorb heat from the furnace, thus reducing the temperature, and will carry large quantities of heat to the chimney. Mechanical stokers are generally designed to ensure the proper application of the coal, and the draught must be regulated to give the right air supply. Generally, the thicker the fire, the stronger must be the draught. Instruments, which record the percentage of CO_2 in the flue gases, are often installed, and these form a useful indication as to whether suitable conditions for complete combustion are being maintained.

EXAMPLES XV

1. A light oil has the analysis: Carbon 86 per cent., Hydrogen 14 per cent. Find its calorific value per lb.

2. The analysis of a sample of coal is: Carbon 75·81 per cent., Hydrogen 5·22 per cent., Sulphur 0·90 per cent., Oxygen 11·14 per cent., Ash 6·93 per cent. Calculate its probable calorific value.

3. Acetylene has the chemical formula C_2H_2. Its molecular weight is 26. Find the volume of air necessary for the complete combustion of 1 cu. ft. of acetylene, the weight of air necessary for the combustion of 1 lb., the density per cubic foot and the calorific value per cubic foot.

4. What do you understand by the " calorific value " of a fuel ?

Estimate the calorific value of a sample of fuel which contains 84 per cent. by weight of carbon and 6 per cent. by weight of hydrogen.

Obtain, from first principles, the minimum weight of air necessary for the complete combustion of 1 lb. of this fuel.

Calorific value of 1 lb. of carbon, 8,080 C.H.U.

,, ,, ,, ,, ,, hydrogen, 29,000 C.H.U.

4·35 lbs. of air contain 1 lb. of oxygen. U.E.I.

5. A boiler uses coal having a composition by weight of carbon 0·85, hydrogen 0·04, ash 0·11. Calculate the minimum weight of air required per lb. of coal.

In a boiler consuming 1,000 lbs. of coal per hour the air supply is 30 per cent. in excess of the minimum quantity, and its temperature is raised to 250° C. in a heater before passing to the furnace. Calculate the area of a delivery pipe from the heater if the air velocity is not to exceed 60 ft. per sec. Assume the air pressure to be 16 lbs. per sq. in. absolute. (Gas constant R = 96 ft.-lbs. per lb. per degree C. ; 4·35 lbs. of air contain 1 lb. of oxygen.)

N.C.T.E.C.

6. (a) What do you understand by the " higher " and " lower " calorific value of a fuel ?

(b) In an experiment to determine the higher calorific value of coal, the temperature of 1,500 c.c. of water was raised from 14·5° C. to 21° C. The water equivalent of the calorimeter was 250 grammes and 2 grammes of coal were burnt. Calculate the higher calorific value of the coal.

(c) What minimum weight of air is required per lb. of the above coal if it contained 0·85 lb. of carbon, 0·035 lb. of hydrogen, and 0·05 lb. of free oxygen ?

Note. There is 1 lb. of oxygen in 4·35 lbs. of air. N.C.T.E.C.

7. What do you understand by the " higher " and " lower " calorific values of a fuel ?

An analysis of 1 lb. of coal gave 0·78 lb. carbon and 0·05 lb. hydrogen. Assuming perfect combustion, state the products of combustion, and determine their respective weights per lb. of coal. Also find the " higher " and " lower " calorific value of each lb. of coal. Given : Atomic weights of carbon, hydrogen and oxygen respectively 12, 1, and 16. The heat evolved during the complete combustion of (a) 1 lb. of hydrogen forming water, 33,850 C.H.U. and (b) 1 lb. of carbon, 8,055 C.H.U. U.L.C.I.

8. Find the weight of air required to burn 1 lb. of carbon to CO_2 and 1 lb. of hydrogen to H_2O. Also calculate the weight of air theoretically required to burn completely 1 lb. of oil consisting of 0·85 carbon and 0·15 hydrogen.

If this oil were used in a boiler furnace and the air supply was 50 per cent. in excess of that absolutely necessary for combustion, how much heat would the excess air carry away up the chimney per lb. of oil burned ? Temperature of air entering the furnace 18° C., and temperature of gases entering the chimney 290° C. Given : Atomic weights of carbon, hydrogen, and oxygen, 12, 1, and 16 respectively. Air contains 23 per.cent. of oxygen by weight. Mean specific heat of air 0·24. U.L.C.I.

9. The analysis of the coal used during a boiler trial gave 87 per cent. carbon, 3·5 per cent. hydrogen, and 4·8 per cent. oxygen.

Determine, from first principles, the amount of air theoretically required for the complete combustion of 1 lb. of coal. Explain why more air is used per lb. of coal in practice than is theoretically necessary.

Atomic weights: carbon 12, oxygen 16, hydrogen 1.

U.L.C.I.

10. The composition per lb. of oil fuel supplied to a boiler consists of 0·85 lb. carbon, 0·13 lb. hydrogen, and 0·02 lb. oxygen. The air supply is 70 per cent. in excess of that required for complete combustion. Calculate the weight of flue gases passing up the chimney per hour when 1,400 lb. of oil are burned per hour. Atomic weights: carbon 12, hydrogen 1, oxygen 16.　　U.L.C.I.

CHAPTER XVI

INTERNAL COMBUSTION ENGINES

116. Introduction. The steam engine is an *external* combustion engine, because the fuel burns in a chamber which is not in direct communication with the inside of the working cylinder. In such a case, the working substance and the fuel do not come into contact. The hot-air engine is also of the external combustion type.

The present century has seen the *internal* combustion engine develop, and become of first-rate importance as a prime mover. In such engines, the fuel mixes with, and becomes a part of, the working substance. The combustion takes place either in the cylinder, or in some chamber directly connected with it. Hence the name "internal combustion."

The fundamental principle of all internal combustion engines is the same. Fuel in the form of a gas or vapour, or else in an atomized form, is mixed with air. The mixture is ignited and with great rapidity heat energy is given to the mixed gases. The accompanying pressure exerts a force on a moving piston and does mechanical work. The principles involved are largely covered by the first seven chapters of this book.

Many fuels, in gaseous or liquid form, are used and the mechanical design of the engine and the nature of its accessories are largely controlled by the kind of fuel used.

Internal combustion engines are divided generally, according to the fuel which they consume, into the following classes : Gas engines. Light oil engines. Heavy oil engines. The last named is becoming of rapidly increasing importance and is treated in a later chapter.

117. Otto Cycle. In 1876, Otto produced an engine working on a cycle, stated fourteen years earlier by Beau de Rochas. This cycle is now known as the Otto or Four-stroke Cycle. It is completed in four successive strokes as follows :

1st Stroke. Air with gas or atomized fuel is drawn into the cylinder by the moving piston.

2nd Stroke. The mixture is compressed in the clearance space as the piston returns. On the completion of compression, the mixture is ignited.

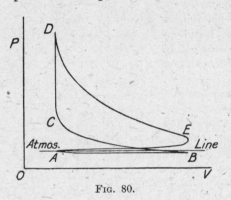

FIG. 80.

3rd Stroke. The pressure thus set up causes the piston to be forced forward and we have the working stroke. At the end of it, exhaust opens.

4th Stroke. The products of combustion are swept out through the open exhaust valve as the piston returns. This is the "scavenging" stroke. Thus the cycle is completed and the engine has made two complete revolutions.

Fig. 80 shows the nature of the resulting indicator diagram. AB, below the atmospheric line, denotes the suction stroke. BC is the compression curve and CD shows the rise of pressure on ignition. DE is the working or expansion stroke and EA shows the exhaust and scavenging. It will be noticed that this diagram consists of two loops. The lower one from A to B represents negative work, whilst the upper and larger one represents the positive work. The effective work done per cycle on the piston is represented by the difference of the two.

118. Clerk or Two-stroke Cycle. This cycle, invented by Dugald Clerk in 1880, was intended to give one working stroke per revolution, and thus increase the power of an engine of given size.

In this engine, the inlet and exhaust ports are both open when the piston is at the outer end of the cylinder. A mixture of air and fuel, slightly compressed, enters through the inlet port, and drives the burnt gases from the previous stroke before it. We then have:

1st Stroke. Compression of charge of air and fuel in the clearance space. At the end of this stroke ignition occurs.

2nd Stroke. The piston is forced forward as a result of pressure generated. Just before the end of this stroke, exhaust opens.

There is no suction stroke, and no scavenging stroke. The commonest form of this engine in use at the present time is the Day two-stroke engine shown diagrammatically in fig. 81. Air and fuel are drawn into the crank-case through a spring-operated valve at I, on the up-stroke of the piston. On the down-stroke the mixture is compressed in the crank-case

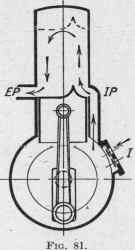

FIG. 81.

below the piston. The piston uncovers the inlet port IP and the exhaust port EP, near the end of its downward stroke and the compressed mixture in the crank-case rushes through IP, driving the exhaust gases before it through EP. The Clerk engine carried out the compression in an auxiliary cylinder, whose piston was driven from the crank pin, or a point on the connecting rod just above the crank pin. There was also an inlet valve at the upper end of the cylinder, and only the exhaust port was uncovered by the piston.

119. The Working Substance. If the student refers

to Article 114, it will be found that nitrogen is always the preponderating item in the products of combustion. There is generally about 80 per cent. of this gas present. Thus the working cylinder mainly contains a gas which takes no part in the combustion.

All that the nitrogen can do, is to absorb heat when ignition of the fuel occurs, and give up that heat again during expansion in the form of mechanical work. Moreover, the percentage of nitrogen present is about the same as the percentage in the air. The thermal properties, therefore, of the cylinder gases are governed by the presence of nitrogen, a fact which is also true of air. Thus it arises that the air standard cycle (see Article 48) becomes the standard of comparison for internal combustion engines, where the combustion takes place at constant volume. This is the case with gas and light oil engines.

120. Gas Engine. It is not intended here to describe the details of a simple gas engine. The student will probably have the opportunity of working on such an engine, and has no doubt gained such knowledge in an earlier year of his course. If approaching the subject for the first time, he will find a section of a gas engine in the Authors' *Mechanics and Applied Heat*, page 316.

The gas used may be town gas obtained by the distillation of coal, Mond gas, blast furnace gas, or producer gas. Town gas is available in most towns in Britain, Mond gas in a portion of the Midlands, blast furnace gas where pig iron is made from iron ore, and producer gas wherever a gas producer plant is set up.

Gas engines usually work on the Otto cycle, and electric ignition is generally adopted in modern engines. They are usually single-acting, though double-acting gas engines have been made.

The heat generated by the combustion of the gas is disposed of chiefly in four ways.

(1) That converted into useful work.

(2) That wasted in friction and windage.

(3) That rejected to exhaust with the hot gases.

(4) That carried away by the water jackets.

The losses (3) and (4) are by far the largest, and are greatly in excess of the heat converted into useful work. Some further knowledge of these losses will be gained on reading chapter XIX.

The air standard efficiency is not reached in actual engines, since neither the expansion nor compression curve follows the adiabatic law.

Given the composition of the gas supplied to an engine, we may calculate, as in the last chapter, the amount of air which should be admitted per stroke. In practice, the best results are obtained by admitting more than this.

Good results have been obtained by admitting about 10 times as much air as gas.

In actual engines, the events of the four-stroke cycle do not occur exactly as described. Particularly must the ignition occur a little before compression

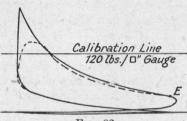

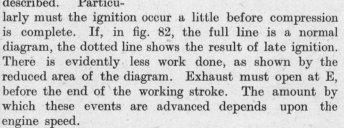

FIG. 82.

is complete. If, in fig. 82, the full line is a normal diagram, the dotted line shows the result of late ignition. There is evidently less work done, as shown by the reduced area of the diagram. Exhaust must open at E, before the end of the working stroke. The amount by which these events are advanced depends upon the engine speed.

121. Governing. The maintenance of constant speed of rotation is effected by a governor. The governor itself is usually of the centrifugal type and its principles are discussed in chapter XX. The way in which it operates upon the supply of power to the gas engine will, however, be dealt with here. There are three methods of importance.

(1) " Hit and miss " governing.
(2) Quality governing.
(3) Quantity governing.

Using the first method, a rise above the permissible speed causes the governor sleeve S (fig. 83) to lift. The lever L lifts the distance piece D, so that the pecker P misses it. In this way the gas inlet valve V is not opened, so that the usual charge of gas fails to enter the cylinder.

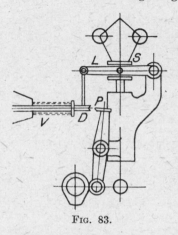

This continues until the speed is reduced and D drops back into position. Thus explosions are missed intermittently, but every charge is of normal strength. This is an efficient method from the point of view of economy in gas consumption.

In *quality governing* the gas supply is not cut out entirely but is reduced in quantity. The governor acts so as to throttle the gas supply. The result is a weak mixture, since the air supply remains the same. The pressure, therefore, is less and the speed falls. A disadvantage of this method is, that with a varying mixture, it is impossible to find a suitable ignition point for all strengths. The thermal efficiency, too, is reduced.

Fig. 83.

Quantity governing consists in throttling both the gas and air supply. A smaller weight of mixture enters the cylinder, but the proportions of gas and air remain about the same. The compression ratio is unaltered and the air standard efficiency does not fall. This method appears to be finding favour, especially for large engines.

Summing up, it may be said that hit and miss governing is most common on small gas engines, and quantity governing is generally found on large engines.

122. Producer Gas. Self-contained plants are obtainable, which consist of a generator for making gas, and a gas engine to use it. The following gives an outline of the principle on which a gas producer works.

If air is forced or drawn through a body of intensely heated carbon the following chemical reaction will occur.

$$2C + O_2 = 2CO$$

We have seen in the last chapter, that if 1 lb. of carbon burns to CO, 2,450 C.H.U. will be generated. If, however, the carbon forms CO_2, 8,080 C.H.U. will be given off. When, therefore, the carbon monoxide given off by 1 lb. of carbon further burns to form CO_2, we obtain

$$8,080 - 2,450 = 5,630 \ \text{C.H.U.}$$

Suppose we use 1 lb. of carbon in producing CO, this gas still contains $\left(\dfrac{5,630}{8,080} \times 100\right)$ per cent. of the calorific value of the carbon ; i.e. 70 per cent. Using gas of this kind, we should send 70 per cent. of the heat in our fuel (carbon) to the engine, and 30 per cent. would remain in the carbon or be used in heating the gas as it goes forward. Some of this heat can, however, be reclaimed by also passing a quantity of steam over the carbon, when the chemical action below may occur :

$$C + H_2O = H_2 + CO.$$

As heat is required to split up the H_2O into hydrogen and oxygen, a large quantity of that waste 30 per cent. can be so used. In this case, it passes on to the engine and can supply heat in addition to the 70 per cent. already referred to. In a gas producer air and steam pass through heated anthracite or coke. The resulting gas is a mixture of hydrogen, carbon monoxide, carbon dioxide, and nitrogen. There is no difficulty in these circumstances in obtaining efficiencies approaching 90 per cent. for the producer.

Fig. 84, reproduced by permission of the National Gas Engine Co. Ltd., Ashton-under-Lyne, shows a section of a gas producer or suction gas plant.

The generator is filled with coke or anthracite to the level of the bottom of the feed hopper.

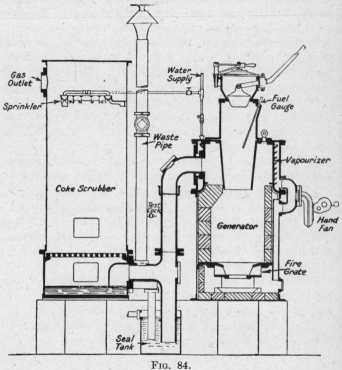

FIG. 84.

The scrubber is filled with coke which is saturated with water from the sprinkler.

The vaporizer consists of a number of projections on the upper part of the inner casing enclosed by the outer casing. Water is supplied to the vaporizer through the pipe marked "water supply."

When the engine is started it draws its supply through the producer. Air enters the vaporizer and picks up steam in its passage through it. The mixture of air and steam passes down the pipe on the right of the diagram into the fire grate. Going through the generator it comes in contact with the incandescent fuel, when the gas is formed. From the upper part of the generator, it passes down the pipe shown, to the bottom of the scrubber.

It then rises through the coke pack, meeting the water from the sprinkler. This removes dust and other impurities, and cools the gas somewhat. Finally, through the gas outlet, it passes on to the engine.

It will be noticed that there is a feed hopper over the generator, which allows charges of fuel to be fed without admitting air from the atmosphere. No air must enter other than that passing in by the vaporizer.

The waste pipe is used in starting up the producer after cleaning, or when it has been out of action for some reason.

123. The Petrol Engine. The principles involved in the working of the petrol engine are exactly the same as in the case of the gas engine. As, however, the fuel is a liquid, it becomes necessary to arrange to vaporize it before entry into the cylinder, and this calls for the use of the carburettor.

Petrol is the lightest of the distillates, obtained from crude mineral oil, in commercial use. In U.S.A. it is known as gasoline and is sometimes called benzine.

The petrol engine differs in its mechanical arrangements from the gas engine, merely to meet practical needs.

Many successful petrol engines are in existence, working, some on the four-stroke cycle, and some on the two-stroke.

In Britain, an arbitrary formula, which gives what is known as the R.A.C. rating, is used to calculate the H.P. for taxation purposes.

This formula is H.P. $= \dfrac{nd^2}{2 \cdot 5}$ where $n =$ number of cylinders, $d =$ diameter of each cylinder in inches. It bears little relationship to the actual horse-power, which may be as much as $3\frac{1}{2}$ times this value even without the use of such special devices as superchargers.

To increase the horse power without increasing the R.A.C. rating has been the aim of designers in this country for some time. With the air standard cycle efficiency in mind, which is

$$1 - \left(\frac{1}{r}\right)^{\gamma - 1} = \text{efficiency},$$

the idea of higher compression ratio at once suggests itself. This line can only be followed to a limited extent, as few petrols will work with a compression ratio exceeding 5·5, without giving rise to pre-ignition.

124. Carburation. To do its work, petrol must be intimately mixed with air in the cylinder. The process of procuring this result is called "carburation," and it is carried out by means of a carburettor. We propose to deal only with the principles of the methods adopted; details of actual carburettors may be easily followed from makers' pamphlets, when the main ideas are understood.

Petrol, on entering the cylinder, should be either in the form of a vapour, or a very fine spray (atomized), or both.

Fig. 85 will serve to illustrate the method of operation of many types of carburettor. PP is the petrol pipe bringing the petrol to the float chamber FC. FF is the float which, through the levers LL, operates the needle valve NV. The level of the petrol in the float chamber cannot rise above a predetermined height. From FC there is a connection to the pilot jet PJ and the main jet MJ. The level of petrol normally stands just a little below the top of the main jet, and considerably below the pilot jet.

The main jet terminates in the throat of the choke tube CT, whilst the pilot jet projects into a much smaller tube. The pilot jet operates during starting and slow running.

When starting, the throttle T is in the position shown. Even the slow motion of the engine, when operated by the self-starter, produces enough suction to draw a plentiful supply of petrol from the pilot jet. As the throttle is opened, the suction on the pilot jet decreases, but a greater rush of air occurs in the main jet. When a fluid passes through a restricted passage, its velocity increases but its pressure decreases (see Boothroyd's *App. Mechs.*, Arts 79 and 87). Hence, a suction is set up in the choke tube sufficient to draw petrol from the main jet. Thus the pilot jet passes out of action, and the main jet begins to function. The fine stream of petrol now flowing mixes with the rapidly moving turbulent stream of air and is

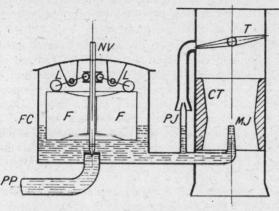

FIG. 85.

atomized. If, in addition, the air is slightly warmed the fuel is also vaporized, at least in part.

The air may be warmed by bringing it in contact at some suitable point with the exhaust system or heat may be obtained from the circulating water.

125. Comparison of the Two Cycles. The Otto and Clerk cycles each have their own advantages.

In gas and petrol engines the Otto Cycle generally gives higher efficiency. This is due to the positive scavenging action during exhaust. Burnt gases are always left behind from the previous stroke, and these dilute the next charge with lower mean pressure as a result. The quantity of burnt gases left in the two-stroke engine is greater than that in the four-stroke. Another reason lies in the fact that, with the two-stroke engine, both inlet and exhaust valves are open at the same time, hence, a portion of the fresh charge often escapes unused through the exhaust port.

The two-stroke engine has an active stroke for every revolution, hence, a more even torque is produced, making it possible to reduce the weight of the flywheel. If crank chamber compression is used the two-stroke engine has a higher power for a given weight. The two-stroke engine will run in either direction if it is designed on the Day principle, that is, if it is of the valveless type. Most internal combustion engines of other types require very cumbersome gear to reverse the direction of rotation.

Examples XVI

1. Why is the term " internal combustion " applied to certain types of heat engines ?
Which of the following are internal combustion engines : gas engine, steam turbine, hot-air engine, petrol engine, reciprocating steam engine, Diesel engine, gas turbine ?

2. Describe the operations of the four-stroke and two-stroke cycles as applied to a gas engine.

3. What are the relative advantages and disadvantages of the four-stroke and two-stroke cycles ?

4. Explain carefully why it seems reasonable to compare the performance of a gas or petrol engine with the air standard cycle.

5. Why is a carburettor necessary to a petrol engine, whilst no similar device is used in conjunction with a gas engine ?

6. The cylinder bore of a petrol engine with six cylinders is 70 mm. Calculate its H.P. according to the R.A.C. rating. What important details affect the actual horse power which the R.A.C. formula does not take into account ?

7. Explain generally or, if you prefer it, in relation to some particular make, what is the function of a carburettor and how it carries out that function.

8. What are the most common methods of governing the speed of small gas engines ? Illustrate your answer by means of neat sketches.
Sketch carefully a good representative indicator card for a gas

engine of the four-stroke cycle type. Show on the diagram, by dotted lines, the variation you would expect :

(a) If the ignition were too early ;

(b) If the mixture were too rich. U.E.I.

9. Sketch neatly and describe a modern type gas producer. Explain how producer gas is made.

It is said that if the process merely oxidized carbon to carbon monoxide, and there were no heat losses, the efficiency of the producer would be at least 70 per cent. Explain this. U.E.I.

10. Describe the series of operations known as the Otto Cycle. Describe, with the aid of an outline sketch, one method of governing an internal combustion engine. N.C.T.E.C.

CHAPTER XVII

HEAVY OIL ENGINES

126. Introduction. Heavy oil engines constitute a very important class of internal combustion engines. These engines use residual oils, heavy mineral oil in the unrefined or crude state, and tar oils obtained from the distillation of solid fuels. On this account they are sometimes called crude oil engines. They differ from petrol and paraffin engines in the method of initiating combustion. In heavy oil engines the fuel is not induced during the suction stroke, but is forced in by means of a pump towards the end of the compression stroke. By this means, pre-ignition is made impossible and dangerous pressures are avoided. This permits of the compression in crude oil engines being much higher than in engines using the lighter fractions, and inducing the oil through a carburettor or vaporizer. Thus the thermal efficiency is higher.

127. Classification. An exact classification of oil engines is not a simple matter as the various types merge into each other. An approximate classification is as follows :

(1) Low compression engines, based on the Hornsby-Ackroyd engine.

(2) Medium compression engines, or cold-starting crude oil engines.

(3) High compression, or Diesel engines.

The high and medium compression engines have no ignition device of any kind, and are known as compression-ignition engines. The reason for this term is that the compression of the air on the compression stroke, which is approximately adiabatic, is carried on until the temperature of the air rises well above the ignition point of the fuel oil. Thus ignition devices, like sparking-plugs, magnetos, coils or lamps, are dispensed with.

128. Low Compression Engines. In the low compression type the heavy oil is heated in a vaporizer, by heat externally applied, before entering the actual cylinder. The oil may be injected either at the commencement of the suction stroke, or towards the end of the compression stroke. In the former case, the oil vapour and air are compressed into the vaporizer. The combined heating effect of the vaporizer and the compression raises the temperature to ignition point, and produces the combustion, no spark being required as with the light oil engine. The compression pressure in this type of engine is from 50 to 100 lbs. per sq. in., depending upon the ignition point of the oil used. The combustion takes place approximately at constant volume.

When the oil is injected towards the end of the compression stroke, the compression pressure may be carried higher without risk of pre-ignition. If, however, the fuel valve leaks, dangerous pressures may be produced due to pre-ignition, but this applies to all pure compression-ignition engines, where the compression pressure is unassisted by hot surface, hot bulb, or lamp.

In the well-known Petter engines the vaporizer is modified to a hot bulb, which is an uncooled portion of the combustion chamber.

The hot-bulb engines are sometimes referred to as semi-Diesel engines ; an incorrect term since there is nothing similar about the engines except that they use the same type of fuel, and that air alone is compressed.

The vaporizer and hot-bulb types of engine follow the Ackroyd principles of low compression and constant volume heat supply. The Ackroyd engine made its appearance in 1889 and was intended to operate on the constant volume thermal cycle.

129. Medium Compression Engines. These engines may be called " sprayer " or airless injection engines, but there are also airless injection engines in the high compression class.

In the medium compression engine the oil is atomized by means of a fine nozzle sprayer, supplied with oil at high pressure from a pump of the ram type. With a sufficiently high hydraulic pressure, a fine bore orifice produces a high degree of atomization, and by suitably arranging the position of the nozzle in the combustion chamber, good penetration of the oil mist into the high temperature air, turbulence, and complete combustion are secured. Pressures in this type of engine at the end of compression are round about 350 to 450 lbs. per sq. in. The oil pressure in the pump system is from 1,200 to 1,500 lbs. per sq. in. Special arrangements of nozzles, pistons and passages to produce turbulence when ignition occurs, form the subjects of many patents, and constitute the difference between crude oil engines from different makers. These arrangements have considerable effect upon the running qualities and efficiency of the engine.

The combustion takes place in these engines partly at constant volume, and partly at constant pressure, with the result that a good mean effective pressure is secured without unduly high maximum pressure. Engines in which this feature is pronounced are said to work on the principle of *Dual Combustion*.

130. High Compression Engines. Sometimes known as airless injection, or compression-ignition engines, these engines are of the sprayer type, but the compression pressure is higher—450 to 550 lbs. per sq. in. The fuel supply is controlled to produce combustion approximately at constant pressure. No ignition device is fitted.

The general design of these engines is similar to that of the Diesel engine. This class of engine has made very rapid progress and appears certain to be the leading type in the future. The main difference between this engine and the Diesel, which is described more fully in Article 129, is that no air compressor is used. The fuel is injected by means of a ram pump accurately timed. It is a type of engine largely used for marine work and power stations, and, at present, is being applied to mechanical road transport. It is thus becoming a competitor of the petrol engine. Its advantages as compared with the petrol engines are absence of fire risk and ignition system. In small units it is largely used for driving ship lighting sets.

131. Nomenclature. There is no uniformity or agreement as to the title by which heavy oil engines are to be known. Various terms are in use such as, semi-Diesel, solid injection, mechanical injection and airless injection.

The term semi-Diesel is applied indiscriminately to crude oil engines following the principles of Ackroyd Stuart's patents, and to high compression engines using pump injection. The latter approach more nearly to the true Diesel, both in mechanical construction, and thermodynamic cycle.

The term "solid" often gives a wrong impression, because the oil is not injected in a solid form nor in a solid stream. In fact, the very opposite is aimed at.

The terms "airless-injection, compression-ignition" or "airless-injection assisted compression-ignition" appear to comprehend the principal features of the main types, but these are cumbersome titles.

Another term coming into use is that of "cold-starting." A cold-starting oil engine is one which does not require a blow-lamp or heater to be applied to a portion of the combustion chamber before the engine can fire.

Cold-starting engines are usually of the medium-compression airless-injection class, but Messrs. Vickers-Petter manufacture an engine which is cold starting and has low compression. It operates on the two-stroke cycle.

132. The Diesel Engine. This engine is unique in many ways. It was the outcome of experiments by Dr. Rudolf Diesel, and was originally intended to use coaldust in the cylinders and work on the Carnot Cycle. So great were the difficulties, that both these ideas were abandoned very early. The Carnot Cycle gives very low mean effective pressures, no matter what the maximum pressures may be, and consequently a massive engine would be needed for but low power. To overcome this difficulty, Diesel conceived the idea of complete adiabatic compression and combustion at constant pressure. The engine, thus constituted, quickly showed its possibilities and is now manufactured all 'over the world. The first engine made in this country was built in 1897 by Messrs. Mirlees Watson of Glasgow, and is still running.

The essential features of the Diesel engine are :
(1) The oil fuel is ignited by compression alone.
(2) The fuel injection is by means of compressed air.
(3) The combustion is regulated so that there is no appreciable rise in pressure during injection.
(4) The combustion commences as soon as injection begins and continues so long as injection is carried on. The combustion begins immediately the oil reaches the compressed air in the working cylinder.

The compression pressure varies from 500 to 700 lbs. per sq. in., and the blast air pressure from 800 to 1,000 lbs. per sq. in. There is no explosive effect in the cycle, and this feature makes for quiet and smooth running.

The heat is liberated by combustion at constant pressure, and at exhaust opening it is removed at constant volume. Thus the thermal cycle has the essential features of constant pressure heat supply and constant volume heat rejection.

133. The Ideal Diesel Cycle. The cycle described is the four-stroke cycle and is carried out as follows :
(1) Air alone is drawn into the cylinder from A to B (fig. 86).
(2) Air alone is compressed adiabatically to high pressure shown by BC.
(3) At the end of compression, fuel oil is sprayed in by means of compressed air and ignites at once. It continues to burn at constant pressure until fuel supply is cut off at D.
(4) From D the gases resulting from combustion expand adiabatically to the end of the stroke shown by DE.

(5) The pressure at E is now greater than that at B and exhaust occurs E to B, which is equivalent to removing heat at constant volume.

The thermal cycle is complete at B and the mechanical cycle is completed in the fourth stroke B to A. The operations of the thermal cycle are thus :

(1) Adiabatic compression.

(2) Heat supply at constant pressure.

(3) Adiabatic expansion.

(4) Heat rejection at constant volume.

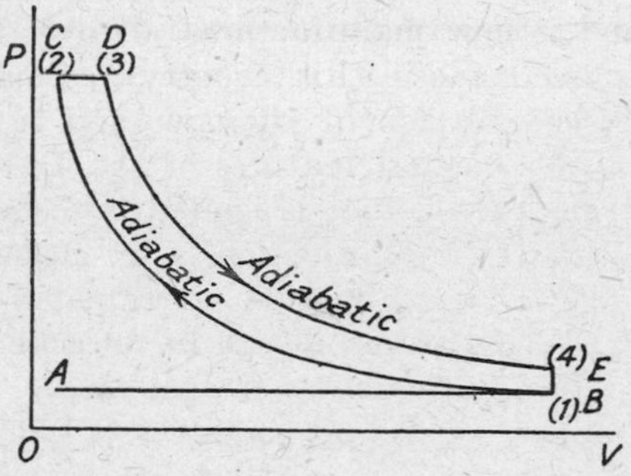

FIG. 86.

The efficiency of the ideal Diesel cycle may be obtained in exactly the same way as the Carnot Cycle efficiency, i.e. by applying the principle of the conservation of energy. Let the figures in fig. 86 become suffixes, and consider 1 lb. of ideal working substance.

Then heat received from C to D = $C_p(T_3 - T_2)$.

 ,, ,, rejected ,, E ,, B = $C_v(T_4 - T_1)$.

∴ Ideal work = Heat supplied − Heat rejected.

∴ Work done per lb. of substance in ideal cycle

$$= C_p(T_3 - T_2) - C_v(T_4 - T_1).$$

Hence the thermal efficiency $= \dfrac{\text{work done}}{\text{heat supplied}}$

$$= \frac{C_p(T_3 - T_2) - C_r(T_4 - T_1)}{C_p(T_3 - T_2)}$$

$$= 1 - \frac{C_v}{C_p}\frac{(T_4 - T_1)}{(T_3 - T_2)}$$

$$= 1 - \frac{1}{\gamma}\left(\frac{T_4 - T_1}{T_3 - T_2}\right) \text{ since } \frac{C_p}{C_v} = \gamma.$$

It can be shown that this efficiency may be written in terms of the ratio of compression, and the cut-off ratio.

Let ρ = cut-off ratio = $\dfrac{V_3}{V_2}$.

n = index of expansion and compression laws
$$PV^n = C.$$

r = ratio of compression = $\dfrac{V_1}{V_2} = \dfrac{V_4}{V_2}$.

Then $\qquad \eta_{ideal} = 1 - \dfrac{1}{r^{n-1}} \cdot \dfrac{1}{\gamma}\left(\dfrac{\rho^n - 1}{\rho - 1}\right).$

When this equation has $n = 1.41$ substituted, it gives the air standard efficiency of the Diesel cycle, which is less than that of the Otto Cycle.

134. Mechanical Considerations. The compression ratio in Diesel engines varies from 14 to 18. It has been mentioned that the blast air is from 800 to 1,000 lbs. per sq. in. pressure, and this is provided by a two-stage or three-stage compressor. This compressor is often built on the engine frame, and serves to provide starting air as well as blast air. The blast air is that which injects and atomizes the oil. The atomization of the oil is secured by smashing it through a series of perforated plates, separated from each other by distance pieces. The perforations are staggered, with the result that the fuel and blast-air form an oil fog, which thoroughly penetrates the high temperature compressed air with considerable turbulence. This brings about complete combustion. The amount of oil admitted is controlled by the fuel pump and by the time of opening of the needle fuel valve, and is always less than the amount which would require all the oxygen in the air charge.

The blast air, expanding through the needle fuel valve, is reduced in temperature by the expansion and therefore cools the compressed air. To maintain a self-ignition temperature in this type of engine, it is necessary to compress through a greater range than would be the case if this cooling did not occur. The air compressor adds to the cost and reduces the mechanical efficiency of the complete engine. It is the custom in this country to take the work expended on the air compressor into account, when calculating the mechanical efficiency of the engine. The air blast contributes a small amount of work to the piston during expansion. A fuel pump is used to pump the oil into the high pressure region occupied by the blast air. The oil rests by gravity upon the bottom of the injection valve chamber until it is blown in by the air. There is not hydraulic continuity in the oil supply system.

The arrangement of the Diesel engine is vertical and there are four valves in the cylinder head. This makes it complicated and considerable trouble arose in the early stages from cracked cylinder heads. With greater knowledge of temperature stresses, and flow and distribution of heat, these difficulties have been overcome. The four valves in the cylinder head are :

(1) The needle fuel valve.
(2) The air inlet, or suction valve.
(3) The exhaust valve.
(4) The air starting valve.

135. Valve Setting in Four-stroke and Two-stroke Engines. Admission of the oil starts from 1° to 2° before dead centre and continues for about 15° to 20° of crank angle movement in the working stroke. Typical valve setting diagrams for four-stroke and two-stroke Diesel engines are shown in figs. 87 and 88 respectively.

136. Cycles used in Heavy Oil Engines. Heavy-oil engines are built to work on the two-stroke or four-stroke cycle. They are also made for single-acting or double-acting operation. The Diesel engine is sometimes constructed to work double-acting, but more frequently is of the single-acting four-stroke type.

137. Methods of Starting. Small units of the low compression class may be started by hand as in the case of petrol engines. When this is done, oil of lower flash point than that of the normal fuel is often used until the

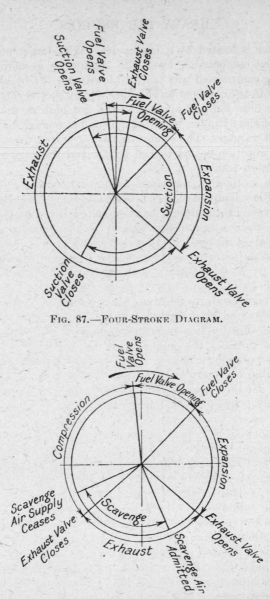

Fuel Valve Opens
Suction Valve Opens
Exhaust Valve Closes
Fuel Valve Opening
Fuel Valve Closes
Exhaust
Suction
Expansion
Suction Valve Closes
Exhaust Valve Opens

FIG. 87.—FOUR-STROKE DIAGRAM.

Fuel Valve Opens
Fuel Valve Opening
Fuel Valve Closes
Compression
Expansion
Scavenge Air Supply Ceases
Exhaust Valve Closes
Scavenge
Exhaust
Scavenge Air Admitted
Exhaust Valve Opens

FIG. 88.—TWO-STROKE DIAGRAM.

cylinder is heated by a few cycles. With larger units in the low compression class, the starting is accomplished (1) by compressed air, (2) by blow-lamp, (3) by electric heater in the combustion chamber, (4) by special cartridge.

The blow-lamp is applied to the hot bulb or uncooled part of the cylinder, until the spot is hot enough to ignite the oil vapour. The engine is then " barred over " and when injection occurs the oil ignites and the engine commences to run.

This method is sometimes modified by using a lighter oil. Blow lamps have often been a source of trouble, but improvements in design have obviated the difficulties.

The electric heater acts exactly as the blow-lamp, but the heat is supplied by electrical means.

Starting by cartridge is a method peculiar to the engine made by Messrs. Petters, Ltd., of Yeovil. It consists of a tube containing a special preparation, which burns in much the same way as a fuse when ignited. The preparation is lighted by an ordinary match and is then screwed into the hot bulb or vaporizer opposite the oil jets. One or two turns of the engine starts the ignition.

A compression relief valve is also used with smaller units to enable the starting to be done more readily.

The medium and high compression oil engines are invariably started by compressed air. The air is used for a few cycles to store up energy in the flywheel and the oil is sprayed in. In multicylinder engines, the cylinders are brought into action one or two at a time. With small engines of this kind, such as are now being used for road vehicles, all cylinders, except one, are cut out. Sufficient energy is then given to the flywheel by hand to cause the one cylinder to fire. When this takes place, as it does after a few quick turns, the other cylinders are brought into action one by one.

The compressed air may be provided by means of :

(a) hand driven compressors for small units,

(b) compressors driven by the engine itself,

(c) separately driven compressors.

P

The last method is most common in marine oil engines, where the compressed air is also used for manœuvring.

In the Diesel air injection engines, the air compressor is mounted on the main frame of the engine, and is driven by it. Starting this engine requires air reservoirs which must be filled by hand at first starting, or if at any time they are allowed to become empty.

138. Governing Oil Engines. Oil engines are usually governed by arranging that the suction valve of the fuel pump shall be held open by levers under the control of the governor. At light loads the valve may be kept open for almost the whole pump stroke. This method is generally known as the "spill" method, since the oil is "spilled" back to the sump. Very often the spill valve is kept quite separate from the pump suction valve. The amount of oil going to the engine is thus regulated according to the power demand. Refinements in the governing of Diesel engines include, (a) control of the fuel valve opening and (b) blast pressure control. This is reduced as the load diminishes in order to secure good combustion at all loads. The centrifugal governor controls a throttle on the compressor suction.

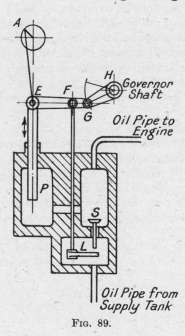

FIG. 89.

The general principle of a simple spill valve will be understood by reference to the diagram, fig. 89. A is the rotating shaft which drives the pump plunger. EG represents a lever which may oscillate about either E or G. F is a point between E and G, to which is connected a light spindle with lever L. The end of the lever is under the stem of the suction valve S. The shaft H is under the control of the governor. It will be evident that as E moves up and down with G fixed, the lever will lift and drop the suction valve. When G moves up under the control of the governor, the suction valve will seat later, with the result that less of the pump stroke will be effective, and a less amount of oil will reach the spray nozzles. The pump stroke is generally much longer than is necessary to deliver the full amount of oil needed at full engine load. This lends itself to better governing.

Another method is to make the governor alter the stroke of the pump and so vary the oil supply to suit the load on the engine.

139. Fuel Consumption. The oil consumption in a good type of heavy oil engine is as low as 0·34 lbs. of good Diesel oil per B.H.P. per hour, and the thermal efficiency is as high as 36 per cent. in the Diesel engine, and about 30 per cent. in the low compression engine.

With the " Still " combined internal combustion and steam engine, the thermal efficiency is as high as 41 per cent.

The advantages of heavy oil engines are as follows :
(1) Being efficient and using cheap fuel they produce power at low cost.
(2) They occupy small space per unit power output.
(3) They require very little in the way of auxiliary plant.
(4) They constitute a self-contained unit.
(5) Fire risk is very small.
(6) The fuel is easily stored and transported.
(7) They are equally efficient in large and small powers.

The disadvantages are :
(1) high initial cost per unit of power, and
(2) restricted output per cylinder, thus requiring a large number of cylinders to produce a moderately large power.

140. Typical Indicator Diagrams. Fig. 90 shows the diagram from a four-stroke oil engine of the hot-bulb type.

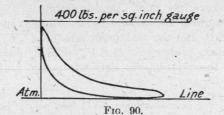

FIG. 90.

Compression ratio 9·32.
Cylinder size 10″ dia. × 18″ stroke.
Speed 260 revs. per min.
Fig. 91. shows a diagram from an airless injection engine with medium compression.

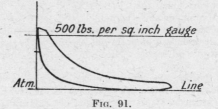

FIG. 91.

Compression ratio 10·5.
Cylinder size 5½″ dia. × 7½″ stroke.
Speed 600 revs. per min. on a four-stroke cycle.
Fig. 92 shows a diagram from a Diesel engine, air injection.

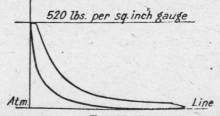

FIG. 92.

Compression ratio 16. Cylinder size $2'-9\frac{7}{8}'' \times 4'-11''$ stroke.

Speed 94 revs. per min. Double-acting.

As the diagrams are calibrated, the student may work out the M.E.P. and the maximum pressures. By writing the ratio, max. pressure $\div$ M.E.P., he will obtain some idea as to the relationship between power and engine forces.

EXAMPLES XVII

1. What is the distinguishing feature of the heavy oil engine ?

2. What do you understand by the term "high compression" as applied to oil engines ?

3. State briefly the principal features of the "low compression" crude oil engines. By what name is the engine often referred to ?

4. "It is not a simple matter to classify heavy oil engines." Explain this.

5. What are the characteristic features of the Diesel engine ?

6. Describe the four-stroke Diesel Cycle, and give an approximate valve timing for this engine.

7. Explain the terms, atomization, penetration, and turbulence.

8. Sketch the indicator diagram which you would expect to obtain from a two-stroke oil engine. Also add a suitable timing diagram for this type of engine.

9. Discuss briefly the suitability of the terms : Semi-Diesel, Solid Injection, and Airless Injection, to describe oil engines.

10. What methods of starting heavy oil engines are in use ? Briefly describe one method. What do you understand by the term "cold starting" ?

11. The weight of air charge in a heavy oil engine is 0·5 lbs. and 0·02 lb. of oil of calorific value 10,000 C.H.U. per lb. is injected. The compression temperature is 500° C. absolute. Find the final temperature. Take $C_p = 0.24$ and assume that combustion is at constant pressure.

12. If the combustion in the engine of question 11 occurs at constant volume, what would be the final temperature ? $C_v = .17$.

13. The compression ratio in a Diesel engine is 16, and the initial temperature of the air charge at the commencement of compression is 80° C. by thermometer. Find the temperature at the end of compression, (a) when the value of n in the compression law is 1·4, (b) when n is 1·3.

14. The volume ratio $\dfrac{\text{volume at fuel cut-off}}{\text{volume at end of compression}}$ is 1·8 for the above engine. Find the temperature at cut-off in both cases (a) and (b).

15. Find the expansion ratio for the engine in exercises 13 and 14. Using this value, find the temperature of the gases in the cylinder at the end of the expansion.

Take $n = 1 \cdot 3$ throughout.

16. The temperature required to ensure the rapid combustion of a given fuel oil is 600° C. absolute. Find the compression ratio (a) when $n = 1 \cdot 3$, (b) when $n = 1 \cdot 4$. Take the initial temperature at commencement of compression as 15° C.

17. Calculate the ideal efficiency of a Diesel engine, compression ratio 18, and cut-off ratio $2 \cdot 133$.

18. Describe any method of governing oil engines.

CHAPTER XVIII

EFFICIENCIES

141. Introduction. The cost of power is an important item in the expenses of a manufacturing company, and it receives very careful attention when engines are to be installed. The cost may be divided into two parts, (a) the overhead charges, (b) the cost of running.

A great part of the cost of running is due to cost of fuel, and it is in this connection that the efficiencies of the engine become important. In this book we are not dealing with overhead or staff charges ; they are mentioned to call attention to the fact that the cost of fuel is not the only item to be considered when calculating power costs.

The user can afford to pay more for a highly efficient engine than for one of moderate efficiency, particularly when large power units are required. Each case must be examined on its merits and the annual fuel charges must be taken with the overhead charges, when deciding which engine will provide the cheapest power.

The cost of fuel per unit of energy output is intimately connected with the efficiency of the engine, and thus the efficiency becomes a very important commercial figure.

142. Efficiencies. There are several efficiencies to be considered for any engine, but no difficulty should arise if it is clearly recognized that any efficiency is a ratio.

The following efficiencies are to be dealt with—
(1) The Mechanical Efficiency.
(2) The Absolute Thermal Efficiency or Thermal Efficiency.
(3) The Standard Thermal Efficiency or Ideal Cycle Efficiency.

(4) The Efficiency Ratio.

(5) The Brake Thermal Efficiency.

In the following definitions all quantities involved are in the same units and for the same period of time.

143. Mechanical Efficiency. The mechanical efficiency of any engine is the ratio

$$\frac{\text{Work available at the engine coupling}}{\text{Work done upon the pistons}}.$$

In calculating the efficiency, these quantities may be taken for any period of time which is the same in both cases, and the quantities may both be expressed in foot-lbs. or heat units.

A convenient basis for calculation is the power unit, because, if the work be expressed in foot-lbs. per minute in numerator and denominator then

Mechanical Efficiency

$$= \frac{\text{Work done at coupling in ft.-lbs. per minute}}{\text{Work done in cylinders in ft.-lbs per minute}}.$$

Dividing numerator and denominator by 33,000, we have

$$\eta_{\text{mechanical}} = \frac{\text{Brake Horse Power}}{\text{Indicated Horse Power}} = \frac{\text{B.H.P.}}{\text{I.H.P.}}$$

This last is not the definition of the efficiency, but the work ratio and the power ratio are equal. It is to be noted that the work available at the coupling is that which would be absorbed on the brake, if a brake dynamometer were applied. The engine only works against a brake during test, but the mechanical efficiency may be determined when the engine is in useful service by means of suitable devices, like a transmission dynamometer of the torsion type. Such a dynamometer is not a brake, but it enables brake horse power data to be taken.

144. Thermal Efficiency. The (Absolute) Thermal Efficiency of any engine is the ratio,

$$\frac{\text{Work done by fluid on the piston (or equivalent)}}{\text{Heat supplied to the engine}}.$$

This is the thermal efficiency of the actual engine and

is sometimes referred to as the Indicated Thermal Efficiency. It is convenient to take both quantities on the basis of unit quantity of substance supplied to the engine, or, to take both quantities in heat units for a period of one hour.

Thus, thermal efficiency

$$= \frac{\text{Work done in cylinder per lb. of substance}}{\text{Heat supplied to engine per lb. of substance}}.$$

This can be done, since the time must be the same in the case of the quantities in both the numerator and denominator.

145. Standard Thermal Efficiency. This is the efficiency of the ideal cycle, which is adopted as the standard of comparison for the particular engine under consideration. In the case of a steam engine or turbine it is the Rankine Cycle, whilst for internal combustion engines it is the Air Standard Cycle (see Arts. 48 and 95).

The Efficiency Ratio is the ratio $\dfrac{\text{Thermal Efficiency}}{\text{Standard Efficiency}}$.

It gives a true measure of the merit of the engine performance, and is an important figure in design.

146. Brake Thermal Efficiency. This is the ratio

$$\frac{\text{Work done at the engine coupling or brake}}{\text{Heat supplied to the engine}}.$$

It is less than the thermal efficiency, because the numerator in this case is less than in the case of the thermal efficiency. This is due to the fact that some of the work done in the cylinder must be expended in overcoming engine friction.

It may be written as the product of mechanical efficiency and thermal efficiency.

Brake thermal efficiency

$$= \frac{\text{Work done at coupling}}{\text{Work done in cylinders}} \times \frac{\text{Work done in cylinders}}{\text{Heat supplied to engine}}$$

$$= \text{Mechanical efficiency} \times \text{Thermal efficiency}.$$

147. Consumption. The consumption of an engine may be defined as the amount of substance supplying the energy taken by the engine per hour. It depends upon the power of the engine and the efficiency. The substance which supplies energy to the engine may be steam, gas, oil, petrol, or coal, and the units will be in accordance with the nature of the substance.

The *Consumption Rate* of an engine is defined as the amount of substance supplied per hour divided by the number of horse power units.

It is stated in lbs. or cubic feet per horse power in one hour, and may be expressed on the basis of either the indicated or brake horse power.

148. The foregoing definitions may now be written as formulæ :

Let P_i = Indicated horse power.

P_B = Brake horse power.

S = Total weight or volume of substance taken by the engine per hour.

E = Heat energy supplied per lb. or cubic foot as most convenient.

η_A = Absolute thermal efficiency of actual engine.

η_B = Brake thermal efficiency of actual engine.

η_s = Standard thermal efficiency of ideal cycle.

η_r = Efficiency ratio for the engine.

C_i = Consumption rate of the engine on I.H.P. basis.

C_B = Consumption rate of the engine on B.H.P. basis.

Indicated thermal efficiency

$$= \frac{P_i \times 33,000 \times 60 \text{ ft.-lbs./hour}}{S \times E \times 1,400 \text{ ft.-lbs./hour}}.$$

$$= \frac{(P_i \times 1,414) \text{ C.H.U. per hour}}{(S \times E) \text{ C.H.U. per hour}}.$$

Note that 1,414 C.H.U. is the heat equivalent of one horse power hour.

Now
$$\frac{S}{P_i} = C_i.$$

∴ Indicated thermal efficiency $= \dfrac{1,414}{C_i \times E}.$

The denominator of this expression is called the *heat consumption* of the engine.

In the case of a gas engine, petrol engine, or oil engine, E is the calorific value of the gas, petrol or oil. With a steam engine or turbine, E is the difference between the heat in the steam at the engine stop valve and the heat of the liquid at feed temperature, both being reckoned from 0° C.

Thus $E = H_1 - h_f$

∴ η_A (for a steam engine or turbine) $= \dfrac{1,414}{C_i \times (H_1 - h_f)}$

$(H_1 - h_f) =$ heat supplied per lb. of steam.

Transposing the above equation, we have

$$C_i = \frac{1,414}{\eta_A \times E} \text{ lbs. (or cu. ft.) per H.P. per hour.}$$

The product in the denominator is the work done per lb. or cubic foot of substance supplied.

Brake Thermal Efficiency

$$= \frac{P_B \times 33,000 \times 60 \text{ ft.-lbs./hour}}{S \times E \times 1,400 \text{ ft.-lbs./hour}}$$

$$= \frac{P_B \times 1,414}{S \times E}$$

but $\dfrac{S}{P_B} = C_B.$ ∴ $\eta_B = \dfrac{1,414}{C_B \times E}.$

The value of C_B is greater than C_i, because P_B has a less numerical value than P_i whilst S is the same.

$$S = P_B \times C_B = P_i \times C_i.$$

The Efficiency Ratio $= \dfrac{\eta_A}{\eta_s} = \eta_r$

$$= \frac{\dfrac{\text{Actual work done per lb. (or unit time)}}{\text{Heat supplied}}}{\dfrac{\text{Ideal work done per lb. (or unit time)}}{\text{Heat supplied}}}.$$

Since the heat supplied in the standard cycle is the same as that supplied in the actual engine, we have

$$\text{Efficiency ratio} = \frac{\text{Actual work done per lb.}}{\text{Ideal work done per lb.}}$$

EXAMPLE. The thermal efficiency of a steam turbine is found by test to be 0·32, and the Rankine Cycle efficiency between the pressure limits of the turbine is 0·4. Find the efficiency ratio.

$$\eta_r = \frac{\eta_A}{\eta_s} = \frac{0·32}{0·4}$$

$$= 0·8 \text{ or } 80 \text{ per cent.}$$

EXAMPLE. The steam supplied to an engine between certain pressure limits gives a Rankine work per lb. of 160 C.H.U. Find the consumption of an engine of 2,000 H.P. if its efficiency ratio is 0·65.

$$\text{Efficiency ratio} = \frac{\text{Actual efficiency}}{\text{Standard efficiency}}$$

$$= \frac{\text{Actual work per lb.}}{\text{Ideal Rankine work per lb.}}$$

$\therefore$ Actual work per lb. $= 0·65 \times 160$

$\qquad\qquad\qquad\qquad = 104$ C.H.U.

Work done per hour by 1 H.P. (in heat units) $= 1,414$ C.H.U.

$\therefore$ Steam required in one hour for each H.P. $= \dfrac{1,414}{104}$

$\qquad\qquad\qquad\qquad\qquad = 13·6$ lbs.

$\therefore$ Total steam required by engine per hour $= 13·6 \times 2,000$

$\qquad\qquad\qquad\qquad\qquad\qquad\qquad = 27,200$ lbs.

EXAMPLE. An oil engine uses 3·6 lbs. of oil per hour of calorific value 10,000 C.H.U. per lb. The indicated horse power is 6·12 and the brake horse power is 4·6. Find the indicated and brake thermal efficiencies, and the consumption rates per I.H.P. and per B.H.P. per hour.

Indicated thermal efficiency $= \dfrac{\text{Work done in cylinders}}{\text{Heat supplied}}$

$$= \dfrac{1,414}{C_i \times E}$$

$C_i = \dfrac{3 \cdot 6}{6 \cdot 12}$ lbs. per I.H.P. per hour

$= 0 \cdot 588$

$\therefore \eta_A = \dfrac{1,414}{0 \cdot 588 \times 10,000} = 0 \cdot 24$ or 24 per cent.

$C_B = \dfrac{3 \cdot 6}{4 \cdot 6} = 0 \cdot 783$ lbs. per B.H.P. per hour.

$\therefore \eta_B = \dfrac{1,414}{0 \cdot 783 \times 10,000} = 0 \cdot 181$ or 18·1 per cent.

149. Relationship between Power and Total Steam Consumption.

The weight of steam per hour taken by an engine increases as the power increases up to the maximum power of the engine. If the engine is governed by throttling the steam, the relationship between *power* and *total steam per hour* is given by a law of the straight line form.

This is known as Willans' Law, because Willans was the first to point out the relationship. It can be shown from theoretical considerations that the law is a straight line law for steam engines, throttle-governed.

If the graph of power and total steam per hour be plotted, the resulting line is known as Willans' Line. Willans' Lines may be drawn for steam turbines, gas engines, oil engines and power stations, but in some of these cases the line is not quite straight. These lines are often drawn for coal as well as for steam in the case of power stations. When drawn for a period of a week or a year they are known as " Parsons " Lines.

Let S = total steam per hour.

P = power developed in cylinders.

a = a constant.

b = a constant.

The Willans Law is $S = aP + b$.

The constant " b " may be looked upon as a constant drain on the boiler, due to condensation and leakage which would occur even if the power fell to zero.

For the fuel relationship,

Let F = fuel used per hour.
   P = power developed.
   A = a constant.
   B = a constant.
Then F = AP + B approximately.

The constant " B " in this case represents the coal

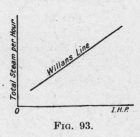

Fig. 93.

used to maintain pressure in the boilers even when the engines are not taking steam. It may be looked upon as the fuel consumption equivalent to heat leakage from the boilers and to drive feed pumps, when the plant is at full pressure but supplying no steam to the engine.

Fig. 93 is a typical graph.

EXAMPLE. The Willans line for an engine is given by S = 21P + 280 where P = the indicated horse power. Find the steam consumption per hour when the power is 300. What is the consumption rate per indicated horse-power-hour ?

$$\text{Total steam per hour} = 21P + 280$$
$$= 21 \times 300 + 280$$
$$= 6,580 \text{ lbs.}$$

$$\text{Steam per horse power per hour} = \frac{6,580}{300}$$
$$= 21 \cdot 93 \text{ lbs.}$$

The steam rate could be obtained in the form of a law by dividing through by P, thus

$$\text{Steam consumption rate} = 21 + \frac{280}{P}$$
$$= 21 + \frac{280}{300}$$
$$= 21 \cdot 93 \text{ lbs. per I.H.P. per hour.}$$

The curve of steam consumption rate plotted on I.H.P. base is shown in fig. 94. When this curve is falling with increasing horse power, the corresponding efficiency curve is rising. It is thus possible to plot the form of efficiency curve without actually evaluating more than one efficiency, and this only for the purpose of obtaining the plotting scale.

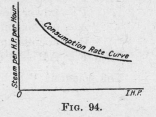

FIG. 94.

EXAMPLE. A test of an oil engine gave a consumption of 14 lbs. of oil per hour when the horse power was 50 I.H.P. When the horse power was 150 the consumption was 45 lbs. per hour. Assuming the consumption to follow Willans' Law for powers higher than 30 I.H.P., find the value of the constants and calculate the consumption rate at 80 I.H.P. and at 120 I.H.P.

$$S = aP + b.$$

At 150 I.H.P. $45 = a \times 150 + b.$

At 50 I.H.P. $14 = a \times 50 + b$

Subtracting, $31 = 100a$

$\therefore \ a = 0·31$

To find $b.$ $14 = 50 \times 0·31 + b$

$b = -15·5 + 14$

$= -1·5$

Hence the law is $S = 0·31 \ P - 1·5.$

The negative sign for b does not imply that there is zero consumption about 5 I.H.P. It signifies that the line is not straight right down to zero horse power. The line in this case would curve upwards from zero and become straight at about 30 I.H.P.

Consumption per hour at 80 I.H.P. $= 0·31 \times 80 - 1·5$

$= 24·8 - 1·5$

$= 23·3$ lbs. of oil.

Consumption per hour at 120 I.H.P. $= 0·31 \times 120 - 1·5$

$= 37·2 - 1·5$

$= 35·7$ lbs. of oil.

Oil consumption rate at 80 I.H.P. $= \dfrac{23·3}{80}$

$= 0·291$ lbs. per H.P. hour.

Oil consumption rate at 120 I.H.P. $= \dfrac{35·7}{120}$

$= 0·297$ lbs. per H.P. per hour.

EXAMPLE. The Willans Law for the above engine in terms of oil per brake horse power per hour is $S = 0·362P_B + 7.$ Find the consumption per hour at 70 B.H.P. and, using the data of the preceding example, find the mechanical efficiency at this load.

$$\text{Oil per hour at 70 B.H.P.} = 0.362 \times 70 + 7$$
$$= 25.34 + 7$$
$$= 32.34 \text{ lbs.}$$

To find the I.H.P. when this is the oil consumption per hour, we apply the Willans equation in terms of I.H.P.

$$S = 0.31 \text{ P} - 1.5$$
$$32.34 = 0.31 \text{ P} - 1.5$$
$$0.31 \text{ P} = 33.84$$
$$\text{P} = 109 \text{ I.H.P.}$$

$$\therefore \text{ Mechanical Efficiency} = \frac{70}{109}$$
$$= 64.2 \text{ per cent.}$$

150. Cylinder Condensation and Wall Action. The presence of water in the cylinder of a steam engine has a great effect upon the steam consumption rate, and probably the greatest improvements in engine efficiencies have been due to elimination of water from the cylinder. The cylinder receives steam from the pipe-range at its highest temperature, and rejects it at its lowest temperature to exhaust. The temperature of the cylinder walls (including cylinder cover and piston surface) fluctuates over a very limited range between these limits, since heat is constantly being exchanged between them and the steam.

Let us consider a quantity of dry steam entering the cylinder. Its walls must be cooler than the steam, hence, a portion of it condenses, giving heat to, and raising the temperature of the cylinder. Owing to this condensation, extra steam must be taken in by the engine. At cut-off there is a film of moisture on the cylinder walls. Expansion now begins which we may suppose to be approximately adiabatic. Heat energy must, therefore, be converted into mechanical work, and hence further condensation occurs.

In the earlier part of expansion the steam continues to give up heat to the walls freshly exposed by the advancing piston. These processes go on during expansion until a point is reached at which the pressure has fallen to such a value that the moisture on the walls can begin to re-evaporate. In doing so, heat equivalent to the latent heat is extracted from the cylinder walls. During the earlier part of the expansion, then, we have condensation taking place due to two causes, and during the latter part of the expansion, there is evaporation at the walls, and condensation in the body of the steam due to the adiabatic expansion. During this latter stage the walls are giving up heat taken from the steam previously. When the exhaust opens, a large proportion of the steam passes out taking with it the heat it contains, and it should be noted that some of this heat has been extracted from the cylinder walls and had originally been taken from the steam during admission and the earlier part of the expansion. The pressure is now very low, either atmospheric, or condenser pressure, and if any water is left in the cylinder, evaporation becomes very vigorous. During this stroke evaporation will continue as long as moisture is available, with consequent cooling of the walls at a rapid rate. The amount of cooling during this period very largely decides the temperature of the walls which will meet the incoming steam at the beginning of the next stroke, and therefore, the amount of condensation which will occur. If there is not enough moisture at the beginning of the exhaust stroke for this evaporation to continue throughout it, then the cooling of the walls will cease when there is no more water to evaporate. If, however, there is ample moisture, this cooling may go on throughout the whole of the exhaust stroke, with consequent heavy condensation at the next admission of steam.

If, as we have just supposed, the steam supply is dry, it is very probable that there would not be sufficient moisture at the end of the expansion for the evaporation to continue throughout the whole of the exhaust stroke, unless there was a very big expansion ratio in the cylinder, when, of course, the amount of condensation during the expansion would be large.

If the steam supply is wet, all the above processes will operate in exactly the same way. The water in the wet steam will be additional to that produced in the way just described, and will be present at the beginning of the exhaust stroke. Evaporation on that stroke will thus be prolonged and may continue throughout the whole of it. Hence, in such a case, initial condensation becomes a maximum, and the amount of extra steam required to make up that condensation is a maximum. The steam used per stroke is increased without any more work being done in the cylinder, and hence the consumption rate is greater. In bad cases, this process builds up and may bring the engine to a standstill.

The reader should carefully note the following facts :

(1) If steam entering the cylinder is condensed and then re-evaporates on the exhaust stroke, the amount of heat drawn from the walls is less than that absorbed by the cylinder metal during condensation.

(2) The cooling of the cylinder walls is caused by the evaporation, during exhaust, of the water which entered as wetness in the steam, and that which condensed during expansion. This is because such water is present, without having given any heat to the cylinder metal. It is this second phenomenon which is the more serious.

151. Wall Temperature. The actual phenomena are very complex and the foregoing may be taken as a statement of the main principles involved.

For any point on the wall surface a diagram of steam and wall temperatures may be drawn on a time or cycle base. The fluctuation of temperature of wall is very small compared with the fluctuation of steam temperature, and study of the diagram will show that the period, during which the wall is hotter than the steam, is longer than that in which the steam is hotter than the wall. Thus the water has ample time to evaporate. The shaded area is known as the condensation area, and, in suitable units, is a measure of the amount of steam which can condense on one square foot of surface at the chosen point. Such a diagram is due to the researches of Callendar and Nicholson in 1895, and is shown in fig. 95.

152. Reduction of Cylinder Condensation. The alternate condensation and re-evaporation may be greatly checked by any of the following means. Improvement in steam consumption follows,

(1) the provision of effective cylinder drains,

(2) the lagging and jacketing of the cylinders (steam jackets are most effective when applied to the cylinder covers but they involve mechanical troubles),

(3) keeping the expansion ratio small in one cylinder,

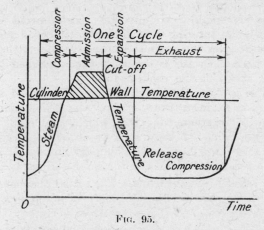

FIG. 95.

(4) compounding the expansion,

(5) using quick revolution engines,

(6) superheating the steam supplied.

Lagging tends to prevent direct loss of heat by radiation, but this loss alone is not serious.

The number of expansions which may be permitted is limited by the effect of wall action. Earlier cut-off involves wetter steam at the end of expansion and longer time for re-evaporation. Hence, long ranges of expansion fail to increase efficiency, owing to the steam taken from the boiler to compensate for the heat removed by re-evaporation.

Quick revolution checks the wall action because there is less time for the steam to condense and evaporate. Any water formed by the adiabatic expansion is flung out at exhaust, before it can drain heat from the metal.

Even moderate superheats, say up to 50° C., will effect considerable economy in steam consumption. The economy in steam is much more than would be indicated by consideration of the Rankine Cycle. This is because superheated steam does not readily give up heat, since the heat conduction from dry steam to dry metal is much less than with wet steam. Hence, the action of the cylinder metal is made to approach nearer to the state of perfection assumed in the Rankine Cycle, consequently, the engine is thermally more perfect in its action when superheated steam is used.

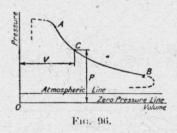

Fig. 96.

153. Weight of Steam at any Point on a P–V Diagram. The calculation of this weight depends upon the relationship between specific volume and total volume (Art. 28).

Let AB, in fig. 96, represent the expansion line for the steam in the cylinder. The cut-off point is at A and the release point at B, consequently with perfect valves and piston there is no leakage of steam from the cylinder between A and B. Suppose that it is required to determine the weight of steam present at the point C. This point may be anywhere on the curve AB, but its exact position must be stated. It is usual to state the position of the chosen point in terms of a fraction of the stroke. The weight of steam at C occupies a total volume V and is at a pressure p lbs. per sq. in. absolute. The volume V includes the clearance space and is not merely the volume swept by the piston up to the point C.

Let W = weight in lbs. of steam present at C.

V_s = specific volume of steam in cu. ft. per lb. corresponding to pressure p.

V = total volume in cu. ft. occupied by the weight W lbs.

V = Clearance volume + volume swept by piston to point C.

Weight × specific volume = total volume.

$$\therefore \ W \times V_s = V$$

$$W = \frac{V}{V_s}.$$

The weight is called the "indicated weight" because it is calculated by means of data obtained from a curve drawn by an indicator, and to distinguish it from the total weight of substance present when the steam is wet.

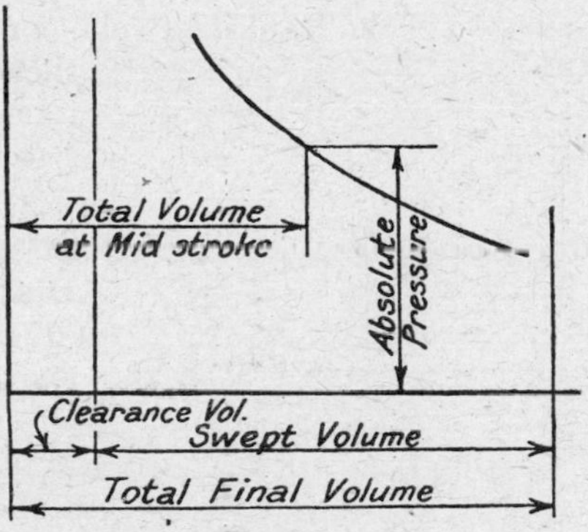

EXAMPLE. The cylinder of a steam engine is 12 ins. diameter and the stroke is 24 ins. Cut-off occurs before mid-stroke, and the pressure at mid-stroke

FIG. 97.

is found from an indicator diagram to be 52·56 lbs. per sq. in. absolute.

The clearance volume is 7 per cent. of the swept volume, and the specific volume of dry steam at 52·56 lbs. per sq. in. is 8·123 cu. ft. per lb. Find the indicated weight of steam at mid-stroke.

$$\text{Swept volume} = \frac{0\cdot7854 \times 12 \times 12 \times 24}{1,728}$$

$$= 0\cdot7854 \times 2$$

$$= 1\cdot571 \text{ cu. ft.}$$

$$\text{Clearance volume} = \frac{7}{100} \times 1\cdot571$$

$$= 0\cdot11 \text{ cu. ft.}$$

Total volume at mid-stroke (fig. 97)

$$= \frac{1\cdot571}{2} + 0\cdot11 = 0\cdot7854 + 0\cdot11$$

$$= 0\cdot8954 \text{ cu. ft.}$$

$$\therefore \text{ Weight of steam present} = \frac{0\cdot8954}{8\cdot123} \text{ lbs.}$$

$$= 0\cdot11 \text{ lb.}$$

154. Indicated Cylinder Feed. The engine takes a certain weight of steam from the boiler each stroke. When this quantity is calculated from the indicator diagram, it

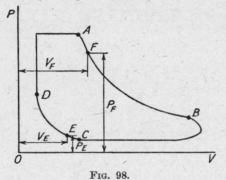

is called the indicated cylinder feed. The previous article shows how to calculate the weight of steam indicated as being in the cylinder at any moment.

If we thus calculate the weights immediately after cut-off and just after compression begins, then, the difference of these quantities will be the indicated cylinder feed.

Fig. 98 shows a complete indicator diagram. The steam weight at A is sensibly the same as that at F. The point F is taken just below A, which is the cut-off point, in order to be certain that the steam supply has ceased. Steam weight at C is sensibly the same as that at E. The point E is taken to ensure that exhaust has stopped.

Weight of steam fed to cylinder per stroke = weight at F — weight shut in clearance space at E.

$$\therefore \text{ Cylinder feed} = \frac{V_F}{V_{sF}} - \frac{V_E}{V_{sE}}$$

where V_{sF} = specific volume at pressure P_F,
and $V_{sE} =$ „ „ „ „ P_E.

EXAMPLE. Calculate the cylinder feed per stroke and per minute for the engine to which the following data relate.

Pressure of steam just after cut-off = 99·56 lbs. per sq. in. from diagram.

Pressure of steam just after closing exhaust = 17·07 lbs. per sq. in. from diagram.

Cylinder, 24 ins. diameter × 48 ins. stroke. Cut-off at ¼ stroke.

Clearance is 10 per cent. of swept volume. Compression begins at 0·88 of back stroke. Speed 80 revs. per min. double-acting.

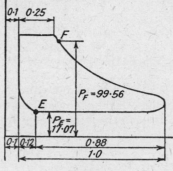

FIG. 99.

Total volume at F = vol. swept at F + clearance.

$$\text{Volume swept at full stroke} = \frac{0·7854 \times 24 \times 24 \times 48}{1,728}$$

$$= 0·7854 \times 16$$

$$= 12·56 \text{ cu. ft.}$$

$$\text{Clearance volume} = 0·1 \times 12·56 = 1·256 \text{ cu. ft.}$$

$$\text{Total volume at F} = \frac{12·56}{4} + 1·256$$

$$= 3·142 + 1·256$$

$$= 4·398 \text{ cu. ft.}$$

From steam tables the specific volume at 99·56 lbs. per sq. in. = 4·46 cu. ft.

$$\therefore \text{Weight indicated at F} = \frac{4·398}{4·46}$$

$$= 0·987 \text{ lb. weight.}$$

Total volume at E = volume of back stroke still to be completed + clearance

$$= 0·12 \times 12·56 + 1·256$$

$$= 1·507 + 1·256 = 2·763 \text{ cu. ft.}$$

From tables, specific volume at 17·07 lbs. per sq. in = 23·25 cu. ft.

$$\therefore \text{Weight indicated at E} = \frac{2·763}{23·25} = 0·119 \text{ lb.}$$

$$\therefore \text{Cylinder feed per stroke} = 0·987 - 0·119$$

$$= 0·868 \text{ lb.}$$

Cylinder feed per min. = cylinder feed per stroke × no. of strokes per min.

$$= 0·868 \times 2 \times 80$$

$$= 138·9 \text{ lbs. per min.}$$

155. Missing Quantity. This term is used in connection with steam engines to denote the weight of steam which passes through the engine cylinder without being indicated on the diagram. It is missing when the indicator diagram is analysed as in the last worked example.

If an engine is measured, indicated, and its exhaust steam is condensed and measured, it is found that the actual measured condensate is always in excess of the cylinder feed quantity calculated as above. This difference is the missing quantity, and may be expressed

(a) as a fraction or percentage of the feed.

(b) as a weight in lbs. per stroke.

(c) ,, ,,   ,,   ,, ,,   ,, minute or per hour.

Let W_A = actual weight of condensate measured during an engine trial.

N = mean number of revolutions per minute during trial.

t = duration of trial in minutes.

W_I = indicated feed per stroke.

Then we have—

Weight passing through cylinder per stroke

$$= \frac{\text{Total condensate weight measured in time } t}{\text{Total number of strokes made in time } t}$$

$$= \frac{W_A}{2Nt} \text{ (for a double-acting engine).}$$

∴ Then missing quantity per stroke $= \dfrac{W_A}{2Nt} - W_I$.

The missing quantity is due to two causes :

(1) Leakage past valves and piston.

(2) Cylinder condensation.

The former depends upon the mechanical condition of the engine whilst the latter depends upon the action explained in Article 150.

Its value varies widely, being from 25 per cent. of the total steam fed in good engines to as much as 60 per cent. in bad cases.

EXAMPLE. In an engine the measured weight of steam per minute was 490 lbs., the speed 110 revs. per min., and it was double-acting. The volume immediately after cut-off was 4·6 cu. ft. and the pressure at this point was 170 lbs. per sq. in. absolute. The volume immediately after compression had begun was 1·32 cu. ft. and the pressure 50 lbs. per sq. in. absolute. Find the missing quantity in lbs. per min. and as a percentage of the actual cylinder feed.

The volumes given in the question are the total volumes at the points referred to.

Specific volume at 170 lbs. per sq. in. = 2·69 cu. ft.

$$\therefore \text{ Indicated weight at cut-off} = \frac{4\cdot6}{2\cdot69} = 1\cdot71 \text{ lbs.}$$

Specific volume at 50 lbs. per sq. in. = 8·51 cu. ft.

$$\text{Indicated weight after compression begins} = \frac{1\cdot32}{8\cdot51}$$
$$= 0\cdot155 \text{ lbs.}$$

∴ Indicated cylinder feed per stroke = 1·71 − 0·155 = 1·555 lbs.

∴ Weight indicated per minute = 1·555 × 2 × 110
= 342·1 lbs.

Missing quantity per minute = 490 − 342·1
= 147·9 lbs.

Missing quantity as a percentage of actual feed

$$= \frac{147\cdot9}{490} \times 100$$
$$= 30\cdot2 \text{ per cent.}$$

EXAMPLES XVIII

1. Explain what is meant by " Thermal Efficiency " of an engine. An oil engine uses 0·34 lb. of oil per I.H.P. per hour of calorific value 10,100 C.H.U. per lb. What is the thermal efficiency ?

2. The overall efficiency of a power station from coal to electrical energy output is 20 per cent. The average daily output of electrical energy is 120,000 kw. Find the cost of fuel per day of 24 hours if the price of the coal per ton is 15s. Calorific value of the coal is 7,500 C.H.U. per lb.

3. A gas engine has a compression ratio of 3·85 and is supplied with gas of calorific value 240 C.H.U. per cubic foot. Find the gas consumption per H.P. per hour if the efficiency ratio is 0·47.

4. A compression-ignition oil engine gave a fuel consumption of 0·43 lb. per B.H.P. per hour, the fuel having a calorific value of 10,150 C.H.U. per lb. The mechanical efficiency was 0·78. Find the Brake Thermal Efficiency, the Thermal Efficiency and the consumption rate on the I.H.P. basis.

5. The thermal efficiency of a steam turbine is 0·3 and the pressure

at the stop valve is 220 lbs. per sq. in. absolute, the feed temperature being 30° C. Find the steam taken per horse power per hour.

6. Some of the steam admitted to a steam engine cylinder condenses early in the stroke. Why does this condensation take place? Describe briefly three methods of reducing this initial condensation and explain the action in each case. U.E.I.

7. A certain governor-controlled steam engine is known to consume 1,300 lbs. of steam per hour at 40 horse power and 2,900 lbs. of steam per hour at 150 horse power. What would you expect the consumption to be when the engine develops 100 horse power? State and explain the law upon which you base your solution.

U.E.I.

8. Explain clearly, and as concisely as you can, how initial condensation in a steam engine cylinder is affected by, (a) variable rates of expansion, (b) quick revolution, (c) steam-jacketing, (d) superheating, (e) compounding.

What is the cause of re-evaporation? In which cylinder of a compound engine is re-evaporation wasteful? Why is it not so in the other cylinder? U.E.I.

9. A four-cycle gas engine has a cylinder 12 ins. diameter; the stroke is 21 ins.; and the volume of the compression space is 594 cu. ins. The mean pressure as calculated from an indicator diagram is 100 lbs. per sq. in.; the calorific value of the gas is 300 C.H.U. per cu. ft. and the consumption is 990 cu. ft. per hour. There are 110 explosions per min. Find:

(a) the compression ratio;
(b) the thermal efficiency on I.H.P. basis;
(c) the standard air efficiency;
(d) the relative efficiency. U.E.I.

10. State briefly and clearly the meaning of the terms " compounding," " superheating," and " condensing " as applied in steam engine practice, and indicate what effect each of these expedients has upon overall efficiency. U.E.I.

11. Steam at a gauge pressure of 200 lbs. per sq. in. with 110° C. of superheat is supplied to a 12,500 kilowatts generator set. At the exhaust of the motor there is a vacuum of 28·4 ins. What should be the steam consumption per kilowatt-hour and per horse power hour supplied to the generator if the guaranteed thermal efficiency of the motor is 23 per cent.?

Assume the mean specific heat of the superheated steam to be 0·56 and atmospheric pressure 30 in. of mercury or 15 lbs. per sq. in.; also that the temperature of the feed is the temperature corresponding to the vacuum. U.L.C.I.

12. In a steam generator set the steam pressure at the stop valve is 210 lb. per sq. in. absolute and its temperature is 340° C. The pressure of the steam at exhaust is 0·5 lb. per sq. in. absolute and the steam consumption per kilowatt hour is 10·7 lbs. Assuming

the mean specific heat of the superheated steam to be 0·53, find the thermal efficiency of the plant. U.L.C.I.

13. The pressure of steam at an engine stop-valve is 195 lbs. per sq. in. absolute and its temperature is 290° C. The pressure of the steam at the engine exhaust is 3 lbs. per sq. in. absolute. Find the thermal efficiency of the engine when it uses 9·75 lbs. of steam per I.H.P. per hour.

Take the specific heat of superheated steam to be 0·55. U.L.C.I.

14. An internal combustion engine working on the four-stroke cycle and having an explosion every cycle had a cylinder diameter of 12 ins. and a stroke of 18¼ ins. During tests of the engine the following data were taken :

Revs. per min,	.	.	199	203	203	205
M.E.P.—lbs. per sq. in.	.		107	87	60	42
Oil used per hour—lbs.	.		20·7	13·5	10	9·5

Draw graphs of oil used per hour on a base of I.H.P.

U.L.C.I.

15. State what is meant by " Willans' Line." A steam turbine uses 4,720 lbs. of steam per hour when developing 220 horse power and 19,200 lbs. per hour when developing 1,120 horse power. Calculate the probable thermal efficiency of the turbine when developing 900 horse power. Dry saturated steam at 180 lbs. per sq. in. absolute is supplied, and the temperature corresponding to the pressure at the exhaust flange is 52° C. (Total heat of steam at 180 lbs. per sq. in. absolute = 666 C.H.U.) N.C.T.E.C.

16. Obtain an expression for the air standard efficiency of an engine working on the Otto Cycle. A gas engine working on the Otto Cycle has a clearance volume of 0·25 cu. ft. and the volume swept by the piston is 1·25 cu. ft. The engine takes in 10 cu. ft. of gas per min. having a calorific value of 275 C.H.U. per cu. ft. as used, and develops 41 I.H.P. Calculate the thermal efficiency and the efficiency ratio. Ratio of specific heats = 1·4. N.C.T.E.C.

17. Explain why initial condensation occurs during admission to a reciprocating steam engine, and state what methods have been adopted to minimize this condensation. N.C.T.E.C.

18. Calculate the engine thermal efficiency in the case of a steam engine taking steam at 180 lbs. per sq. in. absolute, 0·98 dry, if the temperature of the exhaust steam is 70° C. and the steam consumption is 15 lbs. per horse power hour.

If the coal used has a calorific value of 8,000 C.H.U. per lb. and the consumption is 1·8 lbs. per horse power hour, determine the overall thermal efficiency of the plant. N.C.T.E.C.

19. The condensate from an engine is 4,410 lbs. per hour when the I.H.P. is 210, and 6,520 lbs. per hour when the I.H.P. is 362. Calculate the probable steam consumption when the I.H.P. is 280. State the law on which the solution depends. N.C.T.E.C.

CHAPTER XIX

ENGINE TRIALS

156. Objects of Trials. Engine trials are carried out for the purpose of comparing actual results with theoretical or ideal performance. They are also carried out when the builders have entered into an agreement to guarantee a specified efficiency for the engine or turbine. The tests in this case are made to verify the guaranteed efficiency, in order that bonuses or penalties may be paid. The standard of attainment in these tests is often the consumption rate under specified pressure and vacuum conditions in the case of a steam plant, and with fuel of given calorific value in the case of gas, oil or petrol engines.

Tests have been the direct cause of, and incentive to, the improvement in engines and boilers throughout the period of their development. Many steam engines were built before tests were standardized, but the development of the steam turbine, petrol engine and oil engine has been largely due to the interest taken in the cost of engines, and particularly the cost of running them. This interest created a demand for authentic records of engine performance, which could only be satisfied by exhaustive trials carefully observed and calculated.

Heavy oil engine development in this country has been greatly encouraged by the Royal Agricultural Society in offering prizes for the best and most efficient engines. Makers attach great value to these awards.

157. Results Sought. In a comprehensive trial of any heat engine the following are the principal results sought.

(1) The power developed.

(2) The heat supplied per minute or per hour.

(3) The distribution of this heat. This appears in the heat balance or account.

(4) The efficiency of the engine compared to that of the ideal engine using the generally accepted standard cycle.

These items may now be considered in detail and the equipment necessary will be mentioned.

158. Power Developed. The power may be measured (*a*) by indicator or (*b*) by brake.

The indicator is used to take observations which are necessary to calculate the cylinder power. It can only be used for reciprocating engines. In steam turbines the horse power, corresponding to the I.H.P. of the reciprocating engine, can only be calculated by working back from the measured B.H.P., using the results of tests on bearing losses, disc and drum losses, windage and friction.

The brake measures the work available for use external to the engine itself, and gives the useful power.

159. Heat Supply. The heat supply to the engine is obtained in two stages, (*a*) the measurement of the amount of substance going to the engine in a given time say the duration of the test, (*b*) the measurement of the heat carried by each unit of substance. This latter figure is obtained by calorimetry. Where oil, petrol or gas is being used, the calorific value is found during the period of the trial. In steam engine or turbine trials the calorimetry results are recorded in the steam tables and diagrams, hence, steam quality tests only need be taken during the trial.

The weight of steam used during the trial is usually measured by condensing it, and measuring the condensate. This assumes that there is no leakage of steam at drains, glands, etc., between engine stop valve and condenser. When precautions are taken to prevent or measure such leakage, the condensing method is the most reliable.

Another method now in use for measuring daily steam

supply is the installation of a steam meter in the supply steam pipe. In many power stations readings are taken half-hourly or hourly throughout the whole period of twenty-four hours.

In gas engine trials the gas is measured by meter or by means of gas-holders of known capacity. The gas is then supplied at constant pressure and its amount can be accurately determined. Two gas-holders are normally used, one being filled, whilst the other is being drawn upon by the engine. One only may be used if all the conditions are kept constant, and the gas rate is measured for short intervals of time. The engine runs from the main, except during the period of gas flow measurement.

160. Heat Distribution. The determination of the distribution of the heat requires the measurement of water and gas quantities, and their temperatures.

In testing a gas engine an exhaust gas calorimeter may be fitted. In this calorimeter the heat is absorbed by water which rises in temperature, and whose quantity may be measured.

Heat passing through the cylinder walls to the jacket is measured by the quantity of jacket water heated and the amount of temperature rise.

Thus in both these cases,

Heat removed per minute = wt. of water per minute × temperature rise. The heat removed in the steam engine condenser is measured in exactly the same way.

161. Efficiency Ratio. The efficiency ratio is obtained by calculating the indicated thermal efficiency and dividing it by the ideal efficiency for the type of engine under consideration.

162. Observations Made. The observations to be recorded in a thermal test of an engine are as follows :

For the indicated horse power.
  (1) Scale of spring on indicator.
  (2) Diameter of engine piston.
  (3) Diameter of engine piston rod and tail rod, if any.

(4) Length of stroke.

(5) Whether single acting or double acting.

(6) Nature of cycle—two-stroke or four-stroke.

(7) Revolutions per minute, from which working strokes per minute may be calculated. (In the internal combustion engine, an explosion counter may be needed.)

For the calculation for the I.H.P.

Work done per minute = mean effective force × distance travelled by piston per minute whilst under action of force.

= M.E.P. × effective piston area × stroke length × working strokes per minute.

Effective area of one side of piston = area of piston — area of rod.

Thus the work done per minute on one side of the piston may be calculated. If the engine is double acting the work done on the other side is added. It is not correct to multiply the work done on one side of the piston by two, in order to find the whole work per revolution, because the M.E.P.'s from each side often differ considerably, and if the engine has no tail rod the effective areas are different.

The algebraic treatment for the steam engine is now given.

Let D = diameter of cylinder in inches.

d =   ,,   ,, piston rod in inches.

d_t =   ,,   ,, tail rod   ,,   ,,

P_F = M.E.P. from piston rod side of piston.

P_B =   ,,   ,, tail   ,,   ,,   ,.   ,,

L = length of stroke in feet.

N = revolutions per minute.

Then I.H.P.

$$= \frac{P_F\left(\frac{\pi D^2}{4} - \frac{\pi d^2}{4}\right)L \times N + P_B\left(\frac{\pi D^2}{4} - \frac{\pi d_t^2}{4}\right)L \times N}{33,000}.$$

With a single-acting engine, with no tail rod and pressure on back of piston,

$$\text{I.H.P.} = \frac{P_B\left(\frac{\pi D^2}{4} - 0\right) L \times N}{33,000} = \frac{P_B \times \frac{\pi D^2}{4} \times L \times N}{33,000}.$$

With the *gas engine*, single-acting, using above notation.

$$\text{I.H.P.} = \frac{P_B \times \frac{\pi D^2}{4} \times L \times \frac{N}{2}}{33,000}$$ (for four-stroke, with no cycles cut out due to hit-and-miss governing).

$$\text{or I.H.P.} = \frac{P_B \times \frac{\pi D^2}{4} \times L \times N}{33,000}$$ (for two-stroke, with no cycles cut out).

The calculation for the double-acting gas engine is the same as for the steam engine. In all gas engine equations, where cycles are cut out, E must be substituted for N or $\frac{N}{2}$, where E = actual number of charges ignited per minute.

163. Brake Horse Power Observations.

It is necessary to measure the (1) speed, (2) torque.

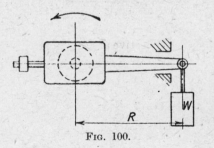

Brake horse power calculations are the same whether some lever type of brake (as the Prony or Froude), or rope type (Hirn) is used.

Fig. 100.

In both cases, work done per revolution
    = resisting torque × angular movement in radians.
The torque in the lever type of brake (fig. 100),
        = effective or equivalent weight × radius.
        = $W_E R$.
W_E is not the weight actually on the lever, but allows for the weight of lever itself and its attachments.

In the rope brake shown in fig. 101, the radius is measured to the centre of the rope. The effective weight lifted is the difference between actual dead weight W and the reading of the counterbalance S.

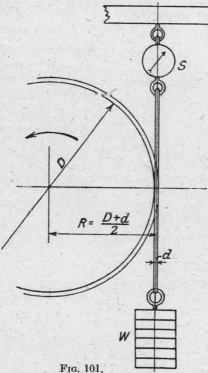

FIG. 101.

$$\therefore W_E = W - S.$$

Assuming a rope brake to be in use,

Let W = weight lifted in lbs.

      S = counterweight in lbs.

      D = diameter of brake wheel in feet.

      d =   ,,   ,, rope   ,,   ,,

      R = effective radius in feet.

Then R = $\dfrac{D + d}{2}$.

Work done per revolution = torque × angle turned in
radians.

$$= (W - S)R \times 2\pi \text{ ft.-lbs.}$$
$$= \pi(W - S)(D + d) \text{ ft.-lbs.}$$
$$= 2\pi R(W - S) \text{ ft.-lbs.}$$

Let N = no. of revs. per minute.
W_E = effective load = $W - S$.
Work done per min. = $2\pi RNW_E$

and Brake horse power $= \dfrac{2\pi RNW_E}{33,000}$.

(If T = the torque in lb. ft. and ω = the angular velocity
in radians, per sec., then B.H.P. $= \dfrac{T\omega}{550}$, and the student is
advised to become familiar with this form.)

164. Thermal Efficiency. The observations to be
made for the determination of thermal efficiency are :

(a) For the steam engine :
  (1) Weight of steam supplied.
  (2) State of steam supply.
  (3) Indicator diagrams.

(b) For the internal combustion engine :
  (1) Weight or volume of fuel supply.
  (2) Calorific value of fuel.
  (3) Indicator diagrams.

It is necessary to measure the substance going to the
engine in a given period of time when the working conditions are steady.

The Indicator. The chief instrument in use is the
indicator. It is an instrument of precision and must be
handled with care and intelligence to secure reasonably
accurate indications.

The precautions to be taken are tabulated below :

(1) The driving cord or wire must move freely over
  guide pulleys.
(2) The cord must be of the right length to ensure that
  the drum does not strike its stop at the ends of

its travel. Cord too long will fall slack, and cord too short will stretch or break.

(3) The correct spring must be chosen for the range of pressure required.

(4) The piston must not strike the stop at either the top or bottom of its stroke.

(5) All parts must be assembled so that there is no backlash.

(6) The pencil must be applied to the paper by means of the small handle usually provided for the purpose. On no account must the fingers touch the pencil mechanism.

(7) The pencil must be applied to the paper as lightly as possible consistent with obtaining a line on the paper. This line may not be visible until the paper is removed. It is a mistake to allow the pencil to trace the diagram time after time.

(8) The indicator cocks must be opened fully. It is a common error to open them partially with the result that the cards are of no use.

(9) The atmospheric line must be drawn before opening the indicator cock.

The motion of the indicator piston is multiplied by a linkwork, which draws a vertical straight line when the drum is not in motion. There are several of these straight line motions which the reader will study in the higher classes in Theory of Machines. The scale of the spring, which is stamped upon it, takes account of this multiplication of motion and also the actual area of the indicator piston. For example, if the spring is actually compressed $\frac{1}{4}$ in. and the pencil moves $\frac{3}{4}$ in., the scale of the spring being 80 lbs. per sq. in. per inch, the pressure increase is $\frac{3}{4} \times 80 = 60$ lbs. per sq. in. Thus each indicator must have its own springs to correspond with pencil movement multiplication and indicator piston area.

The reader should take the opportunity of examining the indicator and indicator rig, when he carries out his laboratory work.

165. Trials. Two trials will now be worked out in full. The first relates to a National Gas Engine and the second to a Cross Compound Condensing Steam Engine. All the observations were made by Third Year Senior Engineering Students in the Wigan and District Mining and Technical College.

166. Gas Engine Trial. The trial was carried out on the above engine operating on the four-stroke cycle and governed on the "hit and miss" principle. The brake was of the rope type, and the counterbalance force was measured by means of a spring balance.

Harding's counters were used, one to measure revolutions and another to record explosions.

The jacket cooling water was measured by means of a calibrated orifice plate in a horizontal plane. Centigrade thermometers were fitted in the supply pipe and in the discharge pipe of the water jacket. The gas supply was measured by means of a gas meter. The reading of the meter was not corrected for temperature or for pressure, since manometers and thermometers were not fitted to the gas supply pipe. When these data are observed, the correction can easily be made by applying the equations of Article 27.

If a determination of the calorific value of the gas is made, the same correction should be applied to the calorific value test result, so that the heat supply to the engine can be accurately obtained.

Three different loads were taken, all other conditions remaining constant. The loads on the brake were as follows :

Series A, 40 lbs. weight.
Series B, 69 ,, ,,
Series C, 97 ,, ,,

The trial for series A was carried out for 15 minutes after the engine had run under this load for sufficient time to allow all parts to reach normal working temperatures, and to obtain uniform readings at all observation points.

Series B and C were run for 10 minutes after allowing

a suitable interval for the engine to adjust itself to the change in load.

SERIES A. Table VI gives the actual observations logged in the engine room for the A trials.

TABLE VI

Call No.	Explosions.	Revolutions.	Weight on Brake.	Spring Balance Reading.	Weight of Cooling Water.	Inlet Temperature.	Outlet Temperature.	Quantity of Gas/5 min.
1	553,800	139,368	40 lbs.	2·5 lbs.	13·7 lbs./min.	8° C.	23·7° C.	0 cu. ft.
2	554,165	140,812	40 ,,	2·5 ,,	13·6 ,,	8° C.	23° C.	19·5 ,,
3	554,527	142,263	40 ,,	3·0 ,,	13·6 ,,	8° C.	22·8° C.	14·25 ,,
4	554,888	143,706	40 ,,	3·0 ,,	13·6 ,,	8° C.	23·1° C.	19·25 ,,

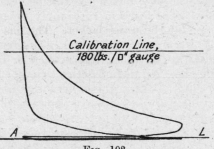

Fig. 102.

Fig. 102 shows the indicator diagram for series A. Gas engine dimensions are as follows:

Diameter of cylinder . . $6\frac{1}{2}$ ins.
Stroke . . . . $11\frac{7}{8}$,, = 0·9896 ft.
Area of piston . . . 33·183 sq. ins.
Brake wheel diameter . . 3 ft.
,, rope ,, . . 1 in.
Engine compression ratio . 3·85

From Table VI we have:
Explosions during trial = 554,888 − 553,800 = 1,088.

Mean number of explosions per minute = $\dfrac{1,088}{15}$ = 72·5.

Revolutions during trial = 143,706 − 139,368 = 4,338.

Mean number of revolutions per minute $= \dfrac{4{,}338}{15} = 289\cdot2$.

Mean deadweight　　　　　$= 40$ lbs.
,,　　spring balance　　$= 2\cdot75$ lbs.
Mean effective brake load $= 40 - 2\cdot75$
　　　　　　　　　　　　$= 37\cdot25$ lbs.
Mean rate of flow of jacket cooling water $= 13\cdot625$ lbs. per min.
,,　　inlet temperature of cooling water $=\ \ 8°$ C.
,,　　outlet　　,,　　　,,　　　,,　　　,,　　$= 23\cdot15°$ C.
,,　　rise in　　,,　　　,,　　,,　　　,,　　$= 23\cdot15 - 8$
　　　　　　　　　　　　　　　　　　　　$= 15\cdot15°$ C.
Total gas used in 15 minutes $= 53$ cu. ft.

Gas used per minute　　　　$= \dfrac{53}{15} = 3\cdot535$ cu. ft.

Calorific value of gas　　　$= 239$ C.H.U. per cu. ft.
Mean height of indicator diagram $+^{\text{ve}}$ loop $= 0\cdot65$　in.
,,　　　,,　　,,　　,,　　　　　　,,　　$-^{\text{ve}}$　,,　　$= 0\cdot028$　,,
　　　　　　　　　　　　　　　　Nett $= 0\cdot622$　,,

Spring scale of indicator　$= 120$ lbs. per sq. in. per inch height
　　　　　　　　　　　　　　　　of pencil travel.
∴ Mean effective pressure $= 0\cdot622 \times 120 = 74\cdot5$ lbs. per sq. in.
Work done per stroke　　　$= 33\cdot183 \times 74\cdot5 \times 0\cdot9896$ ft.-lbs.
There are $72\cdot5$ explosions per min.
∴ Work done per min. $= 33\cdot183 \times 74\cdot5 \times 0\cdot9896 \times 72\cdot5$
　　　　　　　　　　　$= 177{,}000$ ft.-lbs.

$$\text{I.H.P.} = \dfrac{177{,}000}{33{,}000} = 5\cdot37.$$

Brake wheel diameter $= 3$ ft.　Rope $= 1$ in. diameter.
Effective brake weight $= 37\cdot25$ lbs.
Revs. per minute　　　$= 289\cdot2$
Effective radius　　　$= (1\cdot5 + \cdot04)$ ft. $= 1\cdot54$ ft.
Work absorbed by brake per minute $= 2\pi NRW_E$
　　　　　　　　　　$= 2 \times 3\cdot1416 \times 289\cdot2 \times 1\cdot54 \times 37\cdot25$
　　　　　　　　　　$= 104{,}200$ ft.-lbs.

Brake horse power $= \dfrac{104{,}200}{33{,}000} = 3\cdot16.$

In 15 minutes, 53 cu. ft. of gas were used
∴ Consumption per hour　　　$= 53 \times 4 = 212$ cu. ft.

Consumption per I.H.P. per hour $= \dfrac{212}{5\cdot37} = 39\cdot5$ cu. ft.

Consumption per B.H.P. per hour $= \dfrac{212}{3\cdot16} = 67\cdot2$ cu. ft.

Mechanical efficiency $= \dfrac{\text{Work done at brake}}{\text{Work done on piston}}$

$$= \frac{104,200}{177,000} = 0.59$$

or $\qquad\qquad = \dfrac{3.16}{5.37} = 0.59$ or 59 per cent.

Indicated thermal efficiency

$$= \frac{\text{Heat equivalent of work done on piston}}{\text{Heat supplied to engine}}$$

$$= \frac{5.37 \times 33,000}{1,400 \times 3.535 \times 239}$$

$$= \frac{126.4}{845} = 0.1495 \text{ or } 14.95 \text{ per cent.}$$

Brake Thermal Efficiency

$$= \frac{\text{Heat equivalent of work done on brake}}{\text{Heat supplied to engine}}$$

$$= \frac{3.16 \times 33,000}{1,400 \times 845}$$

$$= \frac{74.5}{845} = 0.0882 \text{ or } 8.82 \text{ per cent.}$$

Ideal efficiency $= 1 - \dfrac{1}{r^{\gamma-1}}$

$$= 1 - \frac{1}{3.85^{1.4-1}} = 1 - 0.583$$

$$= 0.417 \text{ or } 41.7 \text{ per cent.}$$

Efficiency ratio $= \dfrac{0.1495}{0.417} = 0.359$ or 35.9 per cent.

The chief results collected are :

Indicated horse power	$= 5.37$
Brake horse power	$= 3.16$
Consumption per I.H.P. per hour	$= 39.5$ cu. ft.
,, ,, B.H.P. ,, ,,	$= 67.2$,, ,,
Mechanical efficiency	$= 59$ per cent.
Indicated Thermal efficiency	$= 14.95$ per cent.
Brake Thermal efficiency	$= 8.82$ per cent.
Ideal efficiency	$= 41.7$ per cent.
Efficiency ratio	$= 35.9$ per cent.

Heat Balance.

Heat supplied per min. by gas $= \dfrac{53}{15} \times 239 = 845$ C.H.U.

Heat at brake $= \dfrac{104,200}{1,400} = 74\cdot5$ C.H.U.

Indicated heat $= \dfrac{177,000}{1,400} = 126\cdot4$ C.H.U.

Heat in engine friction $= 126\cdot4 - 74\cdot5 = 51\cdot9$ C.H.U.

Heat to water jacket $= 13\cdot625 \times 15\cdot15 = 206\cdot5$ C.H.U.

Heat supplied per min. . . . =	845 =	100 %
Brake heat = 74·5	—	—
Friction ,, = 51·9		
Indicated heat	126·4	14·95%
Jacket heat	206·5	24·5%
Exhaust and other losses . . .	512·1	60·55%
	845	100 %

For series B and C the observations, indicator diagrams to scale, and calculated results are given. The reader may carry out the calculations as shown for series A as a valuable exercise.

SERIES B.

Table VII gives the observations logged in the engine room.

TABLE VII

Call No.	Explosions.	Revolutions.	Weight on Brake.	Spring Balance Reading.	Weight of Cooling Water.	Inlet Temperature.	Outlet Temperature.	Quantity of Gas/5 min.
1	555,382	145,143	69 lbs.	7 lbs.	13·6 lbs./min.	8° C.	26° C.	0 cu. ft.
2	555,906	146,579	69 ,,	7·5 ,,	13·6 ,,	8° C.	28° C.	20·75 ,,
3	556,424	148,018	69 ,,	7·5 ,,	13·6 ,,	8° C.	29° C.	19 ,,

Duration of test   = 10 minutes.
Indicator spring scale = 120 lbs. per sq. in. per inch.
Engine dimensions as before.

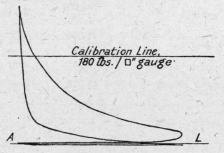

Calibration Line,
180 lbs. / □" gauge

A   L

FIG. 103.

The chief results collected are :

Indicated horse power	= 6·33
Brake horse power	= 5·21
Consumption per I.H.P. per hour	= 37·7 cu. ft.
,, ,, B.H.P. ,, ,,	= 45·8 ,, ,,
Mechanical efficiency	= 82·3 per cent.
Indicated Thermal efficiency	= 15·71 per cent.
Brake Thermal efficiency	= 12·87 per cent.
Ideal efficiency	= 41·37 per cent.
Efficiency ratio	= 37·6 per cent.

Heat Balance.

Heat supplied per min.	=950 C.H.U.	100%
Heat at Brake = 122·1		
,, by Friction = 27·1		
Indicated heat	149·2	15·71%
Jacket heat	267·5	28·2%
Exhaust and other losses	533·3	56·09%
	950	100%

SERIES C.

Table VIII gives the observations logged in the engine room.

TABLE VIII

Call No.	Explosions Counter Readings.	Revolution Counter Readings.	Weight on Brake.	Spring Balance Reading.	Weight of Cooling Water.	Inlet Temperature.	Outlet Temperature.	Quantity of Gas/5 min.
1	557,070	149,444	97 lbs.	13 lbs.	13·6 lbs./min.	8° C.	32° C.	0 cu. ft.
2	557,745	150,846	97 ,,	13 ,,	13·6 ,,	8° C.	34° C.	24·5 ,,
3	558,415	152,252	97 ,,	14 ,,	13·6 ,,	8° C.	35° C,	25·0 ,,

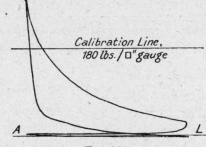

Calibration Line,
180 lbs. / □″ gauge

A   L

FIG. 104.

Duration of test   = 10 minutes.
Indicator spring scale = 120 lbs. per sq. in. per inch.
Engine dimensions as before.

The chief results collected are :

Indicated horse power   = 8·49
Brake horse power   = 6·9
Consumption per I.H.P. per hour = 35 cu. ft.
    ,,   ,, B.H.P. ,,   ,,   = 43·1 cu. ft.
Mechanical efficiency   = 81·3 per cent.
Indicated Thermal efficiency   = 16·9 per cent.
Brake Thermal efficiency   = 13·72 per cent.
Ideal efficiency   = 41·7 per cent.
Efficiency ratio   = 40·8 per cent.

The student should compare the results of the three tests with one another, when he may draw useful conclusions concerning the theory in the earlier chapters.

Heat Balance.

Heat supplied per min. . . .	1,182 C.H.U.	100%
Heat at Brake = 162·5 ,, by Friction = 37·5 Indicated heat	200	16·9%
Jacket heat	349·5	29·56%
Exhaust and other losses	632·5	53·54%
	1,102	100%

167. Steam Engine Trial. The engine was run as a cross compound condensing engine at constant speed and load.

The observations were :

(1) Indicator diagrams.

(2) Engine revolutions.

(3) Indicator spring scales.

(4) Brake weight and counterbalance.

(5) Stop valve pressure.

(6) Vacuum pressure.

(7) Weight of steam supplied (taken as weight of condensate).

(8) Steam and water temperatures.

Engine Data.

High Pressure cylinder diameter = 7 in.   Stroke = 20 in.
,,   ,,   piston rod ,,   = 1¾ in.   No tail rod.
Low Pressure cylinder   ,,   = 13 in.   Stroke = 20 in.
,,   ,,   piston rod ,,   = 1¾ in.   No tail rod.
Brake wheel   ,,   = 8 ft.
,,   rope   ,,   = 1 in.

Calls were made at five minute intervals.

Duration of test, 25 minutes.

The observations logged in the engine room are recorded in Table IX.

A number of the engine thermometers are Centigrade and others Fahrenheit. The actual observations are recorded.

TABLE IX

Call No.	Engine Revolution Counter.	Brake Weight. Lbs.	Spring Balance. Lbs.	Stop Valve Pressure. Lbs./ Sq. In. Gauge.	Compound Gauge. Lbs./ Sq. In.	Vacuum Gauge. Ins. Mercury.	Condensate Temperature. ° C.	Weight of Condensate. Lbs.	Quantity of Cooling Water. Gallons.	Inlet Temperature of Cooling Water. ° F.	Outlet Temperature of Cooling Water. ° F.	Exhaust Temperature. ° F.
1	52,968	376	27·5	115	13	22·5	50	—	—	48	80	140
2	53,564	376	27·5	120	12	24·5	51	—	180	49	82	136
3	54,191	376	27·5	112	12	24·9	51·5	—	185	49	83	138
4	54,819	376	27·5	112	12	23·0	52	—	175	50	85	136
5	55,445	376	27·5	111	11·5	23·8	52	—	185	50	85	134
6	56,073	376	27·5	111	11·0	24·5	52	458	185	50	85	134

Calibrated indicator diagrams from the high pressure and low pressure cylinders are shown in figs. 105 and 106 respectively.

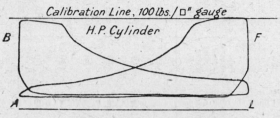

FIG. 105.

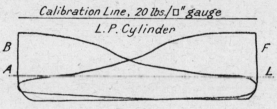

FIG. 106.

Indicator springs.
High pressure = 64 lbs. per sq. in. per in.
Low   ,,   = 20 ,,   ,,   ,,   ,, ,,   ,,

Reduction of Table of Observations on Steam Engine Trial.

Mean speed $= \dfrac{56{,}073 - 52{,}968}{25} = 124$ revs. per min.

Effective brake load $= 376 - 27 \cdot 5 = 348 \cdot 5$ lbs.

Average stop-valve pressure $= 113 \cdot 5$ lbs. per sq. in. gauge
$= (113 \cdot 5 + 14 \cdot 7)$ lbs. per sq. in. abs.
$= 128 \cdot 2$,,   ,,   ,,

Average vacuum $= 23 \cdot 86$ ins. mercury

$\therefore$ Pressure in condenser $= 30 - 23 \cdot 86$ at 30 ins. barometer
$= 6 \cdot 14$ ins. mercury

$= \dfrac{6 \cdot 14 \times 14 \cdot 7}{30}$ lbs. per sq. in. abs.

$= 3 \cdot 01$,,   ,,   ,,

* Corresponding temperature = 63·6° C.
Mean temperature of condensate = 51·41° C.

Weight of condensate per min. $= \dfrac{458}{25}$

$= 18·32$ lbs.
,, ,, ,, ,, hour $= 1,100$ lbs.
Total quantity of condensing water in 25 mins.

$= 910$ gallons $= 9,100$ lbs.

∴ Weight of condensing water per min. $= \dfrac{9,100}{25} = 364$ lbs.

Mean inlet temperature of condensing water

$= 49·33°$ F. $= 9·64°$ C.

Mean outlet temperature of condensing water

$= 83·33°$ F. $= 28·5°$ C.

Temperature rise of cooling water $= 28·5 - 9·64 = 18·86°$ C.
* Mean exhaust temperature at inlet to condenser

$= 136·33°$ F. $= 58°$ C.

I.H.P. Calculations.

(1) High Pressure Cylinder.
Mean height of indicator diagram, back of piston = 0·618 in.
,, ,, ,, ,, ,, front ,, ,, = 0·63 in.
Average mean height $= 0·624$ in.
,, ,, effective pressure = 0·624 × 64
$= 39·9$ lbs. per sq. in.
Area of piston (7 in. dia.) $= 0·7854 × 7 × 7 = 38·5$ sq. ins.
,, ,, ,, rod (1¾ in. dia.) $= 0·7854 × 1·75 × 1·75$
$= 2·406$ sq. ins.
Effective area, back of piston $= 38·5$ sq. ins.
,, ,, front ,, $= 36·094$ sq. ins.
Average effective area $= 37·297$ sq. ins.
Mean force on piston $= 37·297 × 39·9 = 1,486$ lbs.

Distance moved by piston per min. $= 2 × \dfrac{20}{12} × 124 = 412·92$ ft.

∴ Work done per minute in this cylr. = 1,486 × 412·92
$= 615,000$ ft.-lbs.

∴ Indicated horse power $= \dfrac{615,000}{33,000} = 18·62$.

---

* This is less than the value corresponding to vacuum pressure probably due to observational or instrumental errors, or undercooling effect in the steam.

(2) Low Pressure Cylinder.

Mean height of diagram, back of piston	$= 0\cdot716$ in.
,, ,, ,, ,, front ,,	$= 0\cdot724$ in.
Average mean height	$= 0\cdot72$ in.
Average mean effective pressure	$= 0\cdot72 \times 20$
	$= 14\cdot4$ lbs. per sq. in.
Area of piston (13 ins. dia.) $= 0\cdot7854 \times 13 \times 13 = 132\cdot8$ sq. ins.	
Area of piston rod	$= 2\cdot406$ sq. ins.
Effective area (front)	$= 132\cdot8 - 2\cdot406 = 130\cdot394$ sq. ins.
Average effective area	$= 131\cdot597$ sq. ins.
Mean force on piston	$= 131\cdot597 \times 14\cdot4 = 1,895$ lbs.
Distance moved by piston per minute	$= 412\cdot92$ feet.

$\therefore$ Work done per min. in low pressure cylr. $= 1,895 \times 412\cdot92$

$= 784,000$ ft.-lbs.

$\therefore$ Indicated horse power low pressure cylr. $= \dfrac{784,000}{33,000}$

$= 23\cdot75$

Total Indicated Horse Power

$= $ I.H.P. (H.P. cyl.) $+$ I.H.P. (L.P. cylr.)
$= 18\cdot62 + 23\cdot75 = 42\cdot37.$

B.H.P. Calculations.

Effective radius of brake wheel	$= 4$ ft. $0\frac{1}{2}$ in. $= 4\cdot04$ ft.
Effective brake load	$= 348\cdot5$ lbs.
Work done against brake per rev.	$= 2 \times \pi \times 4\cdot04 \times 348\cdot5$
	$= 8,870$ ft.-lbs.
Work done against brake per min.	$= 8,870 \times 124$

$\therefore$ Brake horse power $= \dfrac{8,870 \times 124}{33,000}$

$= 33\cdot3$ horse power.

Mechanical efficiency $= \dfrac{33\cdot3}{42\cdot37} = 78\cdot6$ per cent.

Steam consumption rate per I.H.P. per hour

$= \dfrac{\text{Wt. of steam used per hour}}{\text{I.H.P.}}$

$= \dfrac{1,100}{42\cdot37} = 25\cdot9$ lbs.

Steam consumption rate per B.H.P. per hour $= \dfrac{1,100}{33\cdot3} = 33\cdot08$ lbs.

The consumption rates may also be obtained by dividing 458 lbs. by the number of horse power hours worked during test.

Indicated horse power hours worked $= 42\cdot37 \times \dfrac{25}{60} = 17\cdot63.$

Brake horse power hours worked $= 33 \cdot 3 \times \dfrac{25}{60} = 13 \cdot 88.$

Steam consumption rate per I.H.P. per hour $= \dfrac{458}{17 \cdot 63}$

$$= 25 \cdot 9 \text{ lbs.}$$

,,   ,,   ,,   B.H.P.   ,, $= \dfrac{458}{13 \cdot 88}$

$$= 33 \cdot 08 \text{ lbs.}$$

Indicated thermal efficiency

$$= \frac{\text{Heat equivalent of work done on piston}}{\text{Heat supplied to engine}}$$

Total heat at 128·2 lbs. per sq. in. abs. and dry $= 664 \cdot 9$ C.H.U.
Liquid heat at 3·01   ,,   ,,   ,,   ,, $= \quad 63 \cdot 6$,,

Heat supplied per lb. of steam $= 601 \cdot 3$,.

$\therefore$ Indicated thermal efficiency $= \dfrac{60 \times 33,000}{1,400 \times 25 \cdot 9 \times 601 \cdot 3}$

$$= \frac{1,414}{25 \cdot 9 \times 601 \cdot 3}$$

$$= 0 \cdot 0908 \text{ or } 9 \cdot 08 \text{ per cent.}$$

Brake thermal efficiency $= \dfrac{1,414}{33 \cdot 08 \times 601 \cdot 3}$

$$= 0 \cdot 0711 = 7 \cdot 11 \text{ per cent.}$$

Rankine Efficiency.

Using the equation of Article 99 to find the Rankine work and modifying it to allow for the fact that no superheater was fitted to the engine, we have Rankine work for dry steam per lb.

$$= (T_1 - T_2)\left(1 + \frac{L_1}{T_1}\right) - T_2 \log_e \frac{T_1}{T_2}$$

$$= (447 \cdot 4 - 333 \cdot 8)\left(1 + \frac{488 \cdot 1}{447 \cdot 4}\right) - 333 \cdot 8 \times 2 \cdot 3026 \times \log 1 \cdot 327$$

$$= (108 \cdot 6 \times 2 \cdot 09) - 336 \cdot 6 \times 2 \cdot 3026 \times 0 \cdot 1229$$

$$= 237 \cdot 4 - 94 \cdot 4 = 143 \cdot 0 \text{ heat units.}$$

$\therefore$ Rankine efficiency $= \dfrac{143 \cdot 0}{601 \cdot 3}$

$$= 0 \cdot 238 \text{ or } 23 \cdot 8 \text{ per cent.}$$

Efficiency ratio $= \dfrac{0 \cdot 0908}{0 \cdot 238}$

$$= 0 \cdot 381 \text{ or } 38 \cdot 1 \text{ per cent.}$$

The chief results collected are :

Indicated horse power	= 42·37
Brake horse power	= 33·3
Mechanical efficiency	= 78·6 per cent.
Consumption rate per I.H.P. per hour	= 25·9 lbs.
,, ,, ,, B.H.P. ,, ,,	= 33·08 lbs.
Thermal efficiency	= 9·08 per cent.
Brake thermal efficiency	= 7·11 per cent.
Rankine efficiency ratio	= 38·1 per cent.

Heat account on a one-minute basis.

	C.H.U.	per cent.
Heat supplied to engine in steam per min. =	11,000	100
Indicated heat $= \dfrac{42\cdot37 \times 33,000}{1,400}$ =	996	9·08
Brake heat $= \dfrac{33\cdot3 \times 33,000}{1,400}$ =	784	
Friction heat =	212	
Heat in condensing water = 364 × 18·86	6,860	62·3
Other losses	3,144	28·62
		100·00

EXAMPLES XIX

1. In a test of a gas engine the following observations were made :

Diameter of piston	= 6½ ins.
Stroke	= 12 ins.
R.P.M.	= 324·6
Explosions per min.	= 143
Brake weight	= 60 lbs.
Spring balance	= 2·25 lbs.
M.E.P.	= 71·4 lbs. per sq. in.
Gas per min.	= 4 cu. ft.
Calorific value of gas	= 240 C.H.U. per cu. ft.
Jacket water per min.	= 12·75 lbs.
Temperature rise in jacket water	= 27·5° C.
Compression ratio	= 3·85
Effective circumference of brake wheel =	9·92 ft.

Find : (a) The I.H.P. (b) The B.H.P. (c) Mechanical Efficiency. (d) Consumption rate per B.H.P. and per I.H.P. per hour. (e) The thermal efficiency, brake thermal efficiency and efficiency ratio.

Also draw up the heat balance sheet on a basis of one minute.

2. The following observations were taken during a test of a

S

small gas engine working on the four-stroke cycle and governed by the hit and miss method.

Cylinder diameter = 6½ ins. stroke = 1 ft.

Brake wheel diameter = 3·185 ft.

Area of mean indicator diagram (positive loop) = 1·084 sq. in.

,, ,, ,, ,, ,, (negative loop) = 0·064 sq. in.

Length of diagram	= 3·2 ins.
Scale of spring	= 240 lbs. per in.
Duration of trial	= 30 mins.
Total revolutions	= 9,999
Calorific value of gas	= 240 C.H.U. per cu. ft.
Brake weight	= 38 lbs.
Total explosions	= 2,871
Spring balance	= 2·5 lbs.
Quantity of jacket water per min.	= 4·2 lbs.
Temperature rise in jacket water	= 22° C.
Total gas	= 83·4 cu. ft.

Reduce the observations and write down—

(1) I.H.P. hours and B.H.P. hours worked.

(2) Indicated and Brake Thermal Efficiencies.

(3) Draw up a heat balance sheet on a minute basis, giving results as quantities of heat and also as percentages.

3. The following data were recorded during the test of a gas engine — I.H.P. 560, B.H.P. 447, revs. per min. 300, gas consumption (reduced to 15° C. and 30 ins. of mercury) 32,500 cu. ft. per hour, lower calorific value of the gas per cu. ft. 71·2 C.H.U., jacket water used per hour 2,870 gallons, temperature of the jacket water at inlet and outlet respectively 18·1° C. and 54·3° C. Determine :

(a) The mechanical efficiency of the engine. (b) The thermal efficiency of the engine. (c) The percentage heat energy of the gas carried away by the jacket water. (d) Neglecting waste of heat by radiation, etc., find the percentage heat energy of the gas carried away by the exhaust gases. U.L.C.I.

4. The following data are the results of a test of a gas engine having a diameter of 8 ins. and stroke of 15¾ ins.

Duration of test, 1 hour ; Revolutions per min. 280 ; Explosions per min. 110 ; M.E.P. from indicator diagrams 82·7 lbs. per sq. in. ; B.H.P. 14·4 ; Gas used during test 475 cu. ft. ; Calorific value of gas per cu. ft. 270 C.H.U. ; Weight of water passing through the jacket 700 lbs. ; Rise of temperature of jacket water 34° C.

Determine (a) the I.H.P. and (b) the thermal efficiency of the engine. Draw up a heat balance for the engine. U.L.C.I.

5. Describe, with the aid of sketches of apparatus used, the method of determining the mechanical efficiency of an engine.

U.L.C.I.

6. A ship is driven by two sets of eight-cylinder internal combustion engines working on the four-stroke cycle with an impulse

stroke every cycle. Diameter of cylinders 19·7 ins. ; stroke 26 ins., revs. per min. 145·3, average mean effective pressure for all cylinders 74 lbs. per sq. in. The thermal efficiency of the engines is 44 per cent.

Find the total I.H.P. driving the ship and the weight of oil used per I.H.P. per hour and per day's run of 24 hours. The calorific value of the oil is 9,890 C.H.U. per lb.   U.L.C.I.

7. The mean effective pressure in an internal combustion engine working on the two-stroke cycle was 91·4 lbs. per sq. in. The total fuel consumption per hour was 126·7 lbs. and the calorific value of the fuel was 10,120 C.H.U. per lb. The B.H.P. was 327·3 and the speed 125 revs. per min. Diameter of cylinder 22 in., stroke 36 in. Determine the mechanical efficiency, the indicated thermal efficiency and the brake thermal efficiency.   U.L.C.I.

8. The area of an indicator diagram taken from a double-acting steam engine is 2·1 sq. ins. and its length is 3·5 ins. The strength of spring used is 60 lbs. per inch of height. The diameter of the cylinder is 18 ins. and the piston stroke 26 ins. Speed 150 revolutions per minute. Find the I.H.P. of the engine and also the B.H.P., the mechanical efficiency being 78 per cent. U.L.C.I.

9. Draw up a heat balance sheet for an oil engine from the following data, taking quantities in C.H.U. per hour.

Oil per hour 3·08 lbs., calorific value 10,200 C.H.U. per lb., indicated horse power 5·8, brake horse power 4·4, cooling water per hour 385 lbs., rise in temperature of cooling water 36° C.

U.E.I.

10. The following particulars were obtained from a test of a four-stroke cycle gas engine :

Cylinder diameter 6½ ins., stroke 12 ins., diameter of brake wheel 5½ ft., effective brake load 60 lbs., revolutions per min. 306, explosions per min. 128, area of indicator card 0·68 sq. in., length 2·25 ins., spring $\frac{1}{300}$, gas used per hour 453 cu. ft. calorific value 530 B.Th.U. per cu. ft.

Calculate the I.H.P., B.H.P., mechanical efficiency, gas consumption per B.H.P. per hour, and the brake thermal efficiency.

U.E.I.

11. The results of a gas engine test gave the following : I.H.P. 7·6 ; B.H.P. 6·1 ; Jacket water 700 lbs. per hour ; Mean temperature rise 35° C. ; gas used, 175 cu. ft. per hour ; Calorific value of gas, 344 C.H.U. per cu. ft.

Draw up a heat balance sheet, taking quantities in C.H.U. per hour, and state the indicated and brake thermal efficiencies.

U.E.I.

12. In a one-hour trial of a Diesel engine the I.H.P. was 60·2 and the mechanical efficiency 70 per cent. The cooling water entered the jacket at 10° C. and left at 50° C., and 141 gallons were circulated. The calorific value of the fuel was 9,100 C.H.U. per lb.

and 22·1 lbs. were used. Calculate the brake thermal efficiency; the heat given to the jacket water; the heat carried off by the exhaust gases and otherwise; and draw up a heat balance sheet. U.E.I.

13. The following results were obtained during a one-hour test of an oil engine : I.H.P., 25·2 ; B.H.P., 20·6. The oil fuel was of specific gravity 0·75, lower calorific value 6,600 C.H.U. per lb. and the consumption for the run was 2·4 gallons. The weight of water passed through the jacket was 540 lbs., the inlet and outlet temperatures being respectively 16° C. and 66° C. The exhaust gases on leaving the cylinder were conducted through an exhaust calorimeter, and raised the temperature of 950 lbs. of water from 16° C. to 70° C. Calculate the mechanical and thermal efficiencies of the engine ; and draw up a heat balance sheet, showing the distribution of heat in C.H.U. per minute. U.E.I.

14. In a recently reported test of a pumping plant, the following results were obtained :

Boiler. Coal fired per hour, 688 lbs.
  Calorific value per lb., 8,340 C.H.U.
  Feed water per hour, 6,630 lbs.
  Temperature of feed water, 92° C.
  Pressure of steam, 200 lbs. per sq. in absolute.
  Amount of superheat, 70° C.·

Engine. Indicated horse power, 566.
  Steam used per hour, 5,618 lbs.

Find (a) the thermal efficiency of the boiler;
  (b) the thermal efficiency of the engine;
  (c) the thermal efficiency of the plant.

Note. There is a leakage of steam between the boiler and the engine and (c) must be calculated as the overall efficiency under the actual conditions of the test. Assume in (b) that the steam reaches the engine in the same condition as it leaves the boiler.

N.C.T.E.C.

15. The following particulars were obtained during a test of a four-stroke-cycle gas engine :

Duration of test, 40 minutes. Average revs. per min., 204. Average explosions per min., 100. Mean effective pressure in cylinder, 96 lbs. per sq. in. Net load on brake, 262 lbs. Effective diameter of brake pulley, 6 feet. Diameter of piston, 12 in. Stroke, 1·5 ft. Gas used during period of test, 334 cu. ft. Calorific value of 1 cu. ft. of gas, 500 B.Th.U. Quantity of water passing through jacket, 738 lbs. Rise in temperature of jacket water, 74° F.

Draw up a heat balance and calculate :

(a) The indicated horse power.
(b) The brake horse power.
(c) The mechanical efficiency of the engine. N.C.T.E.C.

16. You are required to test a condensing steam engine developing about 20 I.H.P. in order to determine the mechanical and thermal

efficiencies and to construct a heat balance sheet. Make a list of the observations which would be necessary and briefly describe how you would measure the necessary quantities. N.C.T.E.C.

17. The following observations were made during a test of a gas engine. Gas used, 396 cu. ft. per hour; calorific value of gas, 270 C.H.U. per cu. ft.; brake torque, 510 lbs.-ft.; speed, 172 revs. per min.; explosions, 78 per min.; mean effective pressure, 70 lbs. per sq. in.; cylinder diameter, 10 in.; stroke, 18 in.

Calculate the indicated horse power, brake horse power, mechanical efficiency and brake thermal efficiency. N.C.T.E.C.

CHAPTER XX

SPEED CONTROL

168. It is essential that the speed of rotation of a heat engine should never be allowed to attain a value which would throw undue stresses upon its working parts. The speeds of steam locomotives, motor-cars and similar machines are controlled by the driver whose personal safety usually ensures that he will not allow excessive speed.

In many other cases, however, it is necessary that the speed be kept within limits, which are sometimes very narrow, as in the case of engines driving cotton spinning machinery and electrical alternators when running in parallel.

There are two causes of speed variation :
(1) the fluctuating torque on the crank shaft ;
(2) alteration in the load which the engine has to take.

Each of these has to be corrected separately, and though absolute uniformity of speed is not attainable, the variations may be kept within narrowly defined limits.

The first of these types of fluctuation is dealt with by the flywheel entirely. These are known as cyclic variations because they occur with regularity. This part of the subject is not treated here, but will be found fully discussed in chapter IX of *Applied Mechanics*, by Mr. J. Boothroyd, B.Sc.

169. Governing. The governor is a device whose function is to check variations in speed when a change in the load occurs. If an engine is working against a load with a uniform rate of steam supply and the load decreases, the result will be an increase in speed. A decrease in speed will follow an increase in load. By decreasing the rate of steam supply in the first instance and increasing it in the second the governor will prevent a change of speed in excess of a certain percentage which has been decided upon.

A governor functions either (a) by throttling the main steam supply, (b) by altering the cut-off, or, (c) by both these means at the same time.

170. Centrifugal Governor. The principle generally made use of in governors is that of centrifugal force. Two weights placed diametrically opposite to each other are capable of moving outwards when speed is increased, and through a system of levers the throttle valve is partially closed or the cut-off is made earlier.

171. Watt Governor. The diagram (fig. 107) shows in outline the governor used by James Watt. It revolves

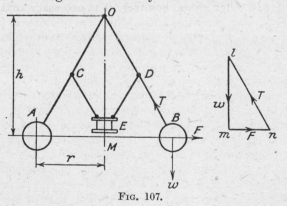

FIG. 107.

about the axis OM which is caused to rotate by direct connection with the engine shaft. OA and OB are arms pivoted at O and carrying weights at A and B. Links attached at C and D operate a sleeve E, which transmits its movement to a bell crank lever connected to the steam control arrangement. Increased speed causes A and B to move outwards owing to increased centrifugal force, thus raising the sleeve. A decrease in speed is followed by an inward movement of A and B and a lowering of the sleeve.

The vertical height from the centre of one of the weights to O is called the height, h, of the governor, and this is obviously a ruling factor in the working of the governor, since it decides the position of the sleeve.

Let w = the weight of one of balls in lbs.

   r = distance from centre of a weight to axis OM in ft.

   F = centrifugal force on one weight in lbs.

   ω = angular velocity of rotation of weights in radians per second.

Consider the equilibrium of weight B.

Three forces act upon it, (a) gravitation, w lbs., (b) centrifugal force, F, (c) tension in the arm OB, T lbs.

The triangle lmn is the triangle of forces for the equilibrium of the ball. It is obviously similar to the triangle OBM.

$$\therefore \quad \frac{OM}{BM} = \frac{lm}{mn}$$

$$\therefore \quad \frac{h}{r} = \frac{w}{F}$$

$$\therefore \quad h = \frac{wr}{F} \text{ but } F = \frac{w}{g}\omega^2 r.$$

$$\therefore \quad h = wr \times \frac{g}{w\omega^2 r}$$

$$= \frac{g}{\omega^2}.$$

h and r are supposed to be in feet.

EXAMPLE. Find the height of a Watt governor for speeds of 20, 60, and 90 revolutions per minute.

Note that the value of the weights and length of arms are of no importance.

1st *Case*. $\quad h = \dfrac{g}{\omega^2} = \dfrac{32 \cdot 2}{\left(\dfrac{2\pi \times 20}{60}\right)^2} = \dfrac{32 \cdot 2 \times 3 \times 3}{4\pi^2}$

$= 7 \cdot 34$ ft.

If the arms OA and OB were shorter than 7·34 ft., they would hang down against the axis.

2nd Case. $h = \dfrac{g}{\omega^2}$

$$h = \frac{32 \cdot 2}{\left(\dfrac{2\pi \times 60}{60}\right)^2}$$

$$= \frac{32 \cdot 2}{4\pi^2}$$

$$= 0 \cdot 816 \text{ ft. or } 9 \cdot 8 \text{ ins.}$$

3rd Case. $h = \dfrac{g}{\omega^2}$

$$= \frac{32 \cdot 2}{\left(\dfrac{2\pi \times 90}{60}\right)^2}$$

$$= \frac{32 \cdot 2 \times 4}{4\pi^2 \times 9}$$

$$= 0 \cdot 363 \text{ ft. or } 4 \cdot 36 \text{ ins.}$$

172. Porter Governor. The results of the above example show that at low speeds the governor would need unreasonably long arms, whilst at speeds which are now considered low, the variation in height, and consequently the movement of the sleeve, would be so small as to make governing difficult. This has given rise to other types, important amongst which is the Porter or loaded governor. In its normal form it is shown diagrammatically in fig. 108. A and B are rotating weights carried by arms OA and OB whilst arms BC and AD attach the weights to the sleeve.

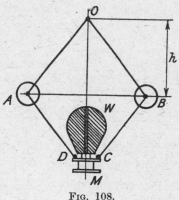

FIG. 108.

On the sleeve rests a weight, W, which is free to slide up and down the central axis with the sleeve. Usually it is arranged that the four arms OA, OB, BC and DA form a parallelogram.

The height of the governor is defined as before.

To find an expression for the height of this governor, produce OB to meet the horizontal through D in E, and consider the equilibrium of the link BD by taking moments about E. We take the particular case, which is the common one, where all arms are equal.

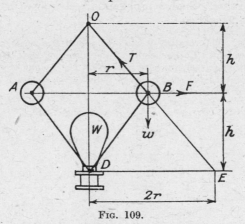

FIG. 109.

Let w = weight of each rotating weight in lbs.

W = ,, ,, central load in lbs.

h = height in feet.

F = centrifugal force on each weight in lbs.

ω = angular velocity in radians per second.

The forces acting on BD are F, w, and T at B, with $\dfrac{W}{2}$ at D. For equilibrium, the moments of these forces about E must be zero. Hence, neglecting weights of all arms we have

$$Fh - wr - \frac{W}{2} \cdot 2r = 0$$

$$\therefore Fh = r(W + w)$$

$$\text{but } F = \frac{w}{g}\omega^2 r$$

$$\therefore\ h = r(\mathrm{W} + w) \times \frac{g}{w\omega^2 r}$$

$$= \frac{g}{\omega^2} \cdot \frac{\mathrm{W} + w}{w}.$$

If the arms are not equal, or if their weights are to be accounted for, the same method of attack gives the solution to the problem, but it leads to a formula too complicated to be of value. Such a problem is best worked from first principles as above.

EXAMPLE. The rotating weights of a Porter governor are each 5 lbs. in weight. If the height of the governor is to be 10 ins. when rotating at 200 revs. per min., find the weight of the load. What percentage increase in speed will lift the sleeve 1 in. if all the arms of the governor are equal ?

$$\omega = \frac{2\pi \times 200}{60} \text{ radians per sec.}$$

$$= 20\cdot92$$

$$h = \frac{g}{\omega^2} \frac{\mathrm{W} + w}{w}$$

$$\frac{10}{12} = \frac{32\cdot2}{20\cdot92^2} \cdot \frac{\mathrm{W} + 5}{5}$$

$$\mathrm{W} + 5 = \frac{10 \times 5 \times 20\cdot92 \times 20\cdot92}{12 \times 32\cdot2}$$

$$= 56\cdot5$$

$$\therefore\ \mathrm{W} = 56\cdot5 - 5 = 51\cdot5 \text{ lbs.}$$

To lift the sleeve 1 in. the height of governor must become $9\frac{1}{2}$ ins.

$$\therefore\ \frac{9\cdot5}{12} = \frac{g}{\omega^2} \cdot \frac{51\cdot5 + 5}{5}$$

$$\omega^2 = \frac{32\cdot2 \times 12}{9\cdot5} \cdot \frac{56\cdot5}{5}$$

$$= 459$$

$$\therefore\ \omega = 21\cdot44 \text{ radians per sec.}$$

$$\text{Revs. per min.} = \frac{21\cdot44 \times 60}{2\pi}$$

$$= 204\cdot6$$

$$\therefore\ \text{Increase in speed} = 204\cdot6 - 200 = 4\cdot6 \text{ revs. per min.}$$

$$\text{Increase per cent.} = \frac{4\cdot6}{2} = 2\cdot3 \text{ per cent.}$$

It will be seen that, since $\dfrac{W + w}{w}$ is under our control,

by suitably choosing values for W and w, we may give h any reasonable value for a given speed. The great disadvantage, therefore, of the Watt governor is overcome.

173. Effect of Friction. The frictional resistance in the linkwork connected to a governor has a serious effect upon its operation. It will oppose the movement of the sleeve whether it is upward or downward.

In allowing for this friction, it is reduced to a force at the sleeve. This force can be found only by experiment and may be tested by a spring balance when the engine is stationary.

The central load in a Porter governor acts directly on the sleeve, hence the force due to friction may be added to or subtracted from the weight of the central load.

Let the force at the sleeve due to friction $= f$, then, when the governor is rising, the resistance at the sleeve will be $W + f$. If the governor is falling, then the downward movement of the sleeve will also be opposed by the friction. The effect will be to decrease the effective value of the central load, and the governor will behave as if the value of the central load were $W - f$.

The formula of the last article, therefore, may be written in the form

$$h = \frac{g}{\omega^2} \frac{W \pm f + w}{w}.$$

The positive sign is taken when the speed is increasing, and the negative when it is decreasing.

EXAMPLE. In the example of the last article, find the limits of speed of the governor between the heights 10 ins. and $9\frac{1}{2}$ ins., if the friction is equivalent to 8 lbs. at the sleeve.

Before the governor can rise to a smaller height than $9\frac{1}{2}$ ins., the friction and weight must be overcome.

∴ we take $W + f$.

$$h = \frac{g}{\omega^2} \cdot \frac{W + f + w}{w}$$

$$\frac{9\cdot5}{12} = \frac{32\cdot2}{\omega^2} \times \frac{51\cdot5 + 8 + 5}{5}$$

$$\omega^2 = \frac{32\cdot2 \times 12 \times 64\cdot5}{9\cdot5 \times 5} = 524$$

$$\therefore\ \omega = 22\cdot9 \text{ rad. per sec.}$$

$$\text{Revs. per min.} = \frac{22\cdot9 \times 60}{2\pi} = 218\cdot7.$$

At the lower limit of speed, when the height = 10 ins., before the sleeve can move downwards, the load must overcome the friction and its effective weight is thus reduced. Hence W — f must be taken.

$$h = \frac{g}{\omega^2} \cdot \frac{W - f + w}{w}$$

$$\therefore\ \frac{10}{12} = \frac{32\cdot2}{\omega^2} \cdot \frac{51\cdot5 - 8 + 5}{5}$$

$$\omega^2 = \frac{32\cdot2 \times 12 \times 48\cdot5}{10 \times 5} = 375$$

$$\omega = 19\cdot4 \text{ rad. per sec.}$$

$$\text{Revs. per min.} = \frac{19\cdot4 \times 60}{2\pi} = 185\cdot3.$$

This is a rather extreme case, but, when compared with the range of speeds in the last example, it shows how serious the effect of friction may be.

174. Hartnell or Spring-loaded Governor. In the governors just treated, gravity has been the force which centrifugal action had to overcome. The Hartnell governor and its many modifications use a spring in either compression or tension for this purpose. The sketch gives the main idea of a spring-loaded governor.

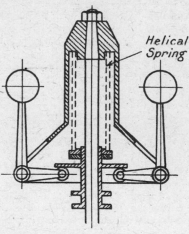

Helical Spring

Fig. 110.

Two bell crank levers carry a weight at one end whilst the other end operates on the sleeve. The pivots of the levers are carried by a bracket which rotates with the spindle. On the sleeve a spring in compression acts. When the rotational speed increases the spring is compressed further due to the outward movement of the weights. The spring has an initial compression given to it, so that the governor will only begin to function when the centrifugal force, acting on the levers, is sufficient to compress the spring further. That can be at any predetermined speed. There is so great a freedom of choice in weights, and stiffness of springs, that a governor on this principle can be made to meet almost any conditions. With modifications in design, it can be made to work with its axis horizontal, which is often an advantage.

The principle of this governor is very simple and no formula need be deduced to deal with it. The following example will illustrate the method of calculation.

EXAMPLE. The weights of a Hartnell governor are each 4 lbs. The vertical members of the levers are 5 ins. long and the horizontal members 6 ins. long. The radius of the circular path of the weights is 7 ins. The initial compression on the spring is 90 lbs. and its stiffness is 40 lbs. per in. Find the speed at which the governor will begin to function, and the speed when the radius of the path of the weights is $7\frac{1}{2}$ ins.

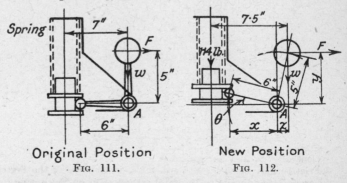

Original Position
FIG. 111.

New Position
FIG. 112.

Fig. 111 shows the arrangement.
Only half the force on the spring acts on each lever.

Let F = centrifugal force on one weight.

Then, when the sleeve is just on the point of rising, we have

$$F \times 5 = \frac{90}{2} \times 6$$

$$\text{but } F = \frac{w}{g}\omega^2 r = \frac{4 \times 7 \times \omega^2}{32 \cdot 2 \times 12}$$

$$\therefore \frac{4 \times 7 \times \omega^2 \times 5}{32 \cdot 2 \times 12} = \frac{90}{2} \times 6$$

$$\therefore \omega^2 = \frac{90 \times 6 \times 12 \times 32 \cdot 2}{2 \times 4 \times 7 \times 5}$$

$$= \frac{9 \times 6 \times 3 \times 32 \cdot 2}{7}$$

$$= 746$$

$$\omega = 27 \cdot 33 \text{ radians per sec.}$$

$$\text{Revs. per min.} = \frac{27 \cdot 33 \times 60}{2\pi} = 261.$$

The stiffness or rate of a spring is the force per inch of compression or elongation.

When the radius increases by $\frac{1}{2}$ in. the rise of the sleeve will be $\frac{1}{2} \times \frac{6}{5} = 0 \cdot 6$ in. for this example. Total force on spring with extra compression $= 90 + 0 \cdot 6 \times 40$.

$$= 114 \text{ lbs.}$$

$$\therefore F \times y + w \times z = \frac{114}{2} \times x \text{ (see fig. 112)}$$

$$\frac{w}{g}\omega^2 r \times 5 \cos \theta + w \times \tfrac{1}{2} = \frac{114}{2} \times 6 \cos \theta$$

$$\frac{w}{g}\omega^2 r \times 5 + \frac{w}{2 \cos \theta} = 57 \times 6$$

$$\frac{4 \times 7 \cdot 5 \times 5 \times \omega^2}{32 \cdot 2 \times 12} + \frac{4}{2 \cos \theta} = 342.$$

Cos θ is very nearly equal to 1.

$$\therefore \frac{4 \times 7 \cdot 5 \times 5}{32 \cdot 2 \times 12} \omega^2 = 342 - 2 = 340$$

$$\omega^2 = \frac{340 \times 32 \cdot 2 \times 12}{4 \times 7 \cdot 5 \times 5}$$

$$= 876$$

$$\omega = 29 \cdot 6 \text{ radians per sec.}$$

$$\text{Revs. per min.} = \frac{29 \cdot 6 \times 60}{2\pi} = 282 \cdot 5.$$

Generally wz may be neglected.

Friction may be taken into account as in the case of the Porter governor by adding it to the total compression on the spring for a rising governor, and subtracting it for a falling governor.

175. Range of Speeds. Any governor must be so designed, that at the lowest speed in its range, it will give the engine full steam supply. At the highest point it should so reduce the steam supply, that the engine will not gain speed, even when all external load is removed. On account of this, flywheel control and governor control have to be properly regulated relatively to each other.

Suppose, for instance, a governor allows a maximum variation of 10 revs. per min. Let the flywheel allow the same cyclic variation. Then, in every cycle (usually one revolution), the governor sleeve would move from its lowest position to its highest position and back again. As this would happen during each revolution, whether load was great or small, the governor would be of no use. When these conditions exist, or even if they are approached, a phenomenon known as " hunting " arises.

It is necessary, therefore, that the flywheel should only permit cyclic variations which are considerably smaller than those permitted by the governor.

EXAMPLES XX

1. Why is it necessary in practice to control the speed of an engine ?

Distinguish between the function of a flywheel and a governor.

2. Give reasons why it is impossible to maintain absolutely uniform speed of rotation.

3. For what range of speeds will a Watt governor vary in height from 12 ins. to 6 ins. ?

Why is the Watt governor not used in modern practice ?

4. A Porter governor with equal arms has a load of 45 lbs. and rotating weights each 4 lbs.

What is its height at a speed of 240 revs. per min. ?

5. In a spring loaded governor the compression on the spring is 80 lbs. The ball-arms of the bell-crank levers are 5 ins. long and the sleeve-arms 6 ins. long. The radius of the path of the balls is 7 ins. and the weight of each is 5 lbs. Neglecting friction, at what speed must the governor rotate to satisfy the given conditions ?

6. The governor of question (4) has friction equivalent to a force of 4 lbs. at the sleeve. At what speed will it begin to fall from the given position and at what speed will it rise ?

7. A spring loaded governor has a compression in the spring of

60 lbs. The spring compresses 1 in. for a force of 40 lbs., and friction is equivalent to a force of 6 lbs. at the sleeve. If the radius of the path of the balls is 7 ins. when the spring has the above compression and if both ball-arms and sleeve-arms are 6 ins. long, find the increase in speed for a rise of 1 in. in the sleeve. Assume that the lower limit of speed is as low as possible and that the balls weigh 8 lbs. each.

8. Distinguish between the governing of a steam engine by (a) throttling and (b) variable expansion, and illustrate your answer by showing the effect of each method on an indicator diagram.

Give a sketch of a spring loaded governor and explain its action.

U.L.C.I.

9. Obtain a formula for the height h of a Porter governor in terms of the central load W, the weight of each ball w, the frictional resistances f, and the angular velocity ω radians per second. Assume the pendulum arms and the suspension links of equal length and that they intersect on the main axis.

Using this formula, calculate the amount of central weight required so that the links, each 15 ins. long, shall be inclined at 45° to the main axis when the speed is 150 revs. per min. You may assume the speed to be increasing. The weight of each ball is 4 lbs. and the resistance on the sleeve due to moving the governor gear is 3 lbs.

U.E.I.

10. Prove that h, the height in feet of a loaded governor of the Porter type with equal arms and links, is given by the equation

$$h = \frac{W + w}{w} \cdot \frac{2,934}{N^2}$$

N = no. of revs. per min., w = weight of each ball,
W = weight of central load.

If $w = 4$ lbs., $W = 56$ lbs., and the height does not alter when the speed increases suddenly from 250 to 255 revs. per min., calculate the force opposing the rising of the sleeve. U.E.I.

11. A Porter governor with equal arms runs normally at 180 revs. per min. If the height at this speed is $7\frac{1}{2}$ ins., what is the ratio of the central load to the weight of one of the balls ? If the frictional resistance on the sleeve be equal to 10 per cent. of the central load, what is the proportional increase of speed before the governor acts ? If you use a formula, show, if you can, how it is derived. U.E.I.

CHAPTER XXI

STEAM TURBINES.

176. Introductory. The steam turbine is the result of much experiment and research. Many attempts to produce a rotary engine had been made prior to 1880, at which time several inventors were endeavouring to perfect their respective machines. It was not until the year 1892 that the inventiveness, skill, and courage of the late Honourable C. A. Parsons produced a turbine which became a competitor with the reciprocating steam engine.

His first mechanically successful turbine was produced in 1884 and now occupies an honourable place in the Engineering Museum at South Kensington. This turbine developed 10 horse power and was used to drive a dynamo. Its steam consumption was so high that it could not hope to displace the high class steam engines of that day. Such progress, however, was made in the next eight years that the turbine thereafter rapidly gained popularity, and in 1905, the famous *Mauretania* was engined with turbines to develop 75,000 horse power.

The production of electrical energy on the scale of modern demands would be impracticable without the steam turbine. The horse power developed by a single turbine set is now as much as 200,000, whilst there are one or two sets in the world designed to develop even higher powers than this. In the field of marine engineering, the turbine is supreme for high powered ships, and it is worthy of note that the turbines of *H.M.S. Hood* develop 144,000 horse power, and that the latest transatlantic liners have turbines developing over 160,000 horse power in four units.

The turbine is very different from a piston engine, both in the manner in which the steam delivers its energy as work, and also in the mechanical construction and general appearance of the machine. If the controlling gear be excepted, there are no parts of a steam turbine moving with reciprocating motion. The moving parts are all rotating and are entirely enclosed. Consequently, there is no very evident sign to indicate that anything is taking place in the turbine. A slight vibrational hum, some radiated heat, and the speed indicator, are the only means of detecting the fact that heat is in process of transformation into work.

In the case of the piston engine, the pressure of steam as registered by a pressure gauge (known as the statical pressure) is the means of propulsion. Although the pistons may be moving at speeds as high as 1,000 feet per minute, and the steam is following up the pistons at this speed, the kinetic energy of the steam is negligible. The steam velocity is small.

In the steam turbine the statical pressure is not used directly as the means of creating the propulsive force. It is used to create high steam velocities, in some cases as high as 4,000 *feet per second*. The propulsive force on the moving parts of the turbine is produced by changing the direction of this high velocity steam and thus changing its momentum. The force set up by this means on the working elements is a dynamic force, (i.e. one set up by change of motion) as distinct from the static force exerted by steam on the sides of its containing vessel. There is, therefore, a double transformation of energy in the steam turbine, first from heat into kinetic energy, and second, from kinetic energy into force and thence into mechanical work. The piston engine does the transformation directly, namely from heat into mechanical work on the piston.

Notwithstanding these important differences between the reciprocating steam engine and the steam turbine, the calculations set out in Chapter XIII are equally applicable to both types of engine, and the term " all steam engines " in the second line of art. 95, includes steam turbines.

177. Advantages of the Turbine. The chief advantages of the turbine engine are as follows :—

I. Very large units can be constructed as indicated in the last article.

II. Since the turbine is a high speed machine it develops high power per unit volume occupied.

III. It can utilize high vacuum very advantageously.

IV. No internal lubrication is needed. Therefore condenser tubes can be kept free from oil and a high rate of heat transmission maintained in the condenser. The boiler feed water is also free from oil with resulting freedom from overheating of tubes. No special oil elimination treatment of the feed water is necessary to maintain high heat transmission rates in the boiler.

V. Heavy foundations are unnecessary as the machine can be accurately balanced.

VI. The high rotational speed of the turbine makes it very suitable for electrical power generation.

VII. Considerable overloads can be carried at the expense of slight reduction in overall efficiency.

VIII. The construction of a turbine readily lends itself to the process of cascade or series feed water heating, or to the provision of steam at reduced pressures for processes such as distilling, heating, humidifying, digesting, etc.

IX. The condenser inlet can be made large and the condenser itself can be placed very close to the last working blade ring. This enables the expansion of the steam to be carried down to condenser pressure and therefore the expansion in a steam turbine is complete, as in the Rankine cycle.

X. The turbine can be operated against any reasonable back pressure and it can be arranged to use high pressure steam, low pressure steam, or both ; and also steam exhausted from reciprocating engines.

178. The Simple Turbine. The essential features of a simple steam turbine are illustrated in fig. 113. The steam pipe from the boiler terminates in the main stop valve M. Close to this valve is placed a second valve G under the control of the turbine governor. The steam

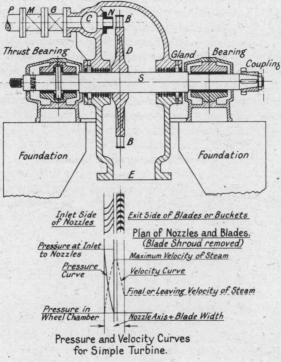

Pressure and Velocity Curves
for Simple Turbine.

FIG. 113.

enters the nozzle chest C through the pipe P. The nozzle chest consists of a special steam pipe curved so that its centre line coincides with the mean path of motion of the working blade. Passages of special shape, known as nozzles and indicated at N, lead the steam from the nozzle chest to the working blades B. During its passage through the nozzles the steam falls in pressure and increases enormously in velocity. It is directed towards the blades by the nozzles which are inclined to the plane in which the blades move, as shown in the plan. The blades are shaped and arranged somewhat as indicated with the result that the steam which leaves the nozzle enters the blade passages and literally blows the blades along. Special shapes of nozzles and of blades are used to increase the driving force of the steam upon the blades. The steam leaves the blade wheel on the right and flows downwards through the exhaust passage E into the condenser. The work done on the blades is transferred to the shaft S by means of the turbine wheel or disc D.

179. The Turbine Stage. The word stage used in this connexion means a pressure stage. A pressure stage is any portion of the turbine in which a pressure drop occurs followed by the development of mechanical work in a moving element or blade ring. It follows from this definition that fig. 113 illustrates a single pressure stage turbine. This simple turbine forms the basis of the calculations treated in this chapter.

180. General Description of the Steam Turbine. A complete steam turbine of the impulse type, by the Metropolitan-Vickers Electrical Co., Ltd., is illustrated in section in fig. 114. It consists of fourteen pressure stages, the first of which is compounded for velocity as in the Curtis turbine. The remaining thirteen stages are simple pressure stages as in the Rateau turbine, and this arrangement is known as the Rateau system. Each of the fourteen stages comprises a unit turbine and the complete machine illustrated is said to be pressure compounded. The last two stages embody the makers patent multi-exhaust construction, part of the steam going direct to the condenser after passing through the outer portion K, of the thirteenth stage working blade. The steam passing through the inner portion L, expands through the nozzles M and does work on the fourteenth set of blades I. This construction is adopted to avoid excessively long blades in the last stage and at the same time to take advantage of the highest

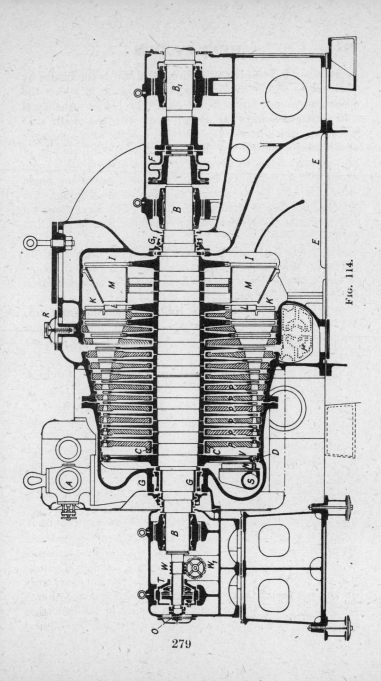

Fig. 114.

vacuum. To make the working portions clearer, the first eight pressure stages have been repeated in fig. 115, and both figures are similarly lettered except that in the latter figure, N_2, N_3, N_4, etc., represent the successive nozzles after the first, whilst B_2, B_3, B_4, etc., represent the corresponding blades attached to their respective wheels W_2, W_3, W_4, etc., which rotate.

The steam is supplied to the first stage nozzles N, through the nozzle box S. The expansion in the first nozzles is usually sufficient to remove any superheat from the steam and thus avoid temperature stress distortion in the casing and wheels. The velocity of the steam leaving the first nozzles N is higher than at any other point in the turbine and this enables two rings of moving blades to be used for the first pressure drop with a directing ring D, of blades between them.

The two moving rings are clearly shown on the first wheel V. This arrangement is known as velocity compounding.

The first nozzles do not extend round the full circumference of the wheel V. The second and third sets of nozzles are formed in steel blocks attached to the diaphragms P. These diaphragms consist of cast steel plates fitted into grooves formed in the casing. Casing and diaphragms are in halves in the horizontal plane containing the axis of the shaft. All stages after the third have the nozzles cast in the diaphragms with the exception of the last one M, in which the nozzles are built up. Usually the arc of admission to successive pressure stages increases until, in the last stages, the full circumference is utilized, although full circumferential admission in the early stages is frequently used to reduce windage losses.

Blade heights and nozzle heights increase in the successive stages in order to accommodate the increasing volume of steam. The increasing nozzle arc also assists in providing this accommodation. Overloads in this type of turbine can be met by increasing the number of first stage nozzles in action, or by supplying steam through the overload valve A to the chamber between the first and second

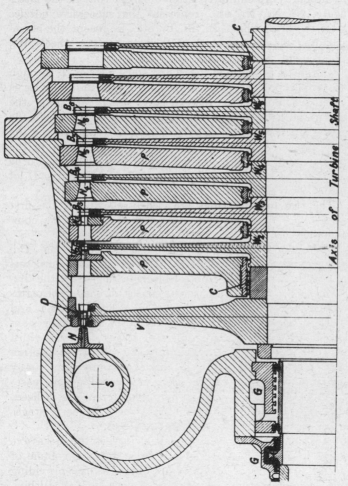

FIG. 115.

stages. Between the tenth and eleventh stages, steam is extracted from the turbine to heat the feed water in the heater H. Also at this point a relief valve R is fitted, to warn the attendant of unusual conditions and to protect the casing from accumulation of pressure. The steam not extracted passes on through the multi-exhaust stages to the condenser and leaves the turbine at EE.

The pressure on the left-hand side of each diaphragm is greater than on the right. It is, therefore, necessary to prevent steam from passing in considerable quantity through the essential working clearances between the inner edges of the diaphragms and the outer surfaces of the wheel bosses. This is practically accomplished by means of labyrinths which consist of rings with projecting fin edges as shown at C. The packing edges are thinned down to a few thousandths of an inch to prevent " seizing " if contact should occur. In the event of contact taking place, the heat generated is localised in the fin which is softened and gives way until a clearance is again established. The principle on which this packing operates is that of throttling the pressure down through a very restricted opening as explained in Articles 56 and 57.

The remaining features of the turbine illustrated in fig. 114 are common to large turbines and differ, in machines from different makers, in constructional detail only.

The two main bearings BB carry the rotor and are supplied with oil under pressure as is also the alternator bearing B_1.

The turbine and alternator shafts are connected by a flexible coupling at F, the flexibility being provided by the bellows shape of the coupling sleeve close to the letter.

At the points where the shaft passes out of the casing, steam and water sealed glands are fitted. The gland G prevents leakage of steam from the casing to atmosphere, and the gland G_1 prevents air from leaking into the condenser where it would interfere with condensation. At starting, both glands are steam sealed to prevent air from entering the casing since the vacuum is created before the turbine is started. When the turbine has run up to speed water is supplied to the glands and a forced vortex is created as a means of preventing leakage. This method has long been in use on Metropolitan-Vickers turbines.

A detail of a high pressure gland is shown in fig 116, whilst a water gland is shown in fig. 117. The gland shown in fig. 116 is of the comb type and consists of nine rings P of special form supported at the outer circumference by springs F, and having axial projections overlapping similar radial projections on the packing sleeve Q. The high pressure steam acts at A. The space B is at low pressure and is connected either to drain or to condenser. The spaces B and C are separated by another packing ring known as the leak-off ring. Steam passing from B to C is sometimes allowed to leak through the passage E, into the atmosphere where it indicates, by its quantity, the state of the packing. In the case of turbines fitted with the water gland, no leakage to the atmosphere takes place. There is some evaporation due to the heat generated in the gland, but this can be piped to the condensing system. This evaporation is made up continuously.

It will be noted that each comb consists of five throttling orifices. The shaft is indicated at SS and D is a ring which throws oil and water off the shaft and also keeps them separate.

In fig. 117 the packing rings R are simpler than those of fig. 116, and are similar to those employed in the diaphragm glands. The impeller I produces a water pressure which seals the gland by slightly different radial depths of water, that on the higher pressure side being less than that on the low pressure side.

A typical double thrust Michell bearing is illustrated in fig. 118. This bearing is used to register the rotor accurately in an axial direction and thus keep the distance between the outlet edges of the nozzles and the inlet edges of the blades the correct amount. This registration is accomplished by adjusting the thickness of the serrated rings S. The thrust collar is indicated at T and the

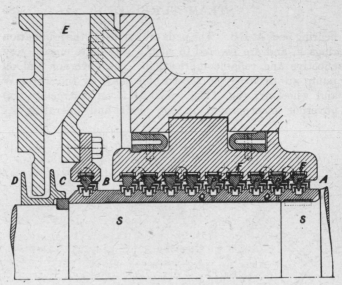

FIG. 116.
High Pressure Gland — 12,500 KW. Turbine

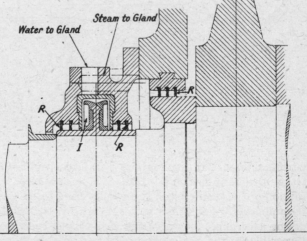

FIG. 117.

bearing pads at BB. The pads are carried in the foundation rings F, and are pivoted in such a way as to ensure very effective and reliable lubrication. The governor and oil pump are driven from the turbine shaft by the worm W and wheel W_1 (fig. 114), whilst O is an emergency trip governor incorporated in the shaft and operating by

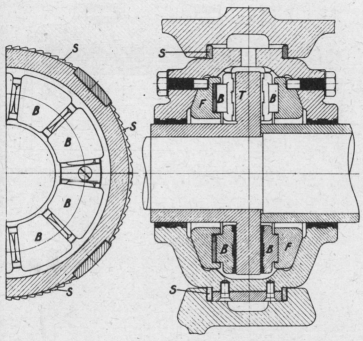

FIG. 118.

centrifugal force. It is restrained by a light spring so long as the predetermined safe speed is not exceeded. The situation of the thrust block is indicated at T in fig. 114.

Examination of figs. 114 and 115 will reveal the large working clearances between the blades and casing, and between blades and nozzle diaphragms, which are characteristic of the impulse turbine. The pressure in successive wheel chambers gets less as the steam approaches the condenser, but the pressure on each side of any wheel is the same, holes being provided in the wheels to ensure this. The successive fall in pressure in each Rateau stage is arranged to produce the same leaving velocity at each set of nozzles.

181. The Reaction Steam Turbine. A longitudinal section of a modern turbine of the well-known Parsons reaction type is shown in fig. 119.

This machine, by C. A. Parsons & Co., Ltd., is the direct descendant of the famous 1884 turbine and is remarkable for the comparatively small space occupied by a turbine of its output. It is capable of producing 20,000 kilowatts at full load and its thermal efficiency at its most economical load is 31 per cent.

In this machine the steam is admitted through the pipe S to the steam belt A, and enters the first group of blades round the full circumference of the blade ring as is usual with reaction turbines. This first group, between the belts A and B, consists of six pairs of blade rings on a parallel portion of the rotor R.

The second group between B and E consists of ten pairs on a conical portion of the rotor. When the turbine is called upon to take overloads, steam is supplied through the pipe S_1 and the belt B, to the gap between the first and second groups of blades. This supply is additional to the normal supply through S and A. The next two steam belts E and F, with their respective gaps between the blade groups, are points at which a portion of the steam is led away from the turbine for the purpose of heating boiler feed water or for other heating purposes.

The third group of blades between E and F consists of eleven pairs of rings. The fourth group between F and H, on a parallel portion of the rotor, contains six pairs which increase considerably in height to accommodate the increased volume of steam. The steam pressure at E in the first pass-out belt is 35 lbs. per sq. inch, and at F in the second one, it is $6\frac{1}{2}$ lbs. per sq. inch. At discharge from the fourth group of blades, shown at H, the steam remaining in

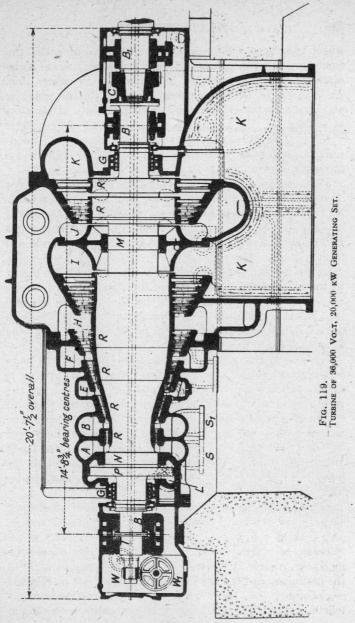

Fig. 119.
TURBINE OF 36,000 VOLT, 20,000 kW GENERATING SET.

287

the turbine divides, part of it passing outside the casing carrying the fixed blades of the fifth group. This latter group occurs between the points H and I. The steam which passes out at H enters the last group at J and expands through the five pairs of blade rings comprising this group into the exhaust passage K and thence downward to the condenser. The remaining steam expands through the six pairs forming the fifth group and also enters the condenser. The portion of the turbine between H and K is the low pressure portion and here the steam has a large specific volume.

The division of the low pressure steam into two parts as explained above, is known as the double flow arrangement. In the turbine illustrated, the steam travels in the same direction through each flow. In many cases the two portions of low pressure steam are arranged to flow in opposite directions so that the thrust set up in one flow is balanced by the thrust set up in the other. The arrangement shown in fig. 119 necessitates a labyrinth steam

Fig. 120.

packing M, between the two low pressure expansions since
the pressure at J is greater than that at I. The reason
for the adoption of the double flow arrangement is the
need for provision of large steam flow area at exhaust from
the last moving ring without using unduly long blades
which would be mechanically weak.

In the reaction turbine, blades attached to the casing fulfil
the function of nozzles and alternate with blades attached
to the rotor. Thus the first blades which the steam
encounters are fixed whilst the last are moving. Both
fixed and moving blades in each pair are identical, but
reversed in direction. This can be followed by reference
to figs. 121 and 133.

The pressure drop across any blade ring is small and
therefore, the increase in steam velocity is also small
compared with that which occurs in an impulse turbine
nozzle. Thus there are more sets of blades in a reaction
turbine than in an impulse turbine for the utilization of
the same heat drop. The blade heights and the mean
diameters of succeeding blade rings progressively increase
along the turbine, and the absolute steam velocities also
increase as the steam flows through the turbine from inlet

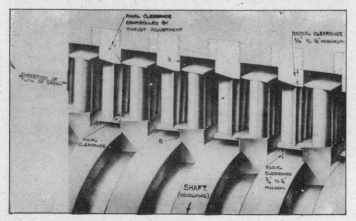

Fig. 121.

to exhaust. As there is a pressure drop across each moving row of blades in a reaction turbine, it follows that there must be some end thrust due to the steam pressure on the blades and on the shaft. To counteract this thrust two dummy pistons N.P. are provided at the steam end of the turbine. The piston N balances that part of the blading between A and E, while piston P balances the blading between E and H. The space L is connected to the low pressure port H.

Any out of balance still remaining is taken up by the thrust block T. As in the impulse turbine, this block serves also to register the rotor accurately in its casing.

Leakage to or from the casing is prevented by steam sealed carbon glands G, one of which is illustrated in fig. 120.

This figure also shows the shaft bearing with its oil throwing rings and the end of the rotor R with its blading.

The flexible coupling C, of the Parsons claw type, with the end of the alternator shaft B_1 can be seen on the right in fig. 119, and the governor and oil pump driving worm W and wheel W_1 on the left.

Reaction blading is very efficient, especially in low pressure sections. In the high pressure sections, where the steam is relatively dense and the blades short, the essential radial clearances were formerly the cause of considerable steam leakage. The whole of the steam did not pass through the blade channels with the result that the efficiency was reduced. This leakage has been overcome by means of Parsons patent end tightened blades which are illustrated in fig. 121.

The projecting blade shrouds reduce the clearance between fixed and moving parts of the turbine and serve as labyrinth packings. The shrouds on the blades fixed to the cylinder have forked ends, the lower one almost touching the foundation ring B of the adjoining blades, whilst the upper one serves to guide the steam into the moving blades without shock.

The feather edges ensure freedom from damage if contact should be made between tightening strip and foundation ring. By the use of this blading, the radial clearance can be increased as shown in fig. 121, with consequent less risk of blade stripping and without the excessive leakage of steam which would otherwise accompany the use of larger radial clearances.

It must be pointed out that this type of turbine is really an impulse-reaction turbine since both impulse and reaction are operating. A pure reaction turbine would have moving nozzles which would move in a direction opposite to the steam flow.

A pure impulse machine would have no expansion or generation of kinetic energy in the moving blades. In the Parsons turbine, the blades fixed to the casing perform the same function as the nozzles of an impulse turbine and the blades fixed to the rotor perform the same function as the moving nozzles of the pure reaction turbine. Thus the working blades are also nozzles and this is the reason for the name reaction.

Usually the term nozzle is applied to fixed passages, but it is applicable to any part of a turbine where controlled expansion and generation of kinetic energy occur. The difference between impulse and reaction turbines is further explained in Articles 186 and 187.

182. The Steam Nozzle. It will be noted from Articles 178 and 180, that the portion of the elemental turbine in which the steam operates to do work consists of (*a*) the nozzle passage, (*b*) the working blade which moves. The function of the steam turbine nozzle is threefold, first it must expand the steam from the higher pressure at inlet to the lower pressure at exit. In doing this, the nozzle allows the heat energy in the steam to be converted into velocity or kinetic energy. Secondly, it must deliver the steam with a maximum of kinetic energy for which reason it needs to be smooth and of correct shape ; thirdly it must direct the steam into the blade channels and for this purpose it is set at an angle to the path of motion of the blades.

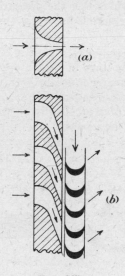

FIG. 122.

There are two principal types of nozzle used in turbine practice, (*a*) the convergent nozzle, (*b*) the convergent-divergent nozzle. The convergent nozzle is indicated conventionally at (*a*) in fig. 122, whilst (*b*) of the same figure shows how the nozzle is arranged in the turbine diaphragm.

The cross-sectional area of a convergent nozzle diminishes from inlet section to outlet section. In other words the outlet section is the least section of the nozzle. This type of nozzle is used when the ratio, $\dfrac{\text{absolute presssure at exit section}}{\text{absolute pressure at inlet section}}$ is not less than about 0·58. This ratio in any type of nozzle is known as the pressure ratio of the nozzle and the actual value of the limiting ratio for convergent nozzles depends on the value of the index *n* in the expansion law of the steam. For example, if the steam expands through the nozzle according to the law $PV^{1.135} = C$

then the ratio is 0·58, whilst if the law is $PV^{1·3} = C$ the ratio becomes 0·5457. The latter value is used in all cases except those in which the steam is initially wet. Thus with n equal to 1·3 the least pressure at the exit section of a convergent nozzle will be $0·5457 P_1$, where P_1 is the pressure at inlet to the nozzle. This least pressure is known as the *critical pressure* of the nozzle.

It will be shown in the next higher stage of this subject that when the exit pressure from a convergent nozzle reaches the value indicated by the above pressure ratio the nozzle is discharging its maximum weight of steam. The lower pressure referred to is that in the nozzle itself and this pressure is not necessarily that in the chamber into which the nozzle discharges.

EXAMPLE. The steam supply to a convergent nozzle is at 200 lbs. per sq. inch absolute. Assume the expansion law to be $PV^{1·3} = C$ and calculate the least theoretically correct exit pressure.

$$\frac{\text{Exit pressure}}{\text{Inlet pressure}} = 0·5457 \quad \text{when } n = 1·3.$$

∴ Exit pressure $= 0·5457 \times 200 = 109·1$ lbs. per sq. inch absolute.

The pressure at exit could be any value higher than 109·1 lbs. per square inch but the nozzle would not in this case discharge its maximum amount of steam.

EXAMPLE. The pressure in front of certain nozzles is 80 lbs. per sq. inch absolute. The exit pressure is 48 lbs. per sq. inch absolute. What type of nozzle is indicated ?

$$\text{Pressure ratio} = \frac{48}{80} = 0·6.$$

Since this is higher than 0·58 or 0·5457, the nozzles are convergent irrespective of the value of n. If this ratio had fallen between 0·58 and 0·5457 it would have been necessary to state the value of n to be used.

The convergent-divergent nozzle is illustrated in fig. 123.

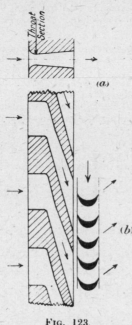

Throat Section

(a)

(b)

FIG. 123.

(*a*) indicating as before the conventional nozzle and (*b*) the nozzle arranged in the turbine casing. This nozzle consists of the convergent nozzle of fig. 122 with a diverging portion added, and it is used when the pressure at exit is less than $0.5457\ P_1$.

The object of the diverging portion is to expand the steam to a lower pressure *in the nozzle* than the critical pressure. The effect is to control the expansion down to lower pressures than can be done with the convergent nozzle. By this means, higher steam velocities can be attained with a convergent-divergent nozzle than with a convergent nozzle.

The least cross section of this combination nozzle is known as the *throat* section and it corresponds to the exit section of the convergent nozzle. Beyond this section the nozzle widens until the exit section is reached. The explanation is briefly as follows. During the expansion of the steam and its passage along the nozzle its pressure falls continuously, and expansion is complete as in the Rankine Cycle. The heat released produces a continuous increase in velocity and the fall in pressure produces increased volume in the steam. At first the volume increase is not at sufficient rate to keep pace with the velocity increase and thus the nozzle can be reduced in section. At the throat the limit of this condition is reached and thereafter the specific volume increases at a greater rate than the velocity.

Hence this portion of the nozzle must **diverge** to accommodate the steam.

EXAMPLE. A nozzle is required to expand steam from 200 lbs. per sq. inch absolute to 20 lbs. per sq. inch absolute. What type of nozzle is needed ?

Pressure ratio $= \dfrac{20}{200} = 0 \cdot 1$. Since this is less than $0 \cdot 5457$, the nozzle must be convergent-divergent.

EXAMPLE. A nozzle of the convergent-divergent type is required to expand steam from a pressure of 180 lbs. per sq. inch dry, to 2 lbs. per sq. inch. The expansion law is $PV^{1 \cdot 3} = C$. Find the pressure and specific volume of steam at the throat and the specific volume at exit. Both pressures are absolute.

Pressure at the throat $= 0 \cdot 5457 \times 180$
$$= 98 \cdot 2 \text{ lbs. per sq. inch absolute.}$$

From steam tables the specific volume at 180 lbs. per sq. inch absolute $= 2 \cdot 562$ cu. ft.

$P_1 V_1^{1 \cdot 3} = P_T V_T^{1 \cdot 3}$ Suffix 1 referring to inlet and T to throat.

$$\therefore V_T = \left(\frac{P_1}{P_T} \right)^{\frac{1}{1 \cdot 3}} V_1$$

$$= \left(\frac{180}{98 \cdot 2} \right)^{\frac{1}{1 \cdot 3}} \times 2 \cdot 562$$

$$= 1 \cdot 83^{0 \cdot 77} \times 2 \cdot 562$$

$$= 1 \cdot 592 \times 2 \cdot 562$$

$$= 4 \cdot 08 \text{ cubic feet per lb. at the throat.}$$

$P_1 V_1^{1 \cdot 3} = P_2 V_2^{1 \cdot 3}$ Suffix 2 refers to exit.

$$\therefore V_2 = \left(\frac{P_1}{P_2} \right)^{\frac{1}{1 \cdot 3}} \times 2 \cdot 562$$

$$= \left(\frac{180}{2} \right)^{0 \cdot 77} \times 2 \cdot 562$$

$$= 90^{0 \cdot 77} \times 2 \cdot 562$$

$$= 31 \cdot 97 \times 2 \cdot 562$$

$$= 82 \cdot 0 \text{ cubic feet per lb. at exit.}$$

183. Calculation of Steam Velocity. The calculation of the velocity with which steam leaves a nozzle is based on the law of the conservation of energy. The steam expands freely through the nozzle from a pressure P_1, to a pressure P_2. There is no piston upon which the steam can do work, hence it does work upon itself and sets itself in motion. The heat energy rendered available by the expansion between the two pressure limits is converted into kinetic energy. The amount of energy available in the ideal case for each pound of steam, is the Rankine cycle work (see pages 150 *et seq*). For convenience this quantity is called the heat drop or available heat.

Since the heat available per pound of steam is operating to increase the kinetic energy of one pound weight of steam we have, in the ideal case,

Heat drop = Increase in kinetic energy of one pound weight.

$$\text{That is } H_R = \frac{V^2}{2gJ}$$

Where H_R = Rankine heat drop in C.H.U. per pound.

      V = Velocity of steam in feet per second.

      g = 32·2 pounds per engineers unit of mass.

      J = Joule's mechanical equivalent of heat = 1,400 ft. lbs. in this case.

EXAMPLE. Dry steam is supplied to a nozzle at 200 lbs. per sq. inch absolute. The exit pressure is 1 lb. per sq. inch absolute. Calculate the final dryness of the steam and the velocity of efflux from the nozzle assuming that the steam is initially at rest and that the flow is adiabatic and frictionless.

To determine the final dryness the entropy quantities will be used. The heat drop will be calculated by the method given on page 157.

$$x_2 = \frac{1\cdot5538 - 0\cdot1323}{1\cdot9724 - 0\cdot1323} \quad \text{See page 276.}$$

$$= \frac{1\cdot4215}{1\cdot8401}$$

$$= 0\cdot773$$

Total heat at A, before expansion = 669·69 C.H.U. per pound.

,,   ,, at B, after   ,,   = 38·63 + 0·773 × 573·83

                     = 38·63 + 443·57

                     = 482·2 C.H.U. per pound.

∴ Heat drop = 669·69 — 482·2

i.e. H_R = 187·49 C.H.U.

∴ $V = \sqrt{2g\,J\,H_R}$

      $= \sqrt{2 \times 32\cdot2 \times 1400 \times H_R}$

      $= \sqrt{2 \times 32\cdot2 \times 1400} \times \sqrt{H_R}$

      $= 300\cdot2 \times \sqrt{H_R}$

      $= 300\cdot2 \times \sqrt{187\cdot49}$

      $= 300\cdot2 \times 13\cdot69$

      = 4110 feet per second.

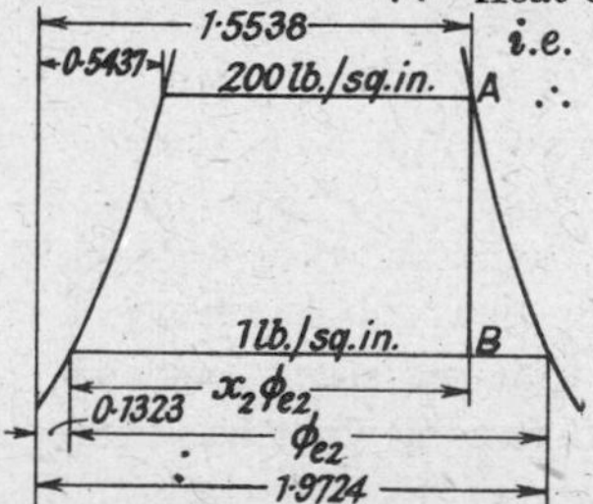

FIG. 124.

It should be noted that such a steam velocity is rarely met in practice. The large range of pressure is divided into portions to give approximately equal heat drops and equal increments of velocity.

Reference to Article 96 and to the worked example on page 155 will show that

$$H_R = \frac{n}{n-1} \ P_1 V_1 \left[1 - \left(\frac{P_2}{P_1} \right)^{\frac{n-1}{n}} \right] \text{ foot pounds.}$$

Therefore $V = \sqrt{2g \ \dfrac{n}{n-1} \ P_1 V_1 \left[1 - \left(\dfrac{P_2}{P_1} \right)^{\frac{n-1}{n}} \right]}$ and this

equation can be used to calculate the steam velocity when the value of n is known.

EXAMPLE. Steam expands through a nozzle according to the law $PV^{1.3} = C$. The initial pressure is 150 lbs. per sq. inch absolute and the exit pressure is 20 lbs. per sq. inch. absolute. Calculate the velocity with which the steam issues from the nozzle assuming that the steam is at rest just before the inlet section.

$$V = \sqrt{2g \ \frac{n}{n-1} \ P_1 V_1 \left[1 - \left(\frac{P_2}{P_1} \right)^{\frac{n-1}{n}} \right]}$$

$$= \sqrt{2 \times 32 \cdot 2 \times \frac{1 \cdot 3}{0 \cdot 3} \times 144 \times 150 \times 3 \cdot 041 \left[1 - \left(\frac{20}{150} \right)^{\frac{0 \cdot 3}{1 \cdot 3}} \right]}$$

$$= \sqrt{18,330,617 \cdot 5 \left[1 - \frac{1}{7 \cdot 5^{0 \cdot 2307}} \right]}$$

$$= \sqrt{18,330,617 \cdot 5 \left[1 - \frac{1}{1 \cdot 592} \right]}$$

$$= \sqrt{18,330,617 \cdot 5 \ [0 \cdot 372]}$$

$$= \sqrt{6,818,989 \cdot 7}$$

$$= 2,613 \text{ feet per second.}$$

184. Effect of Friction.

The walls of a nozzle are made as smooth as possible, but even when this has been done they are not devoid of some degree of roughness. Thus no actual nozzle is without its frictional effect. There are also frictional effects in the body of the steam itself.

The net result of these effects is that the steam velocity at exit from an actual nozzle is always somewhat less than the ideal velocity which would be generated with the same heat drop.

Let V_a = actual steam velocity at exit from the nozzle in feet per second.

V_i = ideal or theoretical velocity at exit from the nozzle in feet per second.

Then the ratio $\dfrac{\text{actual exit velocity}}{\text{ideal exit velocity}}$ is known as the velocity coefficient of the nozzle. The value of this coefficient varies from 0·92 to 0·98 and is usually denoted k.

Thus actual velocity at exit = k × ideal exit velocity

$$= k \times \sqrt{2g \text{ J } H_R}$$

EXAMPLE. If the velocity coefficient of the nozzle in the last exercise, Article 183, is 0·96, what is the actual velocity of the steam as it leaves the nozzle ?

Actual steam velocity = 0·96 × 2613
= 2508 feet per second.

The principal object of the nozzle is to convert the available heat energy of the steam into kinetic energy. In a frictionless nozzle all the heat drop would be converted. Friction reduces the velocity of the steam and the actual kinetic energy of the steam at exit from the nozzle is less than the ideal kinetic energy.

The ratio, $\dfrac{\text{actual kinetic energy per lb. at exit}}{\text{ideal kinetic energy per lb. at exit}}$ is the nozzle efficiency and this quantity will be denoted η_n

Using the above notation, we have

Actual kinetic energy at exit per pound of steam

$$= \frac{V_a^2}{2g} \text{ foot pounds.}$$

Ideal kinetic energy at exit per pound of steam

$$= \frac{V_i^2}{2g} \text{ foot pounds.}$$

$$\therefore \; \eta_n = \frac{\dfrac{V_a^2}{2g}}{\dfrac{V_i^2}{2g}} = \frac{V_a^2}{V_i^2} = \left(\frac{V_a}{V_i}\right)^2 = k^2$$

Also $\quad \dfrac{V_i^2}{2g} = JH_R$

$\therefore \quad \eta_n = \dfrac{V_a^2}{2g\,JH_R}$

or $\quad V_a^2 = 2gJ\,\eta_n\,H_R$

i.e. $\quad V_a = 300\cdot2\sqrt{\eta_n\,H_R}$ when H_R is in Centigrade
Heat Units.

EXAMPLE. Dry steam is supplied to a nozzle which expands it from 180 lbs. per sq. inch absolute to 14·7 lbs. per sq. inch absolute. The expansion is adiabatic. Find the velocity of the steam at exit from the nozzle if the efficiency of the nozzle is 0·9.

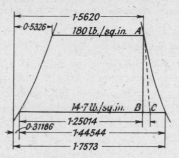

The process of adiabatic expansion with friction is shown by the line AC in fig. 125. The line AB is the ordinary frictionless adiabatic expansion line.

FIG. 125.

$$\text{Dryness at B} = \frac{1\cdot5620 - 0\cdot31186}{1\cdot7573 - 0\cdot31186}$$
$$= 0\cdot865$$

Total heat at A before expansion $= 668\cdot53$ C.H.U.

,, ,, ,, B after ,, $= 100 + 0\cdot865 \times 539\cdot3$
$= 566\cdot49$ C.H.U.

$\therefore$ Heat Drop $= 668\cdot53 - 566\cdot49$
$= 102\cdot04$ C.H.U.

Actual energy converted $= 0\cdot9 \times 102\cdot04$
$= 91\cdot836$ C.H.U.

$\therefore$ Exit velocity of steam $= 300\cdot2 \times \sqrt{91\cdot836}$
$= 2875$ feet per second.

Assuming that no heat enters or leaves the steam during expansion in the nozzle, the heat not converted into kinetic energy remains in the steam at exit. The result is that the steam is actually dryer than it would be at exit from a perfect nozzle when the pressure limits are the same. This affects the specific volume of the steam at exit and this quantity is important when the nozzle dimensions are to be found. In the above example, the dryness at the end of the adiabatic frictionless expansion is 0·865. Actually, however, 0·1 of the heat drop remains in the steam as additional heat.

Therefore the improvement in dryness due to friction

$$= \frac{0·1 \times 102·04}{539·3}$$

$$= 0·0188$$

∴ Actual dryness at exit $= 0·856 + 0·0188$

$$= 0·8748$$

The volume of one pound of the wet steam at exit

$$= 0·8748 \times 26·79$$

$$= 23·4 \text{ cubic feet.}$$

In fig. 125, C is the end point of the actual condition line AC. The length BC represents the evaporation which would be produced by 10·204 C.H.U. at the atmospheric exhaust pressure of this example. It is necessary to point out that this heat has been degraded to a lower state of temperature and is therefore wasted since 14·7 lbs. per square inch is the discharge pressure.

185. The Blade Velocity Diagram.

The velocity of steam in the fixed nozzle passages of any turbine is the velocity of the steam relative to the earth. This velocity is known as the absolute steam velocity. The velocity of the steam relative to the blade will depend on the speed of the blades, the absolute steam velocity, and the angle which

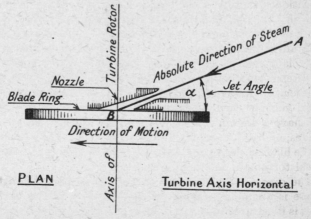

Fig. 126.

the nozzle axis makes with the plane in which the blade moves. The absolute steam velocity is represented by AB in fig. 126. This velocity can be resolved into two components, one parallel to the direction of motion of the blade and the other parallel to the axis of the turbine. The first component is known as the velocity of whirl and the second is known as the velocity of flow. The velocity of whirl is important in calculating the force or work done on the blades and the velocity of flow in calculating the thrust along the turbine axis.

To find the velocity of steam relative to the moving blade, vector velocity diagrams, or equations based upon them, are used.

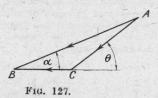

Fig. 127.

Let AB (fig. 127) represent the absolute steam velocity at entry to the blades. Set it down to scale, making an angle α with the direction of motion of the blade. This angle is known as the nozzle angle or the inlet jet angle and is the angle at which the nozzles are set. Now set off, to the same velocity scale, the velocity of the blade along the direction of motion of the blade. Let this be CB. Then a straight line AC indicates the direction, magnitude, and sense of the motion of the steam relative to the blade. This diagram is the inlet triangle and is one of vector subtraction. The blade velocity vector CB is vectorially subtracted from the steam velocity vector AB, giving the vector AC as the difference. Imagine the blade speed to be equal to the whirl velocity then the relative velocity of steam to blade will have a direction at right angles to the direction of the blades, and will be equal in magnitude to the flow velocity. If the blade is stationary, then the relative velocity becomes equal to the absolute steam velocity.

The diagram drawn above is the inlet velocity triangle. There is a similar triangle for the exit edge of the blade. This is illustrated in the third example of this article.

The angle θ (fig. 127) is the angle of the blade at inlet and the steam will glide on to the blade without shock when the conditions of turbine rotational speed, turbine diameter, absolute steam velocity and inlet jet angle enable the diagram to produce the angle θ to agree with that of the actual blade. If the blade velocity, steam velocity and inlet jet angle are known, then the blade angle and relative steam velocity can be found.

EXAMPLE. A steam turbine is 4 ft. mean diameter of blade ring and the nozzle angle is 22°. The turbine speed is 550 r.p.m. and the inlet blade angle is 30°. Draw the velocity diagram and find the absolute steam velocity at entry to the turbine wheel. Also find the inlet whirl and flow velocities.

Blade speed $= \pi$ DN.

$= 3\cdot1416 \times 4 \times 550$ ft. per minute

$= \dfrac{3\cdot1416 \times 4 \times 550}{60}$ ft. per second.

$= 115\cdot2$ ft. per second.

The velocity triangle, fig. 128, is now set out.

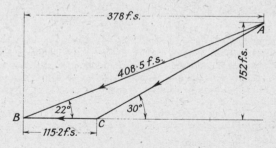

FIG. 128.

Measurement of this triangle gives the following results, absolute steam velocity 408·5 ft. per second ; inlet whirl velocity 378 ft. per second ; inlet flow velocity 152 ft. per second.

EXAMPLE. The ideal heat available in a turbine nozzle is 160 C.H.U. The nozzle discharges the steam into a ring of moving blades, the efficiency of the nozzle being 0·92. The nozzle angle is 20° and the blade angle inlet is 32°. Find the blade velocity assuming no shock at entry.

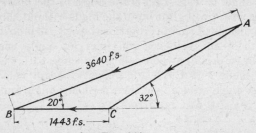

FIG. 129.

Set down any length to represent the unknown blade speed. Draw the line BA, fig. 129, at 20°. Draw CA at 32°. Then AB represents the steam velocity to scale.

This velocity is equal to $\sqrt{2g \, J \, \eta n \, H_R}$

$= 300 \cdot 2 \sqrt{0 \cdot 92 \times 160}$

$= 3640$ ft. per second

The original diagram, from which fig. 129 is reproduced, was set out so that 3 inches represented the blade speed. On measuring the length of AB it was found to be 7·56 inches. This length represents 3640 ft. per second, and thus the velocity scale can be found.

∴ Blade speed $= \dfrac{3640}{7 \cdot 56} \times 3$

$= 1443$ ft. per second.

EXAMPLE. The relative velocity of steam leaving the blades of an impulse turbine is 1,200 feet per second. The blade speed is 460 feet per second, and the angle of the blade at exit is 28°. Draw the exit velocity triangle and find the velocity of whirl, the velocity of flow, and the absolute velocity of steam at exit from the blades. What is the angle which the leaving jet of steam makes with the plane of the turbine wheel ?

The diagram in this case is one of vector addition.

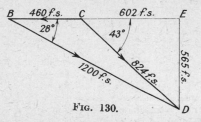

FIG. 130.

Set off the blade speed, 460 feet per second along CB (fig. 130). Also set off 1200 feet per second along BD making an angle of 28°

with the direction of motion.　Complete the triangle by drawing CD. Then CE = whirl velocity = 602 feet per second ; ED = flow velocity = 565 feet per second ; CD = absolute leaving velocity = 824 feet per second and $\theta = 43°$ = exit jet angle.

186.　The Simple Impulse Blade Velocity Diagram. This diagram consists of two velocity triangles, one for the inlet edge and one for the outlet edge of the blades.　The arrangement is shown in fig. 131, and this allows the blade shape to be inserted in the combined triangles.　The

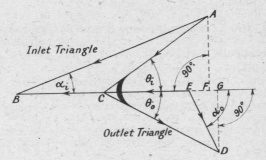

Fɪɢ. 131.

significance of the lines are as follows all being set down to scale and the angles measured with a protractor.

AB is the absolute steam velocity at inlet.

CB ,, ,, ,, blade ,, ,, ,, .

AC ,, ,, relative steam ,, ,, ,, to the blade.

EC ,, ,, blade velocity, repeated for convenience in the second triangle.

CD ,, ,, relative steam velocity at outlet from the blade.

ED ,, ,, absolute steam ,, ,,

α_i ,, ,, inlet jet angle.

α_o ,, ,, outlet ,, ,, .

θ_i ,, ,, inlet blade angle.

θ_o ,, ,, outlet ,, ,, .

If the blade is considered to be frictionless, then the steam leaves it at the same velocity as it enters and in this case the length of CD is the same as the length AC.　If friction is taken into account then the steam leaves the blade with less velocity than it possessed when entering. In this case, the length CD is less than AC and the ratio $\dfrac{CD}{AC}$ is the *velocity coefficient* for the blade. The inlet whirl velocity is represented by FB and the outlet whirl velocity by EG. The inlet and outlet flow velocities are represented by AF, and GD respectively. The arrows indicate the sense of flow in all cases.

The ratio $\dfrac{BC}{AB}$ is called the speed ratio of the blades. For simple impulse turbines, the value of this ratio is usually about 0·47.

EXAMPLE. An impulse steam turbine nozzle is inclined at 20° to the plane of motion of the blade. The steam leaves the nozzle with a velocity of 2,500 feet per second and the blade speed is 1,200 feet per second. Find the relative steam speed at inlet, the inlet blade angle, the absolute steam speed at outlet, and the outlet jet angle. Neglect friction and assume the blades to be symmetrical i.e. $\theta_o = \theta_i$.

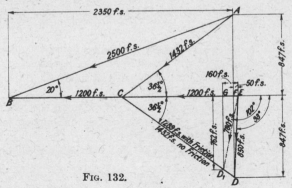

FIG. 132.

Draw the diagram as in fig. 132 with AB = 2,500 feet per second ; CB = 1,200 feet per second ; and $\alpha_i = 20°$. Then relative steam speed at inlet AC, = 1,432 feet per second ; inlet blade angle = 36·5° ; absolute steam speed at outlet ED, = 850 feet per second ; and outlet jet angle = 93°.

EXAMPLE. Write down the whirl and flow velocities from the data of the last example (a) when friction is neglected, (b) when friction reduces the steam speed 10 per cent. whilst the steam is passing through the blade channels.

The whirl velocities will be considered as positive towards the left and the diagram shows that both inlet and outlet whirl velocities are positive.

Measurement of the diagram gives the following results. For no friction, inlet whirl velocity FB, = 2,350 feet per second ; outlet whirl velocity EF, 50 feet per second ; inlet flow velocity AF, 847 feet per second ; outlet flow velocity FD, 847 feet per second.

When friction is taken into account, outlet whirl velocity EG = 160 feet per second ; outlet flow velocity GD_1 = 762 feet per second ; inlet whirl and flow velocities are unchanged. The absolute steam velocities and outlet jet angles change from ED, 850 feet per second to ED_1, 780 feet per second, and from 93° to 102° respectively.

Before leaving the impulse velocity diagram, an important feature which is characteristic of impulse turbine diagrams must be emphasised.

The velocity CD of the steam leaving the blade cannot be higher than the velocity AC of the steam entering the blade. The reason for this is the characteristic of impulse turbines, namely, that there is no fall in pressure from inlet to outlet edge of blades. Hence there is no release of energy of the steam whilst it is in the impulse blade passages.

187. The Reaction Blade Velocity Diagram. In the reaction turbine, the nozzles consist of turbine blades which are fixed to the casing. The moving blades and the fixed nozzle blades are identical, but relatively reversed as shown in fig. 133. As the steam passes through the length of a reaction turbine, the succeeding sets of blades alter slightly in shape, and considerably in height, but so far as a working

Fixed

Moving

Fixed

Moving

Fig. 133.

pair are concerned, they are identical. It is important to

note that there is a pressure fall across both fixed and moving blades with consequent release of energy in each. The release of energy in the moving blade channels causes an increase in steam velocity, whilst the steam is traversing them, and therefore, *the outlet steam velocity relative to the blade is greater than the inlet steam velocity relative to the blade.* The effect of this increase in *relative* velocity is clearly shown in the blade velocity diagram fig. 134, which is lettered to correspond with the impulse diagram of the last article. Note that CD is now greater than AC. Also note that the pressure fall in the moving blade is such as to pull up the relative velocity from AC to CD so that CD = AB. In other words, the relative velocity of the leaving steam is equal to the absolute velocity of the entering steam. Because the blades are identical, but reversed, the inlet and outlet triangles are identical. Thus BC = CE, AB = CD, AC = ED, $\alpha_i = \theta_o$ and $\theta_i = \alpha_o$.

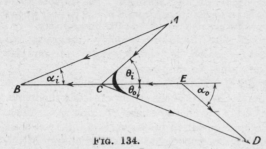

FIG. 134.

EXAMPLE. A reaction steam turbine pair has a blade ring 4 ft. 6 in. mean diameter and the turbine speed is 350 r.p.m. The blade speed is 0·7 of the relative leaving velocity of the steam and the leaving edge of the blade is inclined at 20° to the direction of motion. Draw the velocity diagram on the assumption that the steam enters and leaves parallel to the blade face and find (*a*) the absolute steam velocity at entry, (*b*) the relative steam velocity at entry, (*c*) the absolute leaving velocity of the steam, (*d*) the inlet angle of the blades, (*e*) the inlet whirl velocity, (*f*) the exit whirl velocity.

Blade speed $= 3 \cdot 1416 \times 4 \cdot 5 \times \dfrac{350}{60}$ feet per second.

$= 82 \cdot 5$ feet per second.

$\therefore$ Absolute steam velocity at entry $= \dfrac{82 \cdot 5}{0 \cdot 7}$

$= 118$ feet per second.

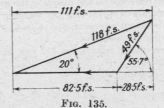

Fig. 135.

Only one triangle need be drawn as shown in fig. 135. From this diagram, relative entering velocity = 49 feet per second ; absolute leaving velocity = 49 feet per second ; inlet blade angle 55·7° ; velocity of whirl at inlet 111 feet per second ; velocity of whirl at exit = 28·5 feet per second.

188. Calculation of Force exerted and Work done by steam on the blades. To calculate these quantities it is necessary to find the change of momentum of the steam *in the direction of motion of the blades*.

Let V_{wi} = whirl velocity of steam at inlet to blades in ft. per second.

,, V_{wo} = whirl velocity of steam at outlet from blades in ft. per second.

,, W = weight of steam flowing through blade channels in lbs. per second.

,, g = engineers unit of mass = 32.2 lbs.

Then momentum at entry per second $= \dfrac{W}{g} V_{wi}$ units

,,   ,,   at outlet   ,, $= \pm \dfrac{W}{g} V_{wo}$,,

$\therefore$ Change in momentum per second $= \dfrac{W}{g} V_{wi} - \pm \dfrac{W}{g} V_{wo}$

$= \dfrac{W}{g} [V_{wi} \pm V_{wo}]$

This quantity is the force on the blades in pounds. The + sign in the last expression is used when the whirl velocity at outlet is opposite in sign to that at inlet as in figs. 131 and 134. The — sign is used when both have the same sign, as in fig. 132.

EXAMPLE. Find the force on the blades in the example relating to fig. 135, when 4 pounds of steam flow per second. What effect will doubling the steam weight per second have on the blade force other conditions remaining unchanged ?

From fig. 135 inlet whirl velocity = 111 feet per second.

    ,,   ,,   outlet   ,,   ,,   = 28·5   ,,   ,,   .

The signs are of opposite kind.

$$\therefore \text{ Force on blades} = \frac{4}{32 \cdot 2}\ [111 + 28 \cdot 5]$$
$$= 17 \cdot 3 \text{ pounds.}$$

The force would be doubled with double steam flow.

The calculation of the work done is now a simple one when the blade speed is known.

Let U = blade speed in feet per second.

Then the work done per second = Force × distance moved per second.

$$= \frac{W}{g}\left[V_{wi} \pm V_{wo} \right] U.$$

EXAMPLE. What is the horse power of the ring of blades in the last exercise ?

Work done per second $= (17 \cdot 3 \times 82 \cdot 5)$ft. lbs.

$$\therefore \text{ Horse power developed } = \frac{17 \cdot 3 \times 82 \cdot 5}{550}$$
$$= 2 \cdot 59$$

189. Efficiency of Turbine Blades. The efficiency of turbine blades is defined as the ratio,

$$\frac{\text{Work done on moving blades per pound of steam.}}{\text{Kinetic energy per pound of steam at exit from nozzle,}}$$

both quantities being in the same units.

Let V_i = absolute velocity of steam at exit from the nozzle in feet per second.

Let V_o = absolute velocity of steam at exit from the blades in feet per second.

Then, when friction is neglected,

Work done on blades per pound of steam

= Change in kinetic energy per pound of steam

$$= \frac{V_i^2}{2g} - \frac{V_o^2}{2g}$$

The latter term is known as the carry over energy, whilst the first term is the kinetic energy at exit from the nozzle.

Therefore, blade efficiency $= \dfrac{\dfrac{V_i^2}{2g} - \dfrac{V_o^2}{2g}}{\dfrac{V_i^2}{2g}}$

$$= \frac{V_i^2 - V_o^2}{V_i^2}$$

The work can be calculated by the method of the last article, either taking into account or neglecting friction.

The blade efficiency now becomes

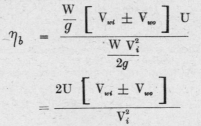

$$\eta_b = \frac{\dfrac{W}{g} \left[V_{wi} \pm V_{wo} \right] U}{\dfrac{W V_i^2}{2g}}$$

$$= \frac{2U \left[V_{wi} \pm V_{wo} \right]}{V_i^2}$$

This efficiency is sometimes called the diagram efficiency because the work done on the blades is calculated from the blade velocity diagram.

EXAMPLE. The speed of the buckets of a de Laval steam turbine is 1,200 feet per second. The inclination of the nozzle to the plane of the wheel is 20° and the velocity of the steam as it leaves the nozzle is 3,400 feet per second. If there is no shock, find the angle of the bucket vane at entrance. Assuming no friction and the vane angle at the steam exit to be the same as at entrance, find (a) the absolute velocity of the steam as it leaves the buckets, and (b) the bucket efficiency.

U.L.C.I.

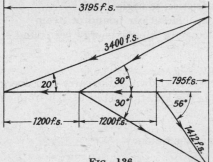

FIG. 136.

From the diagram absolute velocity at exit from buckets
= 1412 feet per second.

Inlet kinetic energy per pound of steam $= \dfrac{3400^2}{64 \cdot 4}$

$= 179,500$ ft. lbs.

Outlet kinetic energy per pound of steam $= \dfrac{1412^2}{64 \cdot 4}$

$= 31,000$ ft. lbs.

$\therefore$ Blade efficiency $= \dfrac{179,500 - 31,000}{179,500}$

$= 0 \cdot 828$ or $82 \cdot 8$ per cent.

Alternatively : Measurement of the whirl velocity at exit shows it
to be 795 feet per second.

$\therefore$ Inlet whirl velocity $= (1200 + 1200 + 795) = 3195$ ft. p.s.
Exit   ,,   ,, $= 795$ feet per sec. and is negative.

$\therefore$ Work done on blades $= \dfrac{1200}{64 \cdot 4} \times (3195 - - 795)$

$= 148,800$ ft. lbs.

$\therefore \quad \eta_b = \dfrac{148,800}{179,500}$

$= 83 \cdot 0$ per cent. as before

EXAMPLES XXI.

1. Explain briefly the difference between the steam turbine and
the reciprocating steam engine confining your attention to the
process of transforming the heat into work.

2. State the principal advantages of the steam turbine.

3. Explain the terms " impulse " and " reaction " as applied to
turbines and also explain why it is necessary to fit a thrust block
on a turbine shaft.   In which type of machine is the thrust the
greater ?

4. Sketch a diagrammatic section through a single wheel impulse
turbine showing clearly the situation of (a) the nozzle chest, (b)

the nozzles, (c) the supply pipe, (d) the working blades, (e) the blade shrouds, (f) the glands, (g) the bearings, (h) the thrust block, (i) the governor driving worm, (j) the flexible coupling (k) the exhaust passage.

5. Sketch and describe the two principal types of steam nozzle used in turbines and state clearly the circumstances under which each type is used.

6. A steam nozzle is supplied at 150 lbs. per square inch absolute and is fully convergent. What is the correct exit pressure if " n " in the expansion law is 1·3 ?

7. Define the terms " nozzle efficiency " and " velocity coefficient." The ideal velocity at outlet from a steam nozzle is 2,800 feet per second. What is the actual velocity of the steam leaving the nozzle if the nozzle efficiency is 0·86 ?

8. Steam is supplied, dry and saturated, to a turbine nozzle at 120 lbs. per square inch absolute the exit pressure being 1 lb. per square inch obsolute. Find the ideal velocity with which the steam leaves the nozzle assuming it to be at rest at the inlet section.

9. If the efficiency of the nozzle in the last exercise is 90%, what will be the leaving velocity ?

10. The exit area of a nozzle is 2 square inches and the steam velocity is 3,000 feet per second. The volume of 1 lb. of the steam as it leaves the nozzle is 140 cubic feet. Find the weight of steam flowing per second.

11. Steam leaves the nozzles of an impulse turbine with a velocity of 1,185 feet per second, the nozzle angle being 15°. The blade speed is 503 feet per second. Find the relative velocity of the steam entering the blade channels, and the inlet blade angle. If the outlet angle of the blades is 18° and the relative leaving velocity is 575 feet per second, find the absolute leaving velocity and the blade velocity coefficient.

12. The absolute velocity of steam entering a reaction turbine blade ring is 207 feet per second. The jet angle is 20°. Find the velocity of whirl at inlet and also the velocity of flow.

13. Find the work done per pound of steam in example 11, and also the blade efficiency.

14. A reaction steam turbine takes 5·5 lbs. of steam per second. The inlet and outlet blade angles are 35° and 20° respectively. The blade speed is 100 feet per second. Draw the velocity diagram and find the horse power developed in one ring of moving blades.

15. What is the increase in steam velocity whilst the steam is passing the moving blade in the last example, and how much heat per pound of steam does this increase represent ?

PROPERTIES OF STEAM. Table X

Pressure Lbs./ sq. in. Absolute.	Temperature C.	Specific Volume Cu. Ft./Lb.	Total Heat of Liquid.	Latent Heat.	Total Heat of Steam.	Entropy of Liquid.	Total Entropy of Dry Steam.
p	t	V_s	h	L	H	ϕ_w	ϕ_s
0·2	11·69	1,524	11·67	588·14	599·81	·0417	2·1068
0·4	22·66	790·7	22·6	582·37	604·97	·0794	2·0482
0·5	26·41	650·5	26·34	580·39	606·73	·0922	2·0299
0·6	29·54	539·1	29·47	578·72	608·19	·1008	2·0148
0·8	34·65	411·1	34·55	576·00	610·55	·1176	1·9906
1·0	38·74	333·1	38·63	573·83	612·46	·1323	1·9724
2	52·27	173·5	52·16	566·51	618·67	·1747	1·9159
4	67·23	90·54	67·1	558·28	625·38	·2197	1·8600
6	76·72	61·91	76·61	552·92	629·52	·2472	1·8277
8	83·84	47·30	83·75	548·82	632·57	·2673	1·8049
10	89·58	38·39	89·51	545·50	635·01	·2833	1·7874
14·7	100·00	26·79	100·00	539·30	639·3	·31186	1·7573
16·0	102·41	24·73	102·43	537·82	640·26	·3184	1·7506
18	105·79	22·16	105·84	535·75	641·6	·3274	1·7414
20	108·87	20·08	108·95	533·87	642·82	·3356	1·7333
25	115·59	16·29	115·76	529·63	645·39	·3531	1·7157
30	121·28	13·74	121·51	526·01	647·54	·3679	1·7016
35	126·25	11·90	126·59	522·77	649·36	·3806	1·6897
40	130·67	10·50	131·08	519·87	650·95	·3918	1·6792
50	138·30	8·52	138·89	514·71	653·60	·4109	1·6620
60	144·79	7·184	145·54	510·22	655·77	·4269	1·6479
70	150·46	6·218	151·37	506·23	657·61	·4407	1·6359
80	155·52	5·487	156·61	502·59	659·20	·4530	1·6256
90	160·9	4·913	161·35	499·24	660·59	·4620	1·6165
100	164·28	4·451	165·71	496·12	661·82	·4739	1·6082
110	168·15	4·07	169·75	493·18	662·93	·4831	1·6007
120	171·75	3·751	173·52	490·4	663·92	·4915	1·5938
130	175·13	3·479	177·07	487·76	664·83	·4994	1·5875
140	178·31	3·245	180·42	485·27	665·69	·5068	1·5818
150	181·31	3·041	183·59	482·9	666·49	·5138	1·5765
160	184·16	2·862	186·61	480·61	667·22	·5204	1·5715
170	186·88	2·703	189·50	478·40	667·90	·5266	1·5666
180	189·48	2·562	192·27	476·26	668·53	·5326	1·5620
190	191·97	2·435	194·94	474·19	669·13	·5383	1·5577
200	194·35	2·32	197·49	472·20	669·69	·5437	1·5538
220	198·87	2·12	202·32	468·38	670·70	·5540	1·5465
240	203·09	1·954	206·88	464·76	671·64	·5635	1·5395
250	205·10	1·880	209·07	463·01	672·07	·5680	1·5362
260	207·04	1·811	211·17	461·31	672·48	·5724	1·5332
280	210·77	1·689	215·25	458·02	673·27	·5808	1·5274
300	214·32	1·583	219·12	454·85	673·96	·5887	1·5219
350	222·45	1·368	228·08	447·44	675·52	·6067	1·5096
400	229·75	1·206	236·21	440·63	676·84	·6228	1·4991

The properties of steam given in Table X (see page 274) are those calculated by the late Professor H. L. Callendar, and are reproduced by kind permission of Messrs. Edward Arnold & Co. More detailed tables are available and may be obtained on application to Messrs. Arnold.

The liquid heats below 100° C. are slightly less than the corresponding temperature, due to the variation in the specific heat of water which is actually less than unity. In practical problems the liquid heat may be taken as equal to the temperature in the absence of the table.

The liquid heats are calculated from the equation

$$h = 0{\cdot}99666t + \frac{V_w}{V_s - V_w} \cdot L - 0{\cdot}003$$

where $\quad t$ = temperature
V_w = Volume of water/lb.
V_s = Volume of steam/lb.

The evaporation entropy is the difference between the entropy of dry steam and the entropy of the liquid, and is equal to latent heat divided by absolute temperature,

i.e. $\quad \phi_e = \phi_s - \phi_w$

$$\phi_e = \frac{L}{T}$$

$$\therefore \frac{L}{T} = \phi_s - \phi_w.$$

Take the figures at 200 lbs. per sq. in. absolute.
$$L = 472{\cdot}2 \text{ C.H.U.}$$
$$T = 273{\cdot}1 + 194{\cdot}35$$

$$\therefore \phi_e = \frac{472{\cdot}2}{467{\cdot}45}$$
$$= 1{\cdot}01$$
$$\phi_s = 1{\cdot}5538$$
$$\phi_w = 0{\cdot}5437$$

$$\therefore \phi_e = 1{\cdot}0101.$$

Use of the entropy columns to determine dryness after adiabatic expansion.

Case (a) dry steam expanding to wet state.

Initial pressure 160 lbs. per sq. in. absolute.

Final pressure 20 lbs. ,, ,, ,,

Total entropy before expansion $= 1\cdot5715$ Ranks.

,, ,, after ,, $= 1\cdot5715$,,

Liquid entropy at 20 lbs./sq. in. $= 0\cdot3356$.

$\therefore$ Entropy of evaporation after expansion $= 1\cdot5715 - 0\cdot3356$.

$$= 1\cdot2359 \text{ Ranks.}$$

Entropy of evaporation when completely dry at 20 lbs./sq. in.

$$= 1\cdot7333 - 0\cdot3356$$
$$= 1\cdot3977$$

$\therefore$ Dryness after adiabatic expansion $= \dfrac{1\cdot2359}{1\cdot3977}$

$$= 0\cdot886.$$

Case (b) steam initially of dryness $0\cdot96$.

Evaporation entropy at 160 lbs./sq. in. $= 0\cdot96 \ (1\cdot5715 - 0\cdot5204)$

$$= 1\cdot01 \text{ Ranks.}$$

Total entropy before expansion at 160 lbs./sq. in. and $0\cdot96$ dry

$$= 0\cdot5204 + 1\cdot01$$
$$= 1\cdot5304 \text{ Ranks.}$$

$\therefore$ Total entropy after expansion to 20 lbs./sq. in. $= 1\cdot5304$ Ranks.

Liquid entropy at 20 lbs./sq. in. $= 0\cdot3356$.

Evaporation entropy after expansion $= 1\cdot5304 - 0\cdot3356$.

$$= 1\cdot1948.$$

Evaporation entropy when completely evaporated at 20 lbs./sq. in.

$$= 1\cdot3977.$$

$\therefore$ Dryness fraction after expansion $= \dfrac{1\cdot1948}{1\cdot3977}$

$$= 0\cdot856$$

ANSWERS

EXAMPLES I

1. 3·9 lbs. per sq. ft., 0·0271 lbs. per sq. in.
2. 16·42 lbs. per sq. in.   **3.** 1,254 ft.-lbs.   **4.** 28,800 ft.-lbs.
5. 15,552 ft.-lbs.   **6.** 26,611 ft.-lbs.   **7.** 3.003 ft.-lbs.
8. 1 sq. in. = 3,240 ft.-lbs., 34·1 lbs. per sq. in.

EXAMPLES II

1. 75·6 I.H.P.   **2.** 960 H.P.   **3.** 606 H.P. and 1,099 lbs./hr.
4. 26,580 lbs.   **5.** 1 H.P.   **6.** 94·6 H.P.   **7.** 1,671 ft. per sec.
8. 180·5 I.H.P., 141 B.H.P.   **9.** 350 revs. per min.   **10.** 2·3 H.P.

EXAMPLES III

1. 658° C.   **2.** 15·9° C.   **3.** 3·843 lbs., 70·2 C.H.U.
4. 35,900,000 ft.-lbs., 1,088 H.P.   **5.** 775 C.H.U. per lb.
6. 1,324 C.H.U. per lb.

EXAMPLES IV

1. 70·2 lbs. per sq. in.   **2.** 320 cu. ft.   **3.** 190·5 cu. ft.
4. 61·7 cu. ft.   **5.** 13·3 cu. ft., 1,925 ft.-lbs., 96·25 ft.-lbs.
6. 1 lb.   **7.** 55° C.   **8.** 5·5 lbs.
9. 29·8 cu. ft., 108·5 lbs. per sq. in.   **10.** PV = 96T, 8·4 C.H.U.
11. 96 ft.-lbs. per lb. per ° C., 2.   **12.** 44·2° C.   **13.** 1,041° C.

EXAMPLES V

1. 235,200 ft.-lbs.   **2.** 212·5 C.H.U., 300 C.H.U.
3. 25·15 C.H.U.   **4.** 119,300 ft.-lbs.   **5.** 12·9 cu. ft.,
0·0775 lbs. per cu. ft.   **6.** 268 C.H.U., 155,500 ft.-lbs.
7. 29,400 ft.-lbs.   **8.** 0·1996.   **9.** 1,086° C., 860 C.H.U.

EXAMPLES VI

1. 37·7 lbs. per sq. in.   **2.** 4·95 cu. ft.   **3.** $PV^{1·087} = C$.
4. 162,000 ft.-lbs.   **5.** 15,900 ft.-lbs.   **6.** 252,000 ft.-lbs.
7. 47,000 ft.-lbs.   **8.** 63·3 C.H.U.   **9.** 123·6 lbs. per sq. in.,
340° C.   **10.** 4·83, 263° C.   **11.** 61·3 lbs. per sq. in., 232° C.
12. 104·5 lbs. per sq. in., 432° C.   **13.** 1·27 cu. ft., 491° C.,
10 : 1, 112,000 ft.-lbs.   **14.** 15·4 C.H.U. wall to gas.

EXAMPLES VII

1. 83 per cent.   **2.** 41·2 per cent.   **3.** 48·5 per cent.
4. 184° C., 1,126° C.   **5.** 46·5 per cent., 18·4 cu. ft. per I.H.P.
per hour.

Examples VIII

1. 702·4 C.H.U. **2.** 674 C.H.U. **3.** 300,000 C.H.U.
4. 555 lbs. **5.** 18·4 lbs. **6.** 5,050 gallons. **7.** 606,000 ft.-lbs.,
65,500 ft.-lbs. **8.** 58,200 ft.-lbs., 797,500 ft.-lbs. **9.** 0·953.
10. 167° C. **11.** 852,000 ft.-lbs., 576,750 ft.-lbs., 59,250
ft.-lbs., 216,000 ft.-lbs. **12.** 829,000 ft.-lbs., 567,000 ft.-lbs.,
62,400 ft.-lbs., 199,600 ft.-lbs. **13.** 0·925. **14.** 0·96, 0·92.
15. 872,000 ft.-lbs., 67,200 ft.-lbs., 754,400 ft.-lbs.,
53,600 ft.-lbs. **16.** 0·98.

Examples IX

2. 65·5 per cent., 9·76 lbs., 13·65 per cent. **4.** 63 per cent.
5. 9·79 lbs. of steam per lb. of coal, 69·3 per cent.
6. 78·2 per cent., 15·45 lbs., 3·92 lbs. **7.** 16·75 per cent.,
10,000 lbs., 20 per cent. **8.** 3·8 barrels, 5,670 C.H.U. per lb.,
76 per cent. **9.** 6.230 C.H.U., 1,039 C.H.U., 46·7 C.H.U.,
78·5 per cent., 627·3 C.H.U.

Examples X

1. 0·47 per cent. **2.** 1·03 per cent. **3.** 25·8° C.
4. 4,250 tubes, 2·37 ft. per sec. **5.** 61,644 galls per hour.
6. 6·42° C., 98·7 per cent., 0·507 cu. ft. **7.** 174,000 lbs.
8. 3,190 galls. per min., 794 tubes. **9.** 2,630 gallons,
13·75 lbs., 5·2 ft. per sec.

Examples XI

1. 66·8 lbs. per sq. in. **2.** 50·9 lbs. per sq. in. **3.** 278 I.H.P.
4. 66·8 lbs. per sq. in., 50·9 lbs. per sq. in. **5.** 11·41 in. dia.,
17·11 in. stroke. **6.** H.P. cyl. 9·48 in. dia., L.P. cyl. 16·42 in.
dia. and stroke. **7.** 12·76 in. dia., 17 in. stroke.
8. L.P. cyl. 32·1 in. dia., 36 in. stroke, H.P. cyl. 17·3 in. dia.,
36 in. stroke. **9.** 8·7 in. dia., 13·05 in. stroke.
10. 92·7 in. dia. **11.** 14·26 in. dia., 40 B.H.P. approx.
12. 0·8. **13.** 0·645. **14.** 15·3 in. dia., 3 ft. stroke.
15. 0·35 of stroke. **16.** 1,635 I.H.P.

Examples XII

1. 1·445 ranks. **2.** 1·068 ranks. **3.** 1·01 ranks.
4. 0·452 ranks. **5.** 1·580 ranks. **6.** 1·277 ranks.
7. 1·761 ranks. **8.** 0·89, 23·8 cu. ft. **9.** 130 − 0·86,
110 − 0·73, 90 − 0·62, 70 − 0·49, 50 − 0·34, 30 − 0·21.

Examples XIII

1. 127,200 ft.-lbs. **2.** 225,000 ft.-lbs. **4.** 229,000 ft.-lbs.,
26·75 per cent. **5.** 264,800 ft.-lbs., 28·6 per cent. **6.** 0·815.
7. 0·84, 53 lbs. per sq. in. **8.** 0·00719 ranks, 0·895 dry.
9. 0·805 dry, 59·2 cu. ft.

EXAMPLES XIV

1. $33\frac{1}{2}°$. **2.** Lead $\frac{1}{16}$ in., 1 in., $\frac{3}{4}$ in. **3.** 0·76, 0·96. **6.** $47\frac{1}{2}°$, 1·25 in., 1·95 in., 25°. **7.** 0·3 in., $1\frac{1}{4}$ in., 0·74 stroke, 0·966 stroke, 0·84 return stroke. **9.** 32°, 1 in., 0·325 in. **10.** 30°, − 4°, 124°, 171°, 310°. **13.** 5·45 in., 1·225 in., $32\frac{1}{2}°$, 0·2 in. **14.** 44°, 0·575 stroke, 0·9 stroke, 0·437 of a rev., 1 in., 1·5 in.

15.

Cut-off	0·7	0·7
Release	0·9	0·9
Outside lap . .	1·15 in.	0·6 in.
Inside lap . .	−0·15 in.	0·29 in.
Max. opening steam . .	0·8 in.	1·25 in.
,, ,, exhaust .	1·25 in.	1·25 in.
Lead	0·1 in.	0·65 in.
Angle of advance . .	39°	39°

EXAMPLES XV

1. 11,010 C.H.U. **2.** 7,260 C.H.U. **3.** 11·9 cu. ft., 13·38 lbs., 0·0729 lbs. per cu. ft., 706 C.H.U. per cu. ft. **4.** 8,520 C.H.U., 11·8 lbs. **5.** 11·22 lbs., 1·475 sq. ft. **6.** 5,680 C.H.U. per lb., 10·83 lbs. **7.** 2·86 lbs. CO_2, 0·45 lbs. H_2O, 7,970 C.H.U., 7,730 C.H.U. **8.** 11·6 lbs., 34·8 lbs., 15·08 lbs., 492 C.H.U. **9.** 11·1 lbs. **10.** 35,460 lbs.

EXAMPLES XVI

6. 18·24 H.P.

EXAMPLES XVII

11. 2,100° C. abs. **12.** 2,760° C. abs. **13.** (a) 1,070° C. abs., (b) 812° C. abs. **14.** (a) 1928° C. abs., (b) 1,460° C. abs. **15.** Expansion ratio 8·9, 758° C. abs. **16.** (a) 11·47, (b) 6·24. **17.** 0·6255.

EXAMPLES XVIII

1. 41·2 per cent. **2.** £1,212. **3.** 30·4 cu. ft. per I.H.P. per hour. **4.** 32·4 per cent., 41·5 per cent., 0·335 lbs. per I.H.P. per hour. **5.** 7·4 lbs. per H.P. per hour. **7.** 2,172 lbs. per hour. **9.** Ratio 5, 31·4 per cent., 47·6 per cent., 66 per cent. **11.** 11·72 lbs. per K.W.H., 8·82 lbs. per H.P. hour. **12.** 24·6 per cent. **13.** 22 per cent. **14.** 55·5 I.H.P. 46 I.H.P., 31·8 I.H.P., 22·4 I.H.P. **15.** 13·2 per cent. **16.** 35·2 per cent., 68·9 per cent. **18.** 16·1 per cent., 9·8 per cent. **19.** 5,382 lbs. per hour.

EXAMPLES XIX

1. I.H.P. 10·32, B.H.P. 5·63, Mech. Eff. 54·5 per cent.,

42·6 cu. ft. per B.H.P. per hour, 23·25 cu. ft. per I.H.P. per hour, 25·4 per cent., 13·86 per cent., 59 per cent. . (Brake heat 132·8 + Friction heat 110·9) = Indicated heat 243·7, Jacket heat 351, Exhaust, etc., 365·3, Heat supplied 960 C.H.U. **2.** I.H.P. hours 3·708, B.H.P. hours 1·79, 26·2 per cent., 12·6 per cent. (Brake heat 84·6+Friction heat 90·3)= Indicated heat 174·9, 26·2 per cent. ; Jacket heat 92·4, 13·8 per cent. ; Exhaust, etc., 399·9, 60 per cent. ; Heat supplied 667·2, 100 per cent. **3.** 79·8 per cent., 34·25 per cent., 44·8 per cent., 20·95 per cent. **4.** I.H.P. 18·15, 20 per cent., Heat supply = 128,000 C.H.U. (Brake heat 20,350 + Friction heat 5,250) = Indicated heat 25,600 C.H.U., Jacket heat 23,800, Exhaust heat 78,600.

6. I.H.P. 1,723, 0·326 lb., 13,480 lbs. **7.** 82·9 per cent., 43·6 per cent., 36·1 per cent. **8.** I.H.P. 180·3, B.H.P. 140·5. **9.** Heat supply 31,400 C.H.U. (Brake heat 6,225 + Friction heat 1,980) = Indicated heat 8,205, Jacket heat 13,850, Exhaust, etc., 9,345. **10.** I.H.P. 11·65, B.H.P. 9·6, 82·5 per cent., 47·3 cu. ft. per hour, 12·15 per cent. **11.** Heat supplied 60,200 C.H.U. (Brake heat 8,630 + Friction heat 2,120) = Indicated heat 10,750, Jacket heat 24,500, Exhaust, etc., 24,950. 17·9 per cent., 14·33 per cent. **12.** 29·6 per cent., Heat supply 201,000 C.H.U., Jacket heat 56,400, Exhaust heat, 59,500 (Brake heat 59,500 + Friction heat 25,600) = Indicated heat 85,100. **13.** 81·8 per cent., 30 per cent., 24·5 per cent., Heat supply 1,980 C.H.U. (Brake heat 485 + Friction heat 108·5) = Indicated heat 593·5, Jacket heat 450, Exhaust heat 855, Radiation, etc., 81·5. **14.** 71·5 per cent., 23 per cent., 13·9 per cent. **15.** Heat supplied per min. = 4,175 B.T.U. (Brake heat 1,290 + Friction heat 797) = Indicated heat 2,087, Jacket heat 1,365, Exhaust heat, etc.,723. **17.** 19·45, 16·7, 86 per cent., 22·1 per cent.

EXAMPLES XX

3. 54 to 76·4 r.p.m. **4.** 7·46 in. **5.** 219 r.p.m. **6.** 230 r.p.m., 249 r.p.m. **7.** 130 r.p.m., 170·5 r.p.m. **9.** 20 lbs. **10.** 2·5 lbs. **11.** $W = 5·93w$, 4·35 per cent.

EXAMPLES XXI

6. 81·86 lb. per sq. in. abs. **7.** 2,598 ft. per sec. **8.** 4,010 ft. per sec. **9.** 3,800 ft. per sec. **10.** 0·297 lb. **11.** 710 ft. per sec., 26°, 185 ft. per sec., $k=0·81$. **12.** 194 ft. per sec., 71 ft. per sec. **13.** 18,500 ft.-lb., 85 per cent. **14.** 9·76 H.P. **15.** 90 ft. per sec. increase, 0·36 C.H.U.

INDEX